Mr. Vanderbilt Webb

with the compliments of

Charmalee Bullio

Mount Hope
May 1939.

HUNGER AND HISTORY

HORSES IN THE HARVEST FIELD
Ancient Egypt

Reproduced here from copies made by Nina M. Davies of paintings in Egyptian tombs, published in 1937 by the University of Chicago in the book, *Ancient Egyptian Paintings.* (See p. 45.)

Horses in the Harvest Field
Ancient Egypt

Reproduced here from copies made by Nina M. Davies of paintings in Egyptian tombs, published in 1937 by the University of Chicago in the book, Ancient Egyptian Paintings. (See p. 45.)

Hunger and History

THE INFLUENCE OF HUNGER
ON HUMAN HISTORY

by

E. PARMALEE PRENTICE

NEW YORK AND LONDON

HARPER & BROTHERS PUBLISHERS

1939

CONTENTS

v

CONTENTS

CONTENTS

alters our intellectual life. Dean Swift on refinements of knowledge and diet. Samuel Johnson in 1751 on the old age of the world. Hallam's question in 1818, Why had not Progress come sooner? Hoskyns' question in 1849, Why had Progress ever paused? Popular movements tend toward inefficient methods. Centralization and stagnation. Freedom and Progress.

CHAPTER IX

THE HISTORY OF THE MILK INDUSTRY

The dairy industry as a great source of food is a very recent development. Civilization and the plough. Pastoral life. Use of milk at place of production. Raw or boiled. Milk as a culture medium for germs. Hesitation to use milk even during famine. Butter. Cheese. Milk trade before railways. Uses for milk in London in the seventeenth century. Wine or ale on oatmeal at breakfast. Milk for invalids. Pasteurizing in the sixteenth century. Milk for infants. Milk and morals. The hunting sow. Margaret and Faust. Milk in cooking. Strawberries and cream. Sugar. Milch asses in London. Cows in the city. Milk trade since the building of railways. The history of ice-cream. The modern milk industry.

CHAPTER X

FIVE CENTURIES OF POULTRY HISTORY

When food for man was short, very little was left for chickens. Verminières. High production on Guernsey at 20 eggs per hen per year. Aristotle, Pliny and others on long eggs and round eggs. Parmentier and Liger settle the question by experiment. When poultry was a subordinate branch of rural economy. Type. Artificial incubation. Value of men like Réaumur—country gentlemen. Trap-nests. Genetics. Nutrition. Poultry diseases. Eggs at the rate of 1,000 per second. Preserving eggs. Egg powders.

CHAPTER XI

ABUNDANCE

Enclosures in England. Bakewell. Richelieu on production of food in the Low Countries. The Po Valley. Plutarch on ancient conditions in the Po Valley. Sismondi on the prosperity of Lombardy during the thirteenth century, a famine century elsewhere. Coryat on prosperity in Lombardy. Prescott on prosperity in the Low Countries in the sixteenth century. The rise of the arts in northern Italy and later in the Netherlands. Carrying water in a sieve. Abundance in a growing population. Malthus on population. Self-restraint unpopular. "It depends on man whether growth of population brings Progress or Misery." Malthus' teaching now generally accepted as incontestable. The ultimate state of agriculture. The example of China.

CONTENTS

CHAPTER XII
THE EFFECT OF ABUNDANCE ON THE HUMAN MIND

Abundance and comfort are very recent achievements. The belief in an aging world. The haunting memory of famine. Abundance as a release. Jean Jacques Rousseau. Sir Henry Maine, David Hume and Lord Acton on Rousseau's influence. Rousseau on the value of his own writings. Godwin on the millennium. Bulwer Lytton and William Hazlitt on the intoxication of prosperity. High prices and low standards of living. The economic philosophy of Mr. Micawber. How can we ensure the permanence of abundance? Two dangers which threaten abundance. Establishing a balance between classicism and liberalism.

ILLUSTRATIONS

HORSES IN THE HARVEST FIELD, ANCIENT EGYPT   *Frontispiece*

Reproduced here from copies made by Nina M. Davies of paintings in Egyptian tombs, published in 1937 by the University of Chicago in the book *Ancient Egyptian Paintings*. See Chapter III hereinafter, p. 45.

Reproduced here from copies made by Nina M. Davies of paintings in Egyptian tombs.

ix

Preface

"The histories of mankind which we possess are in general histories of the higher classes." This complaint by Malthus has been made by many other writers, both before and since his time. What is needed is a history of the common affairs of daily life and instead of this we are given partial histories of some elements of the population, accounts of the development of literature and poetry, endless theology and stories of striking and unusual events. All these things have their importance in varying degrees, as have also the banquets of Lucullus, the magnificence of Le Roi Soleil, political issues and wars. That which would be most valuable, however, if we could have it, would be a knowledge of the every-day interests of private individuals in every walk of life, during previous ages, for it is only by knowing the burdens which men have carried and the pleasures which they have enjoyed that we can hope to understand their outlook upon life, their philosophy of existence, their political views and intellectual progress.

The most important of these every-day human interests is, of course, the nature and adequacy of the food supply and of this, unfortunately, little is told. A young Swede of very simple origin said not long ago, in answer to inquiries, that the subject of food was one on which information could not easily be obtained. "Everybody," he said, "likes to make a good appearance for himself and for his family. One would surely be reluctant to confess that his people had ever gone hungry and nevertheless," he added, "my own grandfather has told me of the times when he used to gather and powder the bark of trees to mix it with grain to make bread." The young Swede could never have heard of Johannis

Dominicus Sala, but in 1628 Sala described in his book *De Alimentis* (p. 7) the practice of making bread from the bark of fir and pine trees which, he said, was often done in Sweden when food was dear. A similar practice was described by Sir Hugh Platt who, during the great dearth of 1590 in England, wrote his book *Sundry Remedies against Famine* where, among other things, it is said that bread may be made of the powdered leaves of the pear tree, apple tree, beech and oak, also of rape "being first scorched and after sodden and then baked" and that "a convenient" drink can be made of beech mast, acorns and the barks of some trees. Doubtless, the barks of trees have been used in all countries to sustain life, from a period long before the dawn of history almost to the present time.

The subject of food and lack of food is one on which we have no such records as we would like to have but there exist old books, published before ancient conditions had wholly passed away, from which much information can be secured. These books are few in number,—not easily bought and mostly scattered in different great libraries where hitherto they could be consulted only by those who could afford the expense of travel and the time which travel involves. Recently, however, the new process of making what are called photostat copies has put many of these books at the service of students. When original printed books can be bought, they are much cheaper and, in most cases, better than copies, but when originals cannot be had—as is commonly the case —the copies are a great resource enabling a reader to use, at his convenience and without haste, a mass of literature which until now has been practically inaccessible.

In this way I have been able, in addition to the more easily available authorities, to consult books mentioned hereafter in the list which precedes the index. Of some of these books it has been possible to secure original volumes while of others it has been

necessary to have copies made, and since the writers are not those
with whom modern readers are generally well acquainted, I have
given under the title of the work the names of some of the principal libraries in which the books can be found, with brief information in regard to the author.

It is impossible to read these books, or others like them, without seeing that they belong to a world that was very different from
anything we know in modern times. Life when the food supply
was short was infinitely harder than it is for us, and nevertheless
the writers of these books are moved by no self-pity and by no spirit
of complaint. They tell us of the only world they knew, just as
we write of the conditions with which we are familiar,—with the
one exception, however, that such pity for the unfortunate as in our
time creates great efforts to reduce human suffering is something
which men of old would have found it difficult to conceive. A world
of inadequate supplies, where inevitably many must die of want
and where the uncertainty of all human conditions affects every
individual, is not a world of pity and ready help for the needy.
"Enough is known," Professor George Beard Grundy says, "of the
spirit and circumstances of antiquity to say that help from outside would not be forthcoming from other political units, which
had probably but little food to spare from the annual yield, to a
political unit which had probably no means of paying for that
which could be spared." Dr. Johnson believed that charity, or ten-
derness for the poor, was one of the fruits of the Christian religion.
"Those ancient nations," he said, "who have given us the wisest
models of government and the brightest examples of patriotism
. . . have yet left behind them no mention of almshouses or hospitals, of places where age might repose or sickness be relieved."
The statement is doubtless too broad and yet, notwithstanding the
best defence that can be made for the ancient world, men of those
times seem to many readers very lacking in the qualities of mercy

and sympathy,—a subject on which John Beckmann gives information in his articles on Orphan Houses and on Infirmaries, Hospitals
for Invalids, etc. in his *History of Inventions, Discoveries and
Origins.*

Most persons probably will agree with Dr. Johnson that Chris-
tianity teaches charity and nevertheless, even with the advantage of
such teaching, progress is slow for there is something more than a
trace of savagery still left in humanity. We are not unacquainted
to-day with sudden outbreaks of cruelty when crowds apparently
delight to inflict pain, but modern life has had so softening an
effect that to the larger part of the population such occurrences are
shocking. The old world, on the contrary, sought these spectacles
and the lust did not pass away with the Roman amphitheatre. The
days are not long gone by when public executions, burnings at the
stake, bear baitings and torturings of animals were celebrations for
a holiday. We read of parks maintained where animals, as Le
Grand d'Aussy says, were fed and protected "in order that their
death might be a pleasure to the owner of the park."

So Plenck says of bulls that, though the flesh is tough and has an
odor so unpleasant that most men refuse it, nevertheless Spaniards
are fond of the meat of a bull killed in a fight with dogs, since this
kind of a death makes the meat tender and pleasant. Even the
poor beasts that were killed for food, Dr. Thomas Muffet said in
1665, "eate much sweeter, kindlier and tenderer," if killed slowly
and painfully, "than if they be killed suddenly by sleight or violence." It improves the meat of an animal if he be destroyed with
"fear dissolving his hardest parts and making his very heart to
become pulpy."

There is every reason for satisfaction that this fierce delight is
less than it was and we may hope that it will constantly decrease,
but we should not judge former days by the standards which we seek
to establish in modern times. Men of old who every day saw about

them want that could not be relieved and who, with want, saw also the diseases which follow in its train, men, moreover, who were themselves always in danger of attack by powerful enemies whom in case of war they must meet in armies fighting hand to hand, would find little call for pity in an exhibition of the pain and death of a few men and animals.

We live at the present time under different conditions for, in the history of our western world, abundance and freedom have come together and we have both. With the abolition of starvation there has been removed from our eyes and from our minds the death and disease which hunger brings and, being supplied with food, we have been able to make great advance in knowledge, establishing settled governments to protect our lives and property. Pity, with help for the needy which has been so generously endowed, especially in America, is a blessing which received great help from the invention of machinery—one of the many gifts to mankind brought by the so-called "industrial revolution."

Great ignorance, Buckle says, is often the fruit of poverty, but it is not the intellect only which fails in conditions of general want, for the moral life fails also and Buckle might have added that callousness and lack of sympathy are other fruits of great poverty.

It is pleasant, of course, to read of abundance with its consequences of an easier life and an amelioration of manners. Abundance, nevertheless, is a relative term depending not only upon the quantity of supplies, but also upon the number of persons to be supplied.

In former times, before the invention of machinery, food was short and famine in greater or less degree always entered into the death rate. Machinery, coming at a time when new land was available, enabled the western world to provide for a much larger population than it then had. The birth rate rose, therefore, in a line which was almost without a curve, as though the world were made up of men and women like the Almoner in Spenser's *Faerie Queene* who

> ". . . feared not once himself to be in need,
> Ne car'd to hoord for those whom he did breede,"

—a good illustration of Malthus' statement that animated life tends to increase beyond the supplies provided for it.

Recently, however, the line has begun to curve. The birth rate is falling both in Europe and America, and since a curve is always the product of more than one force, it is evident that the force which made the rising birth rate has met a new force, and that interaction of old and new forces makes the curve. This new force, whether it be called Malthus' law or be given some other name, was described by him and the great question is whether our still increasing population will continue to grow, so that in the end it will press once more upon our possible supplies, renewing the miseries of the middle ages, or will stop within the numbers that can be fed and made comfortable.

Food is not the only need of a population, and the birth rate may be checked by lack of any other necessary supply as well as by lack of food. What is necessary for one man is not always necessary for another. Primitive men could get along with little and so can the primitive element in every population, while, on the other hand, the needs of educated men are many. The force which causes a fall in the birth rate appears first among the educated members of a people, or among persons who are accustomed to conveniences, while the birth rate among what have been termed the primitive elements still stays high.

The question before every country, therefore, is a question not only of numbers but of the quality of its people.

The present book is concerned, however, not with questions of population but, so far as possible, limits attention to the progress of freedom, to the character of the food supply, and to the effect of want and abundance on the human mind.

During the study of the subjects with which this book is concerned, I have had the advantage of consulting my cousin, Professor William K. Prentice of Princeton University, and Dr. Florian Vurpillot of Washington, D. C., who have made many helpful suggestions.

The pictures of agricultural operations, spinning, weaving, etc. in India were very kindly provided by Mr. Purshottam N. Joshi, Superintendent of Cattle Improvement in the Indian State of Bhavnagar.

For permission to quote from the article by Professor Humphrey Michell, published in the *Contemporary Review*, I am indebted to the kindness of Professor Michell and the *Contemporary Review*.

For permission to copy the pictures of horses and mules in the harvest field by Nina M. Davies, I am indebted to the kindness of the Oriental Institute of the University of Chicago, and I take pleasure in returning my thanks to Professor Prentice, Dr. Vurpillot, the Oriental Institute, Mr. Joshi, Professor Michell and the *Contemporary Review*.

E. P. P.

May, 1939
5 West 53rd Street
New York City

Now for the worke it selfe I am well assured (as all other Bookes and actions) it will be diversly censured as men stand diversly affected: if but three guests meet at a feast, they will hardly accord in one dish; & truely I thinke that as men's fancies (could they be seene) would bee found to differ more then their faces; so are their judgments more different then their tastes: but this common courtesie (due by the Lawes of civility and humanity) I shall crave (which I hope no ingenuous mind will deny mee) that I bee not condemned before I bee understood.

GEORGE HAKEWILL, in *An Apologie of the Power and Providence of God.* (Oxford, 1627) Preface, page 8.

CHAPTER I

HUNGER, HISTORY AND DEMOCRACY

CIVILIZATION presents itself to our attention in many different forms of intellectual progress and of increasing physical comfort. Through the slow experience of the ages, man has learned how to accomplish much that at first was impossible and how to accomplish easily what before had been difficult. The growth of civilization, therefore, has one single cause—the increasing efficiency of man's labor. Savagery is the condition in which man lived when much effort brought small results. Progress comes with decreasing effort and increasing results. Civilization begins when man's effort is so productive that he can diversify his labors, spending for new comforts the labor which had previously been devoted to the maintenance of life. In modern terms, civilization has advanced with the constantly decreasing cost of production. Refinements and amenities, comforts, luxuries, books and all that to the modern world make life worth living, are a surplus arising after primary needs have been met, and these primary needs are insistent. To civilized man, as to the savage, food, clothing and shelter are essential. Man must be fed, protected from the elements and from his enemies, and the search for refinements must wait until these needs are satisfied.

Human progress can, therefore, be measured by the ease with which the necessaries of life are provided. Costly food, costly shelter and costly protection mean comparatively increased effort to provide for essential needs, with consequent decrease in the surplus which makes life worth living.

1

The most conspicuous fact in human history, from one point of view, was the discovery of the New World in 1492. New lands to occupy, new fields of thought to cultivate, were opened by Columbus' voyage, but from another point of view a greater world was discovered three hundred years later. Our ancestors of the time of the American Revolution—even men of a later generation, the grandfathers of persons now in active life—lived very much as men lived in the time of Caesar. Transportation on land in the early years of the nineteenth century was on horseback or in horse-drawn vehicles, though for heavy loads oxen were still used in many places. Transportation by sea was made in sailing ships, bigger and swifter than the ships Caesar knew but involving no new principle. The science of medicine—or what we would to-day call a science of medicine—did not exist in the year 1800. Priestley had discovered oxygen and Lavoisier had laid foundations for chemistry, but our modern science of chemistry did not exist. Benjamin Franklin had sent a kite aloft in a thunderstorm and fortunately had drawn a spark instead of a bolt from the key attached to the kite string, but physical science had not advanced much beyond the time of Archimedes.

The world, nevertheless, was preparing for an advance. Sometime about the middle of the eighteenth century, a change came in the affairs of men, showing itself in the freedom of thought and speculation which, in the nineteenth century, brought railroads, steamships, machinery and all that vast advance of physical science which still—though part of our daily life—is a daily wonder to us all. What happened a hundred and fifty years ago to open to us the treasure chest of knowledge? For thousands of years man lived on earth more or less as his ancestors had lived, and then came advance in every direction. What had been impossible before became possible to the men of the late eighteenth century and of the nineteenth century. What was this change? The question admits of but

2

one answer. It was an increase in the surplus created by men's labor after the necessaries of life had been provided. Sometime, therefore, about the year 1750, man's labor began to be more productive.

The primal daily need of every living being is food, and before the eighteenth century there had been in varying degrees of intensity a constant lack of food. If, therefore, at this time man began to have the leisure for study, which he must have if advance in knowledge is to be made, if men began at this time, in Sismondi's phrase, to meditate and apply to the arts the fruits of their study, it must be because during the eighteenth century food was slowly becoming more abundant and cheaper. Hungry men do not meditate about arts; as Dr. Samuel Johnson says, "He that pines with hunger is in little care how others shall be fed." Abundance of food at prices within reach of all is the first great need for human welfare. Food adequate to relieve this need is the achievement of the eighteenth and nineteenth centuries, and the Conquest of Hunger, the high production which machinery brought to a comparatively small population, is the conquest from which all present-day comforts have sprung.

FOOD AND HISTORY

The state of France in 1793, Jules Michelet said in his *History of the Nineteenth Century*, with its crescendo of miseries accumulated from century to century, will never be understood until a terrible book has been written—the history of Hunger. When this book is written, however, it will not be upon the conditions of life in France only that light will be thrown, for all the world has suffered from hunger during many ages.

It is hard for persons living under modern conditions to realize that we enjoy such widespread abundance and luxury as never could have been imagined in previous times within the range of possi-

3

bility. "I could wish rather than hope," said Sir Thomas More, "that laborers could have glass in their windows and meat once a week." Nevertheless, so much more has been accomplished than the little for which Sir Thomas More wished, but for which he dared not hope, that we now have glass in all windows, while meat is part of the ordinary diet of our people, along with milk and butter and other foods which, in More's time, were luxuries hardly known to princes. There still is suffering in the world, and we are much concerned to relieve it as is right, but the existence of suffering is not adequate ground for destroying society, and such radical counsels come only from those who do not realize what great advances the world has made and is making. The hope of mankind lies in the promise which progress during the last hundred and fifty years holds out, and the soundest program which can be put forward for the future is to continue the methods which have already done so much to reduce human misery.

First, and most important, of recent achievements is what has been termed the conquest of hunger. Of course, complete conquest is impossible, for we will always have the storms, droughts, frosts and blights beyond human control which bring poor harvests. Much suffering, however, has been the result of human folly and ignorance. Among the causes of famine which Mr. Cornelius Walford lists are some which have present importance.

1. The prevention of cultivation or the willful destruction of crops;
2. Defective agriculture caused by communistic control of land;
3. Governmental interference by regulation or taxation;
4. Currency restrictions, including debasing the coin.

Human folly and human error will doubtless last while man lives on earth, but folly and error can be reduced and their effects can be minimized when mankind learns to know their faces and to understand the trouble they bring. The history of the world has been the story of a struggle for daily bread. The primitive arts

4

come from the search of hungry men for food,—a very terrible search of which Count Grégoire in 1804, thinking especially of France, said:

Times of famine were formerly more calamitous than in our days and their scourges were more frequent. Maret, the elder, counts ten famines in the tenth century and twenty-six in the eleventh century.[1]

Battles, tournaments, coronations at Rheims or Aix-la-Chapelle and splendors such as the Field of the Cloth of Gold have been but temporary distractions. The permanent and enduring interest of mankind has been in food, and the degree to which the effort to secure food has been unavailing is told in many books.[2]

"In the eleventh and twelfth centuries," Mr. Farr said of England, "famine is recorded every fourteen years, on an average, and the people suffered twenty years of famine in two hundred years. In the thirteenth century the list exhibits the same proportion of famine; the addition of five years of high prices makes the proportion greater. Upon the whole, scarcities decreased during the three following centuries; but the average from 1201 to 1600 is the same, namely, seven famines and ten years of famine in a century. This is the law regulating scarcities in England."

Some idea of the significance of this brief statement can be se-

[1] *Essai historique*, published as an introduction to *Le théâtre d'agriculture* by Olivier de Serres (Paris, 1804), Vol. 1, p. cxxxvii. Maret, Hughes, *Mémoire . . . sur les moeurs des François . . .* couronné à Amiens, 1771. (Amiens, 1772.)

[2] *The Influence of Scarcities and of the High Prices of Wheat on the Mortality of the People of England*, by William Farr, February 16, 1846. Journal of the Royal Statistical Society, Vol. IX, p. 158. *The Famines of the World: Past and Present*, by Cornelius Walford, March 19, 1878, Journal of the Royal Statistical Society, Vol. 41, p. 433; Vol. 42, p. 79. *Vier Thesen zur Lehre von den Wirtschaftskrisen*, by Otto Karman (Carl Winters Universitatsbuchhandlung, Heidelberg, 1905). *Des chertés en France et de leur influence sur le mouvement de la population*, par A. Legoyt, Journal de la Société de Statistique de Paris, Vol. I, Part I, p. 93; Part II, p. 149.

cured from the following summary which Mr. Walford gives of
famines in Europe during the thirteenth century:

1200	Ireland	"A cold, foodless year."
'03	England	A great mortality and famine from long rains.
	Ireland	A great famine—"so that the priests ate flesh meat in Lent."
'09	England	Famine from a rainy summer and severe winter.
'24	England	A very dry winter and bad seed time, whence followed a great famine.
'27	Ireland	A great famine throughout the country.
'30	Rome	After a deluge of the Tiber.
'35	England	Famine and plague; 20,000 persons die in London; people eat horse-flesh, bark of trees, grass, etc.—Short.[3]
'39	England	Great famine, "people eat their children."—Short.
'43	Germany	Famine.
	England	"By reason of embasing the coin a great penury followed."
'52	England	No rain from Whitsuntide to autumn; no grass, hence arose a severe famine; great mortality of man and cattle; dearness of grain and scarcity of fruit.
'57	England	The inundations of autumn destroyed the grain and fruit, and pestilence followed.
'58	England	North winds in spring destroyed vegetation; food failed, the preceding harvest having been small, and innumerable multitudes of poor people died. Fifty shiploads of wheat, barley and bread were procured from Germany; but citizens of London were forbidden by proclamation against dealing in same. "A great dearth

[3] The entries marked "Short" are based on a book published anonymously in 1749 and credited to Thomas Short by the *Dictionary of National Biography*. Walford mentions this book on p. 277 of his *Famines of the World*, the reference being:

"Dr. Thomas Short, *General Chronological History of the Air, Weather, Seasons, Meteors*, etc., in sundry places at different times, wherein he reviews the famines and dearths which have afflicted the world."

This book is not in the Library of Congress, but a copy can be found in the Surgeon General's Office.

6

followed this wet year pest, for a quarter of wheat was sold for 15s. and 20s. but the worst was in the end; there could be none found for money—though many poor people were constrained to eat barks of trees and horseflesh; but many starved for want of food—20,000 (as it was said) in London."—Penkethman.

'62	Ireland	Great destruction of people from plague and hunger.
'68	Sicily	Terrible famine; also in Vienna.
'71	England	A violent tempest and inundation, followed by a severe famine in the entire district of Canterbury.
	Ireland	Pestilence and famine in the whole of Ireland.
'81	Poland	Famine.
'86	England	Short speaks of a twenty-three years' famine commencing this year.
'89	England	A tempest destroyed the seed, and corn rose to a great price.
'94	England	Severe famine; many thousands of the poor died.
'95	England	No grain or fruits, "so that the poor died of hunger."—Camden.
		Hail, great concussion of elements.—Short.
	Ireland	Great dearth during this and the previous and following years.
'97	Scotland	"Calamitous" famine and pestilence.
'98	England	26 Edward I. An especially calamitous year of the 23-year dearth mentioned by Short, which in that religious age seemed to reach its most dreadful form when wine could not be had to minister the communion in the Churches.

Passing over many years of want which are briefly described, it is noticeable that in many cases the intensity of want is told by reciting the high prices paid for food. Thus:

1437-38	England	Wheat rose from its ordinary price of 4s. to 4s. 6d. per quarter (8 bushels) to 26s. 8d. Bread was made from fern roots.—Stow.
		Rains and tempests.—Short.

7

"In the 17th yeere of Henry the Sixth, by means of great tempests, immeasurable windes and raines, there arose such a scarcitie that wheat was sold in some places for 2 shillings 6 pence the bushell."

'39 England 18 Hen. VI. "Wheat was sold at London for 3s. the bushell, mault at 13s. the quarter, and oates at 8d. the bushell, which caused men to eat beans, peas and barley, more than in an hundred years before; wherefore Stephen Browne, then mayor, sent into Pruse (Prussia), and caused to be brought to London many ships laden with rye, which did much good; for bread-corne was so scarce in England that poor people made their bread of ferne rootes."

1521 England Famine and mortality. "Wheat sold in London for 20s. a quarter."

Many other entries of this sort may be found, telling a story of want among our ancestors in western Europe—and famine in those days, as M. Achille Luchaire remarks, was not merely privation, it was death.

Les riches, les puissants eux-mêmes en souffraient; le chroniqueur de Liège affirme qu'ils étaient réduits à manger des charognes. "Quant à la foule des pauvres, elle meurt de faim."[4]

How great want and suffering has been is suggested in the remark of Bruyerinus Campegius,[5] that the birds known in Latin as corvi— crows or ravens—are not good for human beings, because they live in large part on the dead bodies of men,—as though in his day unburied bodies were no uncommon sight. Lack of adequate food supplies, moreover, did not stop with the year 1600, the last year included in Mr. Farr's summary, but continued, with decreasing frequency in England, nevertheless with much suffering, even into

[4] *La société française au temps de Philippe-Auguste*, by M. Achille Luchaire (Paris, 1909), p. 8. On famine and disease in general, see *Population Problems* by Warren S. Thompson (McGraw-Hill Book Co. of N. Y., 1935), Chap. XIII.
[5] *De Re Cibaria*, Lib. XV., Cap. LXXV, (Lyons edition of 1560), p. 833.

the eighteenth century, and in France the lack of food, following
the short crops of 1788, was one of the moving causes of the great
Revolution of 1789.

M. Parmentier's book on *Nutritive Vegetables which May Be
Substituted for Ordinary Food in Times of Scarcity*, crowned by
the Academy of Besançon in 1772, was translated into English and
published in 1783 in England, with a Preface by the translator
in which, describing the conditions of the time in England, he says:

At the present period of scarcity and dearness of provisions, when the
common people have been already excited to discontent and tumult, by the
distress that has so soon begun to press upon them, and by the prospect of
the still deeper distress in which they will probably be involved before
another harvest, . . . it is incumbent upon every man to propose publicly
whatever means he may suppose likely to avert or alleviate the impending
calamities . . .

The frequent and severe attacks of scarcity, and even of famine, felt in
France, render researches like M. Parmentier's an object of the highest
national importance; and, unhappily, the present year has afforded ample
proof, that no fertility of soil, or skill in husbandry, can absolutely secure
any nation against such disasters.

Twenty years before the Napoleonic wars, therefore, and only a
little more than a hundred and fifty years ago, England, like the
nations on the continent of Europe, was in distress for lack of food
which "no fertility of soil or skill in husbandry" could provide.
Mankind evidently has walked with Hunger and Want. These have
been his daily companions throughout European history and, could
we discover the facts, we would learn that they have been his companions during his whole history. The facts are not wholly hidden
and occasional references to conditions which we know existed can
be found.

No man can be so inhuman and wicked, that when he sees men languish-
ing in the streets, and falling down from hunger, he does not feel a pain
in his heart to think how near he is to the same suffering. It may be that

this want was sent to us by God our Father to punish us and correct us, and it must be suffered patiently for though we die we are but taken from our poverty, misery and pain.[6]

Such expressions as those quoted nevertheless are rare. One would have thought that the want man has endured would have been reflected in every page that man has written, but it is not so. Man has suffered hunger as he has suffered storms and earthquakes, the cold of winter and the heat of summer. The conditions which all have known and lived with, needed no comment from anybody. Abundance, when it came, could be described. Feasts could well be occasions of happy memory, but of daily want so little was said that a world which regards hunger as a wrong from which no person in civilized countries should suffer, finds it somewhat difficult to understand that want and hunger were the lasting conditions under which previous generations lived. Mr. Walter H. Mallory says that the normal mortality of the Chinese may be said to contain a constant famine factor,[7] and the same could be said of Europe during the period before the nineteenth century.

What caused the constant shortage of food, which so often increased in intensity and extended to include so large a territory that it was described as famine, marked by famine prices for the simplest and most necessary foods? The question intimately concerns man's daily life and welfare through all previous ages, for man's first need is food, and a knowledge of the degree to which it has been possible for the human race to supply this need and of the extent to which population pressed upon the food supply and starved, is essential if we are to understand human history and existing conditions.

In the ancient world, as in many centuries also of the Christian era, the extreme uncertainty which attended the course of human

[6] *Carestia e Fame* by Giovanni Battista Segni (Bologna, 1602), p. 108.
[7] *China: Land of Famine* (Am. Geographical Soc., N. Y., 1926), p. 1.

life made it impossible for men to turn their minds to the development of enterprises which, in their nature, belong to settled conditions. Both in the ancient world and during the middle ages, there was always great want, and want brought war, and war always brought pillage.

Le malheur de ce temps est que les calamités s'engendraient l'une l'autre. La famine produisait le brigandage. "Pour ne pas mourir de faim, beaucoup de gens se firent voleurs" . . .[8]

Machinery, mines, mills and improved transportation come only when there is sufficient protection for rights of person and property to arouse ambition.

Men of the ancient world were under a double burden of hunger and constant insecurity. Triptolemus, it is said, in early days invented the plough and Myles the art of grinding grain. The past had seen many improvements and the future, very likely, would see more; but, if the conditions of men's lives suggested no permanence for themselves, their children or their people, the idea of progress, as Professor Bury says,[9] was valueless to them. Moreover, Mr. Hallam shows that when, in the early centuries of the Christian era, European peoples ceased, in their common speech, to use the Latin language, they lost all access to what had been the literature of the civilized world, and with the loss of the ancient books, they lost all written record of such progress as the world had actually made up to that time.

After the middle ages, however, when those influences of which

[8] *La société française au temps de Philippe-Auguste,* par M. Achille Luchaire, p. 9.

It always was (and 'tis reasonable it be) the design and end of all those who make war, to enrich themselves and impoverish the enemy; nor is conquest and victory desired upon any other score.

Florentine History, Machiavelli (London, 1675), Bk. VI, p. 115.

[9] *The Idea of Progress* by Professor J. B. Bury (Macmillan, 1924), p. 5. *The Idea of Progress* by Dr. W. R. Inge. *Outspoken Essays,* Second Series, (Longmans, Green & Co., 1926), p. 158.

Professor Bury and Mr. Hallam speak no longer weighed upon men's minds, there was still a long pause before the world saw that great outburst of achievement which began not far from the opening of the nineteenth century. Apparently, some other cause besides those mentioned was operating still further to delay human progress. Intellectually, as the event showed, mankind was ready to move forward and, nevertheless, the forward movement did not come. What, at this period, was the delaying cause?

Whatever it was, it ceased to operate about a century and a half ago. Outside of Russia, famines no longer visit the western world. Indeed, whatever the future may have in store, we have during the last century so easily raised the food we needed that unless there is some interference by Government, such as caused the Russian troubles, famines seem remote and impossible, like the dragons of fairy books read when we were young—with this difference, however, that the dragons never existed and the famines were very real in times not long past. What has happened to give us of this age so much that the world never before knew?

The answer is simple—we have had freedom. At the time of Louis XIV, Voltaire said, speaking not only of France but of the European world, the arts had not gone beyond the point which had been reached under the Medici in Florence, under Caesar Augustus in Rome during the first century of the Christian era, and under Alexander the Great in Greece during the fourth century before Christ, but slow as progress might be in the arts, human reason at the time of Louis XIV had improved[10] and, with awakened reason, as freedom slowly developed, so grew the opportunity for man to use his released intellectual power.

Without doubt, many causes joined together to produce the great results we see, but growing freedom—freedom of mind, as well as of body—freedom from physical restraint, from regulation by

[10] *Siècle de Louis XIV* (Paris, 1843), Introduction, p. 2.

12

authority and from crushing taxation—was the greatest influence then at work.

Louis XIV died in 1715 and there was little freedom in France at that time, but the change had begun in England with enclosures of a small number of commons and with the introduction both of Dutch agriculture and of market gardens from Flanders. The change, such as it was, did not show itself very clearly to many observers, but as time went on the momentum increased. It was not obvious to Samuel Johnson in 1750, but looking back over history from present times we see what Johnson could not see. We recognize the men of Johnson's time who were beginning to change the face of the world, and we see that among those men ambition and hope had been aroused—the greatest and most inspiring of all changes that can come to humanity. Men were permitted to own their fields, to work out their problems as best they could, and to enjoy the fruits of their labor without regulation by authority and without oppressive taxation. Freedom is the first great achievement of modern times and with it came agricultural machinery, increased supplies of food, intellectual advance, release from ancient superstitions, improved means of communication, steam, electricity, and all the wonders we know so well.

The middle ages instead of freedom and abundance had land used in common, regulation by authority,—and want.

Commons. The tribes which Caesar found in Europe and Britain, and which are very briefly described in his *Commentaries*, were small communities occupying territory which they had taken by the strength of the tribe and which the strength of the tribe was required to defend. In the middle ages, Mr. Edmund Robertson says,[11] the land of the community was divided into:

[11] *Ency. Brit.*, 9th ed., Vol. 6, p. 208, Tit. Commons.

1. Land occupied by the town where the houses of the heads of families were held in severalty;
2. Arable land divided into many plots but subject to regulations as to common cultivation, the most usual of which was the three-field system, the land being fallow every third year and the whole community having rights of pasturage on the fallow portion and on the stubble of the fields under cultivation between harvest and seed time. It was probably a common practice to rotate holdings, perhaps for the purpose of ensuring a fair division of good soil and desirable locations among the peasants, but certainly with the result of taking away from every individual any ambition to improve his property;
3. Land from which the native grasses were cut for hay, which also was common after the cutting;
4. Waste land over which the community had rights of common for pasture, wood-cutting, etc.

It is out of this origin that the rights of common came, which held Europe short of food for so many centuries,—rights which began in the need for common defence and continued because a community upon which such burdens are once fixed can free itself from them only with the greatest difficulty.

Since Mr. Robertson wrote his article on Commons, a great literature on the subject of village communities has arisen,[12] some of it highly controversial in nature. With these controversies we are not now concerned. It is enough for present purposes to know that the open field system of farming with intermixed strips of land in private ownership subject in varying degree to community control, with rights of common in pastures and woods, prevailed in the larger part of England for a thousand years until the en-

[12] See Fustel de Coulanges: *Le problème des origines de la propriété foncière* (Paris, 1889), still the leading work on the subject. Vinogradoff: *The Growth of the Manor* (London, 1905). Meitzen: *Siedelung und Agrarwesen der Westgermanen und Ostgermanen* (Berlin, 1905).

See also *The Open Fields* by C. S. and C. S. Orwin (Oxford, 1938); also *The Enclosure and Redistribution of Our Land* by W. H. R. Curtler (Oxford, 1920), both very instructive and helpful reviews of the subject.

closure acts, chiefly of the eighteenth and nineteenth centuries, put an end to it.[13] With local variations, these communities existed also throughout northern Europe, including northeastern France and extending to the Danube basin. Except in the Pays de Caux, M. Bloch says, the open field system of farming was customary in France north of the Loire and in Burgundy.[14]

The management of agriculture by village communities, wherever it prevailed, was inconsistent with private enterprise but in France, besides community control, there were the great impediments of the ancient régime and the centralized monarchy.

The conditions under which the farming population lived in former times have been described so often that details are unnecessary here. It is a mistake, in looking at crowded districts in modern towns, to think that people are now less comfortable than they were. The dwellings of mediaeval laborers were hovels —the walls made of a few boards cemented with mud and leaves. Rushes and reeds or heather made the thatch for the roof. Inside the house there was a single room, or in some cases two rooms, not plastered and without floor, ceiling, chimney, fireplace or bed, and here the owner, his family and his animals lived and died. There was no sewage for the houses, no drainage, except surface drainage for the streets, no water supply beyond that provided by the town pump, and no knowledge of the simplest forms of sanitation. "Rye and oats furnished the bread and drink of the great body of the people in Europe."[15] Cultivated herbage and roots were unknown in the agriculture of Britain before the end of the reign of Henry VIII. The vicissitudes of Lord Ernle's formidable list—"precariousness of livelihood, alternations between feasting and starvation, droughts, scarcities, famines, crime,

[13] *Ency. Brit.*, 14th ed., Vol. 23, p. 153, Tit. Village Communities.
[14] Marc Bloch: *Les caractères originaux de l'histoire rurale française.* (Les Belles Lettres, Paris, 1931).
[15] *Ency. Brit.*, 9th ed., Vol. 1, pp. 291, 294, Tit. Agriculture.

violence, murrains, scurvy, leprosy, typhoid diseases, wars, pestilences and plagues"—made part of mediaeval life to a degree with which we are wholly unacquainted in the western world of the present day, a matter which deserves emphasis, because in all the discussion now so common of the poverty which it is said accompanied the "industrial revolution," the fact is overlooked that conditions were worse before than after it.

Outside the villages, land was generally cultivated on the plan of a triennial rotation—the first year wheat or rye, the second year barley, oats, beans or peas, the third year fallow. There were no fences, but the land in each part of the rotation was divided into strips, long and narrow, often marked by rough balks of unploughed land, so that every member of the community could know what land was his, and so arranged that every one had a third of his holding in each part of the rotation. In the use of their land, all owners, from the lord of the manor down, were compelled to follow the same system—to plough, sow and reap at the same time. Roots, clover and artificial grasses, as Lord Ernle says, subsequently revolutionized farming. Flax, hemp, hops and other crops could have been raised to advantage as has since been done. More important still would have been the cultivation of potatoes, but no change could be made and no new crops introduced into an open-field farm unless the whole body of farmers agreed to alter their field customs, and this agreement never came.[16]

According to Professor Gras,[17] the scattered strips of arable land assigned to the use of individual farmers in mediaeval England varied in total amount from about fifteen to thirty acres. If one-third of a 15-acre allotment were fallow and 10 acres were planted, the farmer might possibly in good years harvest the

[16] *English Farming Past and Present*, Lord Ernle (Longmans, Green & Co., 1927, 4th ed.), p. 108.
[17] *History of Agriculture*, Professor N. S. B. Gras (Crofts & Co., 1925), p. 90.

16

equivalent of 40 bushels of wheat for bread and 50 bushels of barley for beer.[18] In addition to this, he would have during the summer a small quantity of milk from his cow and a few eggs and some meat from his chickens, ducks or geese. Plutarch says, in his *Life of Lycurgus*, that in ancient Sparta the provision for the master of a family and his wife was about 82 bushels of grain with a suitable proportion of wine and fruits—figures which are not very different from those which Professor Gras gives for mediaeval England.

Beyond the cultivated land lay the pastures—"waste land," as Dr. Anderson said, "in that state of abandonment that we call commons in England," or, in Dryden's phrase, "the bare commons of the withered field"—of which Adam Moore says that horses and oxen raised on upland commons were of little value, while the low commons were pest holes. "Hither come the Poor, the Blinde, the Lame, Tired, Scabbed, Mangie, Rotten, Murrainous and all kinds of diseased scurvie cattel" to infect sound animals, if any such there were.[19] "No individual," Lord Ernle says, "even if he had possessed the genius of Bakewell, could improve his live stock, since infectious diseases were rarely absent from the promiscuously-herded, half-starved cattle of the community."[20]

Almost the entire population of a village were farmers, raising food by methods that were slow and wasteful.

A grown ox seemed to have been little larger than a calf of the present day, and the fleece of a sheep often weighed less than two ounces. Many of the stock had to be killed before winter, and those that survived were

[18] "It is calculated that a man, his wife and five children, living chiefly upon bread, would consume a bushel of wheat a week." *Agriculture* by Sir John Sinclair (London, 1817), p. 82. See post, p. 104.

[19] *Bread for the Poor* by Adam Moore (London, 1653), pp. 23-24.

[20] *Landmarks in British Farming*, Jour. Roy. Ag. Soc., 1892, Third Series, Vol. III, p. 4.

often so weak in the spring that they had to be dragged to pasture on a sledge. Insufficient stock meant insufficient manure, and though the fields were allowed to lie fallow every third year, they were exhausted by constant crops of cereals and gave a yield of only about six bushels of wheat an acre, of which two had to be retained for seed. . . . The result was an alternation of waste and want. . . . Nearly every year was marked by a famine in one part or another of a country and famine was often followed by pestilence.[21]

It is of little use, Professor Gras says, to ask whether the mediaeval farmer could support his family on the small quantity of food which he could raise, for with much suffering he did, in a way, get along except, it may be said, when lack of fertilizing material, bad weather or poor seed brought short crops, which was not an unusual condition.

Of the use of meat, garden vegetables, milk and eggs, something will be said later. It is sufficient here to notice that the supply of these foods was seasonal, and scanty even for the producer's family. As a protection to the general public against ever-recurring scarcity, they were always totally inadequate—a matter of great importance, especially in the case of milk, since a good supply of milk, which is important for all, is necessary for infants. When this supply is lacking, infant mortality is high and when also food for human mothers is short, we have the explanation of one of the most distressing chapters in the long history of human suffering—the chapter which tells of the abandonment and exposure of infants.

There was a column known as the Lactaria Columna in the Vegetable Market at Rome, having no relation to milk, however, beyond a traditional association with an old Roman legend[22] and at this column, according to Festus, it was common to abandon

[21] *A History of Commerce* by Clive Day (Longmans, Green & Co., New York, 1921), pp. 35, 36.

[22] Pliny, *N. H.*, VII, 36; Valerius Maximus, V, 4-7; *Childe Harold*, Canto IV, CXLVIII—CL.

infants, as it was euphemistically said, "lacte alendos,"[23] that is to be fed by strangers with the milk which the parents of the child either would not or could not supply. It is hard to believe that in a great city like Rome, any such practice of public abandonment could exist and nevertheless, if necessary food was actually lacking, an explanation is offered for conduct which otherwise we do not understand. Gibbon says that in his time, above three thousand new-born infants were annually exposed on the streets of Pekin.[24] Mr. Warren S. Thompson said in 1935 that it was not improbable that at that time one-third to one-half of all the babies born in Shanghai were allowed to die or were killed almost immediately after birth and that in Europe it was not until well into the middle ages that infanticide was considered a crime.[25] What was done in one city or at a particular time might have been done in another city at other times, for the question is not one of race and period, but of food, and when the population lacks food, publicity ceases to be as shocking as it would be under the comparatively very easy conditions of our modern world. Albert Babeau, describing life in France four hundred years ago, says:

How often in years of want have the peasant and his wife, seated on stools in the corner of their fire-place, like the wood-cutter and his wife in Perrault's story, mourned because they could no longer feed their children! How often have they groaned, thinking of their empty bread-bin, their exhausted tubs of salted meat and their small harvest of grain that

[23] De Sig. Verb. Lib. X "Lactaria." *The Child in Human Progress* by George Henry Payne (Putnam, 1916), p. 242; *Walks in Rome* by Augustus J. C. Hare (George Allen, London, 1893), Vol. I, pp. 155-156; *History of European Morals* by W. E. H. Lecky (Appleton & Co., New York, 1898), Chap. IV, Vol. II, pp. 24-33. See Chapter on Foundling Hospitals in *History of Inventions, Discoveries and Origins* by John Beckmann (Bohn, London, 1846), Vol. II, p. 434.
[24] *Decline and Fall* (Harper & Brothers, 1905), Chap. XV, Vol. II, p. 135.
[25] *Population Problems* by Mr. Warren S. Thompson (McGraw-Hill Book Company, New York, 1935), p. 7.

had been completely used! Famines have been only too frequent in the last two hundred years![26]

Mr. John Louw Nelson has very recently told of the Hopi Indians who, in times of great drought, sold their children for corn and water,[27] and it is out of such conditions of want that stories arise like the tale of the Babes in the Wood, the fable of Roland and May Bird and other similar stories.

Obviously, then, the middle ages offered no room for ambition and individual initiative. Unless all moved together, no one could move hand or foot. There could be no improved methods of cultivation, no better live stock, without unanimous consent, and the result was increasing exhaustion of the soil, an agriculture that, as compared with the agriculture of the thirteenth century, remained stationary or actually retrograded and, in the end, the breakdown of the manorial system.

The middle ages practised what the present world would call community planning. The profit motive had been successfully eliminated, and the result was starvation. St. Jerome put the gist of the problem in few words when he asked:

Nonne qui arat, laboris sui fruge laetabitur?[28]

Shall not he who ploughs enjoy the fruit of his labor? Surely he will not work long for nothing! And Dr. Samuel Johnson summed the matter up when he said:

It is no wonder that when the prospect of reward has vanished, the zeal of enterprise should cease.[29]

[26] *La vie rurale dans l'ancienne France* (Librairie Académique Didier, Emile Perrin, Editeur, Paris, 1885), p. 100.
[27] *Rhythm for Rain* (Houghton Mifflin Co., 1937).
[28] Letter XXII Ad Eustachium.
[29] *The Rambler*, No. 127. "Now unto him that worketh, is the reward not reckoned of grace, but of debt." *Romans*, IV, 4.

Shakespeare expressed the same idea when he said:

> The sweat of industry would dry and die
> But for the end it works to.[30]

Of the effect of want upon the minds of men, less has been written, but it is because our mental powers become reduced by want that progress was stayed for many centuries. "There is no such thing as 'the energy of despair,' " Mr. Albert Guérard says, "despair is depressing."[31]

[30] *Cymbeline*, Act III, Sc. vi.
[31] *The Life and Death of an Ideal* (Charles Scribner's Sons, New York, 1928), p. 298.

CHAPTER II

PRODUCTION IN A STAND-STILL WORLD. HAND LABOR

THE modern world is so accustomed to the immense volume of production which comes with the use of agricultural machinery, improved seed, chemical fertilizers, flour mills, textile mills and steam transportation, that it seldom occurs to us to speculate as to what our conditions would be were all those aids to safe, comfortable life taken from us, or to consider the problem how the world ever could have procured food, comforts and clothing without them. When we do think of such questions, it becomes immediately obvious to us that a society which lived on the products of hand labor only must have been very simple and subject to frequent periods of want and starvation.

Man as a Hunter. Primitive man found his food in field and forest in the roots and leaves of plants, in berries, fruits, fish and game, but hunting with primitive weapons was difficult and success was not great. All articles of food which could be secured were obtained by hand work, with very little diversification of labor. Every person who was strong and well was fully occupied and effort was great, but the results were so small that want was the rule and comfort rare.

Mr. J. S. Newberry, in an article on *The Food and Fibre Plants of the North American Indians*, published in 1887, gives facts from which it is possible to get a better understanding of the conditions in which primitive man lived than can be secured from all the writings of Rousseau and Chateaubriand.

One article of subsistence, [Mr. Newberry said] sometimes employed by the Indians, is only resorted to when they are driven to great straits of hunger. Around many of the watering-places in the pine forests of Oregon and California, the trees of pinus ponderoso may be seen stripped of their bark for a space of three or four feet near the base of the trunk. This has been accomplished by cutting with a hatchet a line around the tree as high up as one could conveniently reach, and another lower down, so that the bark, severed above and below, could be removed in strips. At certain seasons of the year a mucilaginous film (the laburnum) separates the bark from the wood of the tree. Part of this film adheres to the surface and may be scraped off. The resulting mixture of mucilage cells and half-formed wood is nutritious and not unpalatable so that, as a last resort, it may be used as a defense against starvation. The frequency with which signs of its having been resorted to are met with is a striking indication of the uncertainties and irregularities of the supply department among savages.[1]

Malthus, describing the life of American Indians, says that it was their general custom to separate, at certain seasons of the year, in search of food since, if they remained in their villages, famine was certain. Evidently their crops of maize and gourds were not very reliable supplies. Even when they were scattered in the woods, their sufferings were sometimes extreme. In one case a party of eleven, having eaten the skins they had with them, their shoes and the bark of trees, finally resorted to cannibalism, five only of the party surviving.[2]

What must the condition of want have been, before savages could have discovered that by scraping the trunk of some trees under the bark, at certain periods of the year, they could get food! The wonder, however, does not end there for, as Professor East says, pre-historic man "pounded up and made flap-jacks

[1] Popular Science Monthly, Vol. XXXII, p. 37. This practice, or something like it, seems to have been known in Sweden. See Malthus, *Essay on the Population*, Bk. II, Chap. II, Vol. I, p. 173.

[2] *Essay on the Population*, Bk. I, Chap. IV, Vol. I, p. 39.

or stew out of nearly everything that grows,"[3] while as for meat, men seem to have lived like the hyena. Worms on trees or reeds[4] and dead bodies in the woods, all were used to sustain life, and nevertheless, as Professor and Mrs. C. C. Furnas well say, "the supply of dead or ailing animals must have been distressingly low at times." Practically, primitive man spent all his strength in gathering food and defending himself. On these terms life was uncertain and want was the greatest of all enemies.[5] Men could face death but they knew and feared that shape which Columella called death's most terrible companion, hunger. Savagery is the condition where much effort brings small results, when hunger, cold, pain and want are experiences none can escape. These are the conditions out of which exposure of infants and of the weak and aged, cannibalism and war, have often risen. When there is no assured supply of food and other necessary articles, man rises from savagery only with the greatest difficulty.

Man as a Nomad. It was a step forward when men learned to domesticate animals since from them they could secure an additional food supply so long as the tribe was not too numerous for the animals that could be pastured. When this happened, it was necessary for some of the tribe to take their herds and flocks to new pastures. There was still, however, little diversification of labor, effort was great and results small.

Agricultural Civilization. The development of different trades first began clearly to appear when man found that he could get more food and other necessary supplies by agriculture than he could from the life of the hunter or from the flocks and herds

---

[3] ". . . ingenio hominis nihil intentatum relinquente," Bruyerinus Campegius, Lib. XI, Cap. XXV, p. 624.

[4] ". . . vermes quosdam qui humani digiti crassitudine in arundinibus nascuntur," *De Alimentis*, J. D. Sala, Cap. II, p. 9.

[5] *Man, Bread and Destiny* by Professor and Mrs. C. C. Furnas (Reynal & Hitchcock, N. Y., 1937), p. 280.

THE CROOKED STICK PLOUGH, PERU

A Wooden Plough in Modern India

of the nomad, and probably both of these steps, first from the life of the hunter to pastoral life, and then to agriculture, were, as Mr. Ross thinks, caused in part by the hunger of a growing population goading indolent humanity forward.[6] Little by little, man learned to relieve some of his wants, so that progress is the condition of decreasing efforts and increasing results. Increase of food by farming meant settled habitations, for whose construction carpenters and stone masons were needed. Very soon mechanics appeared to make wagons, ploughs and harnesses. Spinning and weaving assumed new importance since mechanics must be clothed as well as fed out of the products of the farms. Agriculture exists, Montesquieu says, only when there are "many inventions and many degrees of knowledge, and we always see ingenuity, the arts and a sense of want making their progress with an equal pace."[7] It is to be observed, then, not only that diversification of labor began with the increased supply of food and other necessaries which agriculture made possible, but that the extent of diversification was limited by the degree of efficiency which agricultural and industrial methods had attained. "It must ever be true," Malthus said, "that the surplus produce of the cultivators, taken in its most enlarged sense, measures and limits the growth of that part of the society which is not employed upon the land. Throughout the whole world, the number of manufacturers of merchants, of proprietors, and of persons engaged in the various civil and military professions, must be exactly proportioned to this surplus produce and cannot in the nature of things increase beyond it."[8] As agriculture became more and more successful, the supplies increased so that it was possible, as time went on and methods improved, to feed, clothe and house

[6] *Standing Room Only* by Mr. Edward Aylesworth Ross (The Century Company, New York, 1927), p. 179.
[7] *Spirit of the Laws*, Bk. XVIII, Chap. 15.
[8] *Essay on the Population*, Bk. III, Chap. VIII, Vol. II, p. 76.

larger numbers of artisans. New arts, therefore, came into existence and civilization became increasingly complicated, the farmer receiving in new comforts the compensation for his products on which the community lived.

It has sometimes been said that civilization is the search of hungry man for food, but only the beginnings of civilization can be made in this way. Starvation is not productive. Hungry men do not meditate about arts and cannot develop anything beyond the primitive methods of early man. From these methods, however, under favorable conditions, agriculture arose, bringing increased food and a degree of leisure sufficient to permit man to turn his mind to the study of the possibilities before him. Agricultural civilization, then, in Malthus' phrase, is exactly proportioned to the opportunity for study which surplus products of agriculture gave, and if this was a simple civilization which could not rise above the level reached during the long years between the fifth century B. C. and the nineteenth century A. D., the explanation is again in Malthus' statement that, being exactly proportioned, it is exactly limited.

Further progress is possible only with more leisure, under conditions favorable to study, with such inducements as will arouse individual ambition, and with increased individual resources.

The history of man, Le Grand d'Aussy says, begins with the provision of food, his first and most pressing need. Lodging and clothes are not needed in all countries and climates, but food is required everywhere and every day.[9]

The very first day that men opened their eyes in the world they knew hunger and the use of food.[10]

We would expect, then, that agriculture would be the subject to which man would devote his greatest efforts, and that in this field

[9] *La vie privée des Français* by Le Grand d'Aussy, Vol. I, Chap. I.
[10] *Carestia e Fame* by Giovanni Battista Segni (Bologna, 1602), p. 115.

the earliest triumphs of his intelligence would be found. Unfortunately, the improvement of agriculture has been so slow in human history that it has been called the art of the world's advanced age. Moreover, the facts in its development are very difficult to learn. There is no direct and continuous narrative but, as Mr. Hoskyns well says, "from a wide and varied field of research we must be content to gather such indications as lie scattered here and there, sometimes in an incidental digression, sometimes in a parenthetical remark let fall by a writer who little contemplated affording information on a topic like Husbandry."[11]

In modern Europe, the first great forward movement in agriculture was made by the Saracens in southern Spain, whose career from the fifth to the eleventh century forms, perhaps, "the most brilliant episode in the whole history of agriculture."[12] From the tenth to the fifteenth century the best agriculture was in northern Italy, and thereafter, until taken up by England, was carried on in the Netherlands, but neither in Spain, in Italy nor in the Netherlands have we any narrative of operations and methods.

Lord Macaulay remarked that Venice prospered for centuries without bequeathing to mankind the memory of one great name or generous action. The Po valley, nevertheless, of which Venice was a seaport, maintained the lamp of civilization burning during the darkest period of the dark ages. The humble contributions of men who kept the arts of agriculture and industry alive furnished little material for royal chroniclers, and the account of many of their achievements is lost. We do not know the names of those who did so much for human welfare, nor the circumstances of their lives, but we can, from what we know of these lands, of their inhabitants and of events, piece together a story of absorbing interest.

[11] *An Inquiry into the History of Agriculture* by Mr. Chandos Wren Hoskyns, (London, 1849), p. 10.
[12] *Ibid.*, p. 60.

The western countries of Europe are comparatively destitute of natural productions fit for exportation and the success which these countries have achieved in commerce has come from the intelligence and industry of their inhabitants.[13] Natural advantages would have had much less value to a less efficient population.

Northern Italy, however, is a well-watered country of rich herbage where cattle can be pastured all winter and the Netherlands enjoy a similar advantage, having a pasture season so long and grass so abundant that enough hay can be stored in summer to meet winter needs. In both countries, therefore, it was possible to keep cattle in sufficient numbers to give adequate power for the cultivation of the land and also to provide a supply of milk, cheese, butter and meat. Animal husbandry, agriculture and horticulture were thus carried on together and became a source of wealth both to Italy and to the Netherlands, as they were also in some degree elsewhere, as in Artois and Hainault.[14]

With tillage, however, there is no easy profit. In light soils the earliest plough may have been the crooked stick, such as is shown in the illustration, or it may in some places have been an adaptation of the husbandman's tool, as Mr. Hoskyns very reasonably suggests,[15] but it is to those modest tools, as Dr. Savoy says, that the great civilizations of Babylon and Egypt owe their brilliant progress.

Of course, light ploughs such as those first made would be useless in heavy soils and they were never efficient even in light soils. Ploughs were, therefore, made of wood, the point being tipped with iron, and since strains were great, it was necessary to use the strongest wood that could be had, strengthening it by braces as well as possible. Iron ploughs first appeared during the

[13] *Middle Ages*, Hallam (Murray, London, 1853), Chap. IX, Part I, p. 315.
[14] *De Re Cibaria* by Bruyerinus Campegius (Lyons, 1560), Lib. II, Cap. III, p. 84. *La vie privée des Français*, Le Grand d'Aussy, Vol. I, p. 3.
[15] *An Inquiry into the History of Agriculture* (London, 1849), p. 26.

Harrowing in India

SEEDING GRAIN

third century before Christ, but they came slowly into use and indeed never wholly displaced the wooden ploughs which are still employed in backward countries. Pliny says that, in Italy, two or three pairs of oxen were necessary for each plough,[16] these pairs probably being used in succession, fresh animals being taken as the preceding pair was exhausted. Mr. Henry Row says that, in England, the ordinary plough team had eight oxen and, since men had learned by that time how to use animal power, these ox teams were hitched one in front of another.[17] It must have required great strength to guide such a plough and we can well understand that the services of two or three men might often have been needed. In Scotland, only a couple of hundred years ago, ploughing was done with six to a dozen oxen harnessed with ropes of straw, while four men were needed to carry on the work.[18]

The oxen, both in Scotland and in mediaeval England, were stunted and weak from lack of food, but so were the men who drove them and who managed the plough. Moreover, good work was impossible where strength, energy and hope took no part, and the work therefore fared as all work must fare when so done. Conditions in Scotland at the beginning of the nineteenth century were well described by Professor David Low:

Within the memory almost of the living generation, the agriculture of Ayrshire was in a state of utter rudeness. The farm houses were mere hovels built with clay. . . . There were no fallows, no green crops, no sown grasses, no carts, no waggons, no straw yards.

Hardly an esculent root was raised, nor indeed any garden vegetables beyond some Scotch greens which, with milk and oatmeal, formed the diet of the people. . . . The ground was scourged with successive crops of oats after oats so long as it would pay the seed and the labour and afford a small surplus of oatmeal for the subsistence of the family. It then re-

[16] *N.H.*, Lib. XVIII, Cap. 48.

[17] *Manorial Farming*, Nineteenth Century and After. March, 1927, pp. 395-396.

[18] *Scotland* by Mr. Robert Laird Mackie (London, 1916), p. 501.

mained in a state of absolute sterility and covered with thistles until rest
enabled it to produce a scanty crop of corn . . . there being scarcely
any enclosures, the horses and cattle were either tethered during the summer months or intrusted to the discretion of the shepherd and his cur, by
whom they were kept in continued agitation, being impelled, through
famine, to fly from their bare leas and commit continued depredation on
the adjacent crops. The cattle being starved during winter, were hardly
able to rise without assistance in spring, and were never in fit condition
for market. . . . Such was the condition, not of Ayrshire alone, but of a
great part of Scotland during half the reign of George III and down to
the times which men yet living can remember. Ayrshire did not surpass,
in the course of improvement, districts like itself, but rather lagged behind.
Scarcely anything that deserves the name of agricultural improvement was
effected in it until after the disastrous close of the American war; most of
what has been done has been done since the commencement of the present
century, and much of it within a few years.[19]

It is a shocking story. To those who know what Scotland is to-
day, it seems impossible, and nevertheless the conditions which
Professor Low describes were not greatly different from those
which had prevailed generally in Europe but a short time before.
Scotland may have come slowly out of the disasters of the Napoleonic Wars, but doubtless other parts of Europe also came slowly
out of those disasters.

Reaping, before the days of machinery, was done with a sickle
and, until flails were used,[20] grain was separated from the
straw either by going over it with heavy rollers or by the treading
of horses or cattle. With a flail, a man could thresh about eight
bushels of wheat in a day, and of this work Loudon says:

[19] *The Breeds of Domestic Animals of the British Islands* by Professor David
Low (London, 1842), Plate XIII.

[20] If the ears of grain were cut from the straw, these ears "possunt in
horreum conferri, et deinde per hyemem vel baculis excuti vel exteri pecudibus."
If horses or oxen were not available "ipsae spicae melius fustibus tunduntur,
vannisque expurgantur." Columella, Lib. II, Cap. XXI. Evidently, flails were
known in Columella's time.

The expense was very considerable while the severity of the labor almost exceeded the power of the strongest man, especially in unfavorable seasons when the grain adhered pertinaciously to the ear, and could not without difficulty be removed. In such seasons, expense was the smallest consideration . . . it was the quantity of grains unavoidably lost which occupied his attention.[21]

A householder to-day, who might be given a crooked stick plough, or a plough of the ancient heavy kind, with an ancient harrow, a spade, a hoe and a rake, being told at the same time that it would no longer be possible to buy grain or cotton from great fields cultivated by machinery, nor meat, eggs or wool from animals raised on the products of such fields, nor clothes made from materials woven in textile mills, might reasonably regard his future and the future of his family with some concern. Nevertheless, the world lived—and starved—in about that way until very recently. John Arbuthnot, in his tables of Grecian and Roman measures, remarks that the Emperor Augustus had neither glass in the windows of his palace nor a shirt on his back, and though the statement may exaggerate the rarity of glass and linen at that time, nevertheless, in substance the picture which it suggests of the conditions of ancient life accords with the facts.[22] What was true as to food in Greece and Rome of the classical period was true also, in varying degrees, of the early Christian era, and during mediaeval times, and down to a date later even than the American Revolution.

Industrial Civilization. The history of the world before the year 1800 is, therefore, the story of many ages in which the supply of those things which are necessary for the maintenance of

[21] Loudon's *Encyclopaedia of Agriculture* (London, 1857), Sec. 5044. For operations of winnowing and screening, see *English Farming Past and Present* by Lord Ernle (Longmans, Green & Co., 1927), p. 357.

[22] Gibbon, *Decline and Fall* (Harper & Brothers, New York, 1905), Chap. XXXI, note 33, Vol. III, p. 371.

31

life was inadequate to meet the demands of the existing population.

Long before the Christian era, agricultural civilization had reached in some fields a high state of development. Greek architecture, for its purposes, has never been surpassed. Ancient sculpture has been a model for all succeeding ages. Roman law is the basis of that part of our judicial system which arose through the English chancery. The literature and philosophy of Greece and Rome show an intellectual life of a very high order, but having reached this stage of development, the world paused.

How many of us realize what a large part of our civilization is the growth of a night, as it were? There was a spasmodic development of culture [in classical times] which cannot be minimized, in spite of dark ages in which much of the social heritage of mankind seemed by way of being lost; yet the modern development of knowledge . . . which has placed this era so far ahead of previous eras, is the result of an acceleration so recent that it may be dated within the memory of our great-grand-fathers some hundred and fifty years ago.[23]

Professor George Beard Grundy, of Cambridge University, in his excellent article in the *Encyclopaedia Britannica*[24] says that conditions of life during former ages were so different from those which surround us at the present day,

that it is difficult to realize, and perhaps impossible to realize fully, even the main circumstances of an existence in which factors which are in some respects the chief determinants of modern life played no part; and this although life in western Europe up to the end of the 18th century in many ways approximates in respect to its economics more closely to the life of the men of the fifth century before Christ than it does to that of the present day.

To the same effect is the statement of Mr. Austin Freeman that

[23] *Mankind at the Crossroads* by Professor Edward M. East (Charles Scribner's Sons, New York, 1923), p. 18.
[24] 14th ed., Tit. Greece, Vol. 10, pp. 779-780.

CUTTING THE EARS OF GRAIN IN THE FIELD

THE THRESHING FLOOR

the transition from the rough stone implements used by early man to more skilfully worked metal implements indicated no really radical change in the conditions of human life,

nor does any such radical change come into view during the many centuries of advancing civilization that gradually evolved the modern world. Startling as it may appear, it is, nevertheless, true that from the dawn of history to the latter half of the eighteenth century, nothing had occurred substantially to alter the relation of man to his environment.[25]

Possibly Mr. Freeman does not sufficiently emphasize the change from barbarism to a pastoral life, and from the pastoral life to conditions of settled agriculture, but few will question the statement that, from the fifth century before Christ to the beginning of the nineteenth century after Christ, the advance was surprisingly small.

Surely there is something here to think of—a period of 2300 years of human history in which progress was so slight that, at the end of that time, the conditions surrounding the lives of our great-grandparents were more like the conditions surrounding men who lived in the time of Plato or Scipio Africanus than they would be to conditions which prevail in Europe or America to-day! The great changes which distinguish modern life have come, then, since the year 1800 or, in figures, the history of modern civilization divides into two periods, one of 2300 or more years, the other of 139 years. The striking phenomenon of the long pause and the quick growth must be understood if we are to entertain any reasonable ideas of the course of man on earth, and the explanation is in the story of Food and Freedom. Man's outlook upon nature had changed in the course of 2000 years, and the world was ready for an advance. When commons were abolished, the opportunity came. Thereafter, man could control his own field, enjoying, in St. Jerome's phrase, the fruit of his labor, and so an inducement was

[25] *Social Decay and Regeneration* (Constable & Co., London, 1921), p. 80.

offered to private ambition. Once more there was surplus produce and this surplus brought leisure and an opportunity for study. Man could lift his eyes from the ground and his hand from his work and out of it all came machinery and our industrial civilization. Freedom, opportunity and the inducement which the right to enjoy the fruits of one's labor brings, were the source of Progress.

More surprising even than the long stagnation of over 2000 years is, however, the fact that mankind is not yet fully reconciled to what has been accomplished. There are persons still who undervalue intellectual effort, regarding manual labor as the source of wealth[26] and who, as to the use of particular machines, live mentally in the long ages before 1800. The objection to machines, however, is always to new machines. The old machines, locomotives, textile mills, and even the automobile, are now willingly accepted as parts of our necessary equipment. Sir Henry Maine says that universal suffrage would have prohibited the spinning jenny, the power loom and the threshing machine, but no one objects to these machines now. In America, we have seen opposition to the reaper and binder, the linotype machine and the cotton-picker, but the objection seems to pass away with age, and the idea of the cotton-picker, being new, is still unpopular.

It is in most cases a kindly feeling for the man out of a job which leads to a desire to multiply jobs and return to methods which require two men to do the work of one, but the system carried to its logical conclusion leaves two men to live on what is sufficient for one, and with time, as this becomes understood, the necessary economies are gradually accepted.

The subject of machinery is so closely related to the abundant production of all comforts, to the abolition of famine and to what has been called the Conquest of Hunger, that it must occupy an

[26] Non viribus, aut velocitatibus, aut celeritate corporum res magnae geruntur: sed consilio, auctoritate, sententia. Cicero, *De Senectute*, Cap. 6.

important place in the history of our food supply. It deserves attention, too, because the methods which produce abundant food are methods which produce all other comforts of human life and with them the greatest comforts of all—human freedom and the dignity which exists when society is founded upon a recognition of individual rights. We shall find also that human slavery, which during many centuries pressed upon all races of mankind, including the white race of our western world, was the result of inefficient methods of production. It is an important fact in western history that not alone are freedom and food closely inter-related as cause and effect, but their contraries, want and slavery, are also related, so that use of inefficient methods of labor, employing two men to do the work of one, is not a forward movement but is a step backward toward old conditions. We cannot, indeed, expect that slavery of the white man will again return, but decreased human efficiency is possible and if such decreased efficiency come, it will bring with it not only a loss of comforts to which we are accustomed, but will involve also limitations of individual freedom that would so weigh upon our activities and mental life that it would seem an appreciable step backward toward the slavery of the ancient world. Man suffers in mind and body when he lacks the means to supply his essential needs. The spur of necessity and the hope of relief have been the source of human progress, but great want without hope is crushing. Unless man have adequate food and other necessary supplies, his physical growth is stunted, his mind is undeveloped and his activity checked. The machines which the nineteenth century brought, coming at a time when population was small and there was much new land, gave mankind, for the first time in human history, the food, clothing and comfort which made great progress possible.

There was a time when almost the entire population of a country was directly or indirectly engaged in agriculture. At present, in

35

America, those so engaged are comparatively few, and these men, perhaps no more than a quarter of the population, do the farming for all who are engaged in other occupations. So, in the production of all the innumerable articles which modern life demands—prepared foods of many kinds, clothing, medicines, safety razors, fountain pens—one man in every place does the work of many. It is as though every worker stood at the point of a cone providing for the indefinite number of workers in other trades which the great spreading mass of the cone represents. Throughout the country these centers of production, which have been likened to cones, are in inconceivable numbers. Almost every article that need demands or pleasure desires can be had in almost every city and in many towns—all made by one or a few organizations and used by the nation. Moreover, new conveniences, for which we have not yet learned to wish, show themselves every day and some quickly become standard articles which we would not willingly do without. Reduce the use of machinery or the efficiency of labor in any center of production and supplies become smaller, while the price rises beyond the reach of persons having small means. On the other hand, when efficiency is increased, the price goes down, people of small means are able to enjoy what before they could not afford, and new industries appear like magic to provide other articles never before known.

Modern life, therefore, depends on the ability of each worker to provide for many persons who are each in their separate fields working for him.

Many years ago, there was a book written for young people, *How One Man Has Saved a Host*. Modern civilization is built upon that very plan. The medicine must be at the druggist's, the shoes must be at the store, the safety razor or the fountain pen must be where it can be had, or inconvenience begins which

36

TREADING OUT THE GRAIN WITH ANIMALS

WINNOWING GRAIN

soon, if lack increase, will become trouble—and one man can work for many only if he have the aid of machinery.

When Goldsmith wrote the lines:

> Ill fares the land to hastening ills a prey,
> Where wealth accumulates and men decay,

he had in mind only that the small farmers of his time were reluctant to change their ways and objected to the abolition of commons,[27] but he could have profited by the advice which Aaron Burr gave to Mrs. Preston, to "deal less in sentiments and more in ideas." The statement indeed is such as we have learned to expect from a man who does not know the value of money and who, as his friend Dr. Samuel Johnson said, "raised money and squandered it, by every artifice of acquisition and every folly of expense."[28] Goldsmith certainly never intended seriously to say that wealth is bad. Agricultural machinery and textile mills which feed and clothe the world are wealth and upon them the intellectual, as well as physical, activity of the world depends. Books are not evidences of decay because they come from the presses and mills which are part of the wealth of present times. The truth is that

> Ill fares the land where hastening trouble preys
> And population grows while wealth decays,

but that was not what Goldsmith said. He could not look far enough ahead to see the stimulus which private ownership would give to ambition and initiative, nor the large number of people who could

[27] "Mr. Richard Carew, in his survey of Cornwall, saith that before that country was inclosed, the husbandmen drank water, did eat little or no bread (fol. 66, lib. I), their apparel was coarse, they went bare-legged, their dwelling was correspondent; but since inclosure they live decently and have money to spend (fol. 23); when their fields were common their wool was coarse Cornish hair; but since inclosure it is almost as good as Cotswold, and their soil much mended. Tusser, Chap. 52 of his Husbandry is of his opinion, one acre inclosed is worth three common." Quoted in Burton, *Anatomy*, Democritus to the Reader (George Bell, London, 1896), Vol. I, p. 112.

[28] Letter of Samuel Johnson to Bennet Langton, July 5, 1774.

be supported by enclosed fields which, when used as commons, produced little. A poet and a dramatist failed to understand the value, to his country and to the world, of the historic work in which Robert Bakewell was at that very time engaged, and which stirred up, as Dr. Anderson said in 1799, "a species of furor in the breeding line that hath, perhaps, no parallel in history, unless it be the tulipa-mania which, about two hundred years ago, prevailed in Holland."[29] It was a great achievement for a working farmer to teach the world what could be done to improve cattle and sheep and it is his work with cattle that suggested to Amos Cruikshank, the Colling brothers and others, the improvement of British beef animals of which Mr. James Sinclair says that it has made it possible "materially to raise the standard of living of the toiling millions."[30]

In the end, the abolition of commons was a contributing cause for all the progress that the nineteenth century brought.

[29] *Recreations in Agriculture*, etc. by Dr. James Anderson (London, 1799), Vol. I, p. 75.
[30] *History of Shorthorn Cattle* (London, 1908), Chap. I, p. 1.

CHAPTER III

THE FOUNDATIONS OF THE MODERN WORLD.
PRODUCTION IN GREECE AND ROME

MANY tales have been written by imaginative authors of travels in time as well as in space, and not a few of these stories have taken us into the future where we could look backward upon present affairs. It would be very instructive if, instead of going into the realm of fancy, we could take a trip in time back to the old world of Greece and Rome, a world which existed in fact, not in fancy, and could there see for ourselves the life out of which our modern civilization has so recently risen.

Probably, could we take such a trip, our minds before going would be filled with thoughts of the people whom we hoped to meet, and afterward, when once more we returned to our pleasant modern surroundings, we would find that the first questions our friends would ask would be personal questions as to the manner, appearance, conduct and opinions of men who played great parts in periods of history about which the world has thought much. And, while we were listening to these questions, it is probable that our minds would be so filled with new experiences which had been unexpected and overwhelming that our answer would be:

"Yes, I saw these men and later I will tell you about them but first I must tell you how I have been living, for unless you know that, you cannot understand my answers to your questions."

So we would tell of a world where there were no clocks or watches, no dry goods stores, a world where houses had no chim-

39

neys, and rooms heated in cold weather by a fire on a hearth or
fire-pan in the center of the room, were filled with smoke whenever
a fire was started, and where consequently the walls, ceiling and
furniture were blackened and more or less covered by soot at all
times; where light was supplied by smoky oil lamps which, like the
houses in which they were used, had no chimneys, and where eye-
trouble as a result of all this smoke was general. It was a world
having little knowledge as to means of curing disease but having
great faith in empirical remedies. "Medicus nihil est, nisi con-
solatio animi," said Petronius—a doctor is nothing but consolation
for the mind—but the herb-doctor, well known to modern times
on street corners in cities, at country fairs and in the stories of
O. Henry, was in the height of his glory and almost the sole resource of the sick. Roman houses, even though lacking in what we
would think the simplest and most necessary conveniences, were at
least substantial in structure, but Greek dwellings were small and
made of sun-dried bricks. They had no heat in winter, no adequate
sanitary arrangements, no washing facilities,[1] and had beds without
sheets, which in some cases were laid on leather straps for springs,
possibly regarded as an indication of effeminacy, for Plutarch,
when describing the luxury of Alcibiades' life, says that he caused
the planks of his galley to be cut away so that he might lie the
softer, his bed not being placed on boards but hanging upon girths.

In his *Life of Pelopidas*, Plutarch says of Timagoras, the Athenian envoy to Persia, that he not only accepted from the King
presents of gold and silver, but also "a rich bed, and slaves to
make it, as if that had been an art unknown to the Greeks."
Plutarch's indignation suggests, nevertheless, that if the art of
bed-making was indeed known in Greece at that time, the knowledge was probably of recent acquisition, for were it not for this

[1] As to soap, see *History of Inventions*, etc. by John Beckmann, Vol. I, p. 92.

defence, no reflection on domestic manners would be seen in such a gift.

Meals consisted of one simple dish of cooked cereal that the Greeks called sitos, not very different from the dish which the Romans called puls, and that we would call a kind of porridge— or possibly sometimes like the bread now used by peasants in Syria—dough without yeast, rolled or kneaded into thin shapes and baked. Meat was not often to be had except at festivals when the carcasses of sacrificial animals, so far as they would go, were distributed,[2] but there were other things that could be eaten with the cereal, figs or olives, dried dates, an onion or turnip, and, as Professor Zimmern says, "everything that was not sitos was dessert" or, as the Greeks called it, "opson,"[3] whence the Romans brought their word "obsonium."[4]

In such a world as this, what are the possibilities of food which present themselves to us?

Some fish could be had in summer but in winter the sea was rough for ancient sailors, so the fish then available would be chiefly such as had been salted when caught, and summer and winter the supply was small.[5] Moreover, Mediterranean fish were not a luxury and were never offered in sacrifice.[6] Garden vegetables could be raised but there was little fertilizing material, the

[2] See I Cor., VIII, 4.

[3] The Greek Commonwealth (Clarendon Press, Oxford, 1911), p. 46.

[4] Obsonium was deified as the offspring of parents who were none other than Time and Wealth—Saturnus and Ops, the Earth. See Sacrorum Sacrificiorum Descriptio by Johannis Guilielmus Stuckius (Tiguri, 1598), p. 22b.

[5] For salsamenta, see De Re Cibaria by Bruyerinus, Lib. X, Cap. XVI, p. 567.

[6] Plutarch's Symposiacs, Question VIII, Vol. III, p. 423.

Gibbon says, however, that "the Propontis has ever been renowned for an inexhaustible store of the most exquisite fish." Decline and Fall, Chap. XVII, Vol. II, p. 254. Obviously tastes differ—non eodem calopodio omnes calceantur.

Conf. however, Public Economy of the Athenians by Augustus Boeckh. Trans. by Anthony Lamb, from 2nd German edition (Little, Brown & Co., Boston, 1857), pp. 139, 141 et seq.

soil of Greece and much of Italy was not very fertile, rain in summer was rare, and most of the garden products had to be eaten when fresh. Beans and peas could be dried and kept, while turnips and onions would last for a considerable time if properly stored. Food could also be preserved by pickling in brine, and Columella, in his twelfth book, gives many recipes of this sort. Where there were forests producing mast, pigs could forage, and their meat when not eaten fresh could be salted for later use, but these foods were like the two bales of goods which the chorus of smugglers carries in the opera of Carmen—a decoration, not a way of life. The lasting permanent food was grain and the most important work of the farmer was to produce grain, a very serious business when, according to Mr. Hallam,[7] nine or ten bushels were a full average crop per acre of wheat, on which two bushels had been spread as seed, a statement that is borne out by the figures which M. François de Neufchateau gives in his note to *Le théâtre d'agriculture* by Olivier de Serres.[8] In addition to this, however, since in a very physical sense man cannot live on bread or porridge alone, ancient farmers produced also wine and oil. Porridge was the principal food which kept the ancient world alive, but they used olive oil somewhat as we might use butter,[9] or as an unguent, they drank weak wine which they diluted with water, and they had such extras, as we might call them, in the form of fish or pork, generally salted, or vegetables, generally dried or pickled, as good fortune might furnish. Of all these foods, every community was obliged to secure its own supply, and if that supply ran short there was suffering.

The ancient world, then, of Greece and Rome was a world of

[7] *Middle Ages*, Chap. IX, Part II (Murray, London, 1853), Vol. III, p. 363.
[8] Paris edition of 1804, Vol. I, p. 193.
[9] "Oleum recens comedi potest cum pane absque damno: butyrum non potest." *Institutionum Epitome*, Caspar Hoffmann (Paris, 1648), Lib. V, Cap. XIII, pp. 432-434.

hand labor and want. Except for sails on boats, and water power which was used to a slight extent, man had no source of mechanical power to supplement his own strength.

It has been assumed that ancient civilizations had a good, even though perhaps not an adequate, use of animal power. This, however, Commandant Lefebvre des Noëttes denies in his book, *La force animale à travers les âges*, published in 1924, and in his more recent book, *L'attelage et le cheval de selle à travers les âges*, published in 1931, revising and developing the argument of his first book.[10]

Animal Power in Classical Times. Of course, the horse and ox and other animals have been used for draught and pack purposes, as well as for riding, from very early times but, M. des Noëttes says, the methods followed in harnessing draught animals prevented full development of the power which the animals possessed.

M. Alfred Leger over sixty years ago spoke of the fact that the Romans had a poor system of harnessing their horses,[11] although he did not describe the Roman harness nor perhaps appreciate how the failure to use animal power reacted upon Roman civilization. This is the subject which M. des Noëttes has now taken up. In

[10] These two books present a new view of important phases of history and were at once the subject of criticism, the principal attack being made by Professor Gustave Fougères in the Journal des Savants, Vol. 22, N. S. (1924), pp. 229-232. Subsequently, Professor Fougères changed his opinion and adopted M. des Noëttes' conclusions. See *Peuples et civilisations* (Alcan, 1926), Vol. I, pp. 404-405. To the second of M. des Noëttes' books, *L'attelage*, etc., M. Jérôme Carcopino contributed his support in an approving preface. Dr. Emile Savoy in *L'agriculture à travers les âges* (Paris, 1935), Vol. 2, Chap. VI, pp. 91 et seq., also accepts M. des Noëttes' views, as does Professor Gaston Bouthoul in *La population dans le monde* (Payot, Paris, 1935), pp. 64-65. M. des Noëttes' work has been the subject of many articles and reviews in French publications and, although some of them have raised minor questions, his principal conclusions appear to be generally accepted.

[11] ". . . un mauvais système d'attelage,"—*Les travaux publics aux temps des Romains* (Paris, 1875), p. 173.

harnessing horses, he says, the use of shoulder-collars and traces was unknown, and in their place the horses, hitched in pairs, carried a wooden yoke resting upon their withers which, on each horse, was held in place by a girth or surcingle. To this yoke the tongue of the wagon or chariot was attached, the yoke and girth being kept from slipping backward by a strap which M. des Noëttes appropriately calls the garotte strap, passing horizontally from the yoke on the horse's withers forward about his neck. Of this arrangement, Dr. Savoy says:

> The strap formed by a large band of pliant leather which "cravatted" the neck of the animal at the spot where the tracheal artery passes close under the skin, without the slightest contact with the bony structure of the shoulder, was the disabling factor which reduced draught ability.[12]

As soon as the horse began to draw his load, the strap about his neck tightened, interfering with both circulation and breathing. The garotte strap could have been held down from the horse's windpipe by means of a martingale, passing downward from it between the horse's front legs to an attachment on the girth. It seems that this was tried, but the only result was to discover that any strap which held the garotte collar down, necessarily carried part of the draught and became so tight when the horses moved their load that friction on the soft skin between their legs rendered the animals useless in no very long time.[13]

The garotte strap, therefore, not being held down, was always drawn upward by the weight of the load, compelling the horses to raise their heads into the position characteristic of ancient pictures. This threw the center of gravity backward and made it impossible for the horses to put their weight into the business of drawing their load. Some relief could have been found had it been possible to increase the number of draught animals attached to the load, but hitching them abreast never proved satisfactory and

[12] *L'agriculture à travers les âges*, Vol. 2, p. 92.
[13] *L'attelage et le cheval de selle*, etc., pp. 45-46.

no method was known by which one pair of animals could be hitched in front of another. Maximum draught was, therefore, limited to the strength of a single pair of draught animals.[14]

To make matters worse, the method of driving two horses by one pair of divided reins was unknown. There were two reins, therefore, to each horse and as this was more than the driver could easily manage, the ends were often wound about his waist beneath a knife with which, in time of need, they could be cut. This method of harnessing horses is well shown in the illustrations reproduced here from the book, *Ancient Egyptian Paintings*,[15] published by the University of Chicago in 1937, containing copies made by Nina M. Davies of paintings in Egyptian tombs. The original paintings copied in these illustrations were made about 1400 B. C. and it is M. des Noëttes' opinion that the method of yoking horses as described in his book continued until the tenth century of the present era, when the modern rigid shoulder-collar was invented, probably by a Frenchman.[16] These shoulder-collars in their present form are so designed as frequently to leave a clear space the width of three fingers between the horse's windpipe and the pad of his collar. The broad breast-collar, which seems the simplest solution of the problem, was probably of English origin in the twelfth century.[17]

Ancient troubles were not confined, however, to the harness alone,

[14] *L'attelage et le cheval de selle*, etc., pp. 14-20.

[15] Metal bits were used in harnesses long before the date of these paintings. Ancient painters, however, often neglected details and Mr. A. C. Rose regards the failure in these pictures to show bits with reins attached as probably an instance of such neglect.

[16] *L'attelage et le cheval de selle*, etc., p. 123. The ancient harness is well shown by the illustrations in the pamphlet, in the Columbia University Library, *When All Roads Led to Rome*, by Mr. A. C. Rose, Senior Engineer of the Bureau of Public Roads, Department of Agriculture, Washington. This pamphlet describes the highways of ancient Rome and contains an article first published, with four plates, in the Smithsonian Report for 1934, pp. 347-370.

[17] *L'attelage et le cheval de selle*, etc., p. 124.

for no way had been invented of protecting the hoofs of animals by shoes. Fibre boots which covered the hoofs and were attached to the horses' legs by straps, and hippo-sandals or solea—metal plates in a leather boot—were tried by both Greeks and Romans. These contrivances were unsuccessful and nothing was left but to choose for use such horses as had hard hoofs, if any such there were, or to find some method of hardening soft hoofs, if such method could be. Leaving the horses, when not at work, to stand on stones was tried, and pitch was tried. Isidore of Seville[18] says that standing in the swamps near Reate had a hardening effect, and doubtless, if the horses were left in soft swamps long enough, their hoofs might heal. The one possible method of saving horses' feet by iron shoes nailed to the hoof was apparently invented about the ninth century of the present era, appearing at about the same time in Byzantium and in western Europe.[19]

For oxen, wooden yokes were used, not very different from those which are used to-day, but since the cloven hoofs of cattle are more easily injured on hard roads than are the solid hoofs of horses, all the advantage which oxen received from the rational placing of their yoke was lost by the injury to their feet, and both horses and oxen were reduced as draught animals to the same level of inefficiency. What this level was, appears from the provision, De Publico Cursu, in the Theodosian Code, a compilation of previous laws, published in the fifth and sixth centuries.[20] By this

[18] *Etymologiarum*, Lib. XIII, Cap. XIII, Sec. 6. Corpus Grammaticorum Latinorum Veterum (Lipsiae, 1833), Vol. III, p. 422.

[19] *L'attelage et le cheval de selle*, etc., Chap. V, p. 136. Beckmann's *History of Inventions*, etc. (Bohn, London, 1846), Vol. I, pp. 442, 141-142. The subject is not entirely free from doubt: see *The Technical Arts and Sciences of the Ancients* by Albert Neuberger, trans. by Henry L. Brose (Macmillan, 1930), p. 52. *Les travaux publics aux temps des Romains* by Alfred Leger (Paris, 1875), p. 174.

[20] *L'attelage et le cheval de selle*, etc., Chap. VII, p. 158. *Codex Theodosianus*, Theodor Mommsen (Weidmann, Berlin, 1905), Bk. VII, tit. 5, 6; Bk. VIII, tit. 5, lex 8, secs. 1-2, lex 17 pr., lex 28, 30, 47, 48, 364.

MULES IN THE HARVEST FIELD
Ancient Egypt

Reproduced here from copies made by Nina M. Davies of paintings in Egyptian tombs, published in 1937 by the University of Chicago in the book, *Ancient Egyptian Paintings.*

MULES IN THE HARVEST FIELD
Ancient Egypt

Reproduced here from copies made by Nina M. Davies of
paintings in Egyptian tombs, published in 1937 by the University
of Chicago in the book, Ancient Egyptian Paintings.

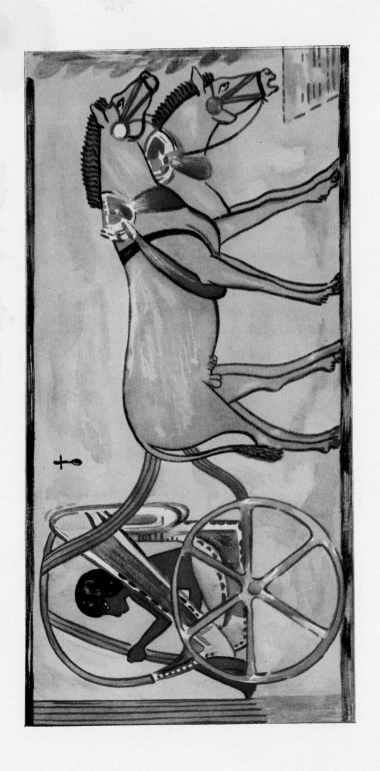

Code, maximum loads, whether drawn by horses, mules or oxen, were limited as follows:

For a birota, light vehicle	145 lbs.
For a vereda carrying travelers or light goods	217 lbs.
For a heavier wagon, the currus	435 lbs.
For the rheda, heavy and slow	726 lbs.
For still heavier and slower transport	1082 lbs.

It is possible to translate the text of the Code so as to make the limit in modern figures a little higher, and M. Alfred Leger calls attention to the fact that where speed was not considered animals could draw heavier weights, but he adds that at the best the loads were so insignificant that pack animals were almost better than any vehicle.[21] Nevertheless, the entire blame for inefficient traction cannot be placed upon the improper method of harnessing horses and mules, for roads were poor, grades were sometimes steep, culverts were weak and vehicles clumsy. Good wheel bearings and hub-boxes were beyond the mechanical ability of former times.[22] Moreover, horses and cattle in ancient days were undoubtedly very small and stunted, as they were much later in the middle ages, if we judge by the mediaeval horse-shoes found in large numbers along the roads of those times,[23] and as they are now in Greece and Syria unless bred from foreign stock and cared for by a horseman who knows something at least of our present day system of feeding and care. Many considerations, therefore, confirm M. des Noëttes' statement that efficient animal power was unknown in ancient times.

[21] *Les travaux publics aux temps des Romains*, p. 173.
[22] *Die Wagen und Fahrwerke der Griechen und Römer und anderer alten Völker; nebst der Bespannung, Zäumung und Verzierung ihrer Zug- Reit- und Last- thiere*, von . . . München, bei dem Verfasser und in der Buchhandlung J. Lentner . . . 1817, by Johann Christian Ginzrot.
[23] *Les travaux publics aux temps des Romains* by M. Alfred Leger, p. 174.

The motor force of animals hardly existed in antiquity; and ancient harness was but a childish affair, differing from modern methods not only in looks but in the principles involved, in its parts and in its effective results. Indeed, the full possibilities of animal power were not actually developed until the tenth century after Christ. The passage from the old system to the new was, therefore, not only a great benefit to humanity, but far beyond this, it was actually nothing less than the dawn of the modern day.[24]

It seems, therefore, that men of the ancient world and what are called the dark ages were unable effectively to use existing animal power. This was a very serious thing, for the quantity of food that could be produced by free hand labor with the small assistance of such animal power as they could develop was insufficient to supply the needs of the population and it was necessary, therefore, to use slaves for the work that should have been performed by cattle. Water wheels, for example, have long been known and were used of old to turn the stones in grain mills, but since pack transportation was insufficient and there was no other land transportation able to supply these mills with grain or to distribute to consumers the flour which the mills produced, water power could actually be used to advantage for grinding grain only in those few places where delivery to and from the mill could be made by water. For the same reason, water power could not be used in shops or forges, and industry had to be carried on in many widely scattered places with great loss of effort. Throughout the country districts, the ass, as the animal which could best get along with much abuse and little food and which, very fortunately, was so shaped, with a low neck and high shoulders, that he could

[24] *L'attelage et le cheval de selle*, etc., p. 4. "The Romans, who had created an Empire, were unable to create a technique adapted to the needs of so vast an organization . . . The decadence of the Empire seems to be due to a lack of inventive genius among the Romans." *La population dans le monde* by Professor Gaston Bouthoul (Payot, Paris, 1935), pp. 64-65. In China the same lack of inventive ability appears, for in this respect the Chinese are no worse than the Romans. *Ibid.*, p. 122, quoting *Le rhythme du progrès* by M. L. Weber.

draw against the yoke like an ox, was used to grind grain,[25] nevertheless, most of the work of grinding had to be done by men, one of the hardest burdens of labor in the old world.

In these conditions human strength found itself faced by such burdensome tasks that forced labor only could effect their execution. Without slavery the material development of the successive civilizations which arose around the Mediterranean would not have been possible. Moreover, the higher the civilization, the greater the number of slaves, and the severer their discipline.

Moral considerations do not weigh against imperative necessity. It was possible in the old world to advocate amelioration of conditions for the slaves; it was not possible to do away with the only effective motor force which ancient civilization could command. No person at that time suspected that the cruel institution of human slavery could ever be abolished.[26]

If shuttles would work by themselves, said Aristotle, we would need no more slaves.[27] But shuttles do not work by themselves and the human race will be clothed and fed, so slaves were necessary.

Animal Power in the Middle Ages. If M. des Noëttes is right, the modern method of using animal power came, over eight hundred years after Christ, with the use of iron shoes nailed to the hoofs of draught animals, with the rigid collar drawing against the shoulders—or later with the broad breast-collar which passes over the animal's chest without pressing upon his windpipe— with the use of traces, that most valuable part of a modern harness, and with the knowledge of the method by which draught animals can be hitched in file, one before the other, so that many animals can be used, putting their whole strength into drawing the load to which they are hitched.[28]

[25] Columella, Lib. VII, Cap. I. The word in *Matthew*, XVIII, 6, which in the King James version is translated millstone, is in the Vulgate rendered mola asinaria.

[26] *L'attelage et le cheval de selle à travers les âges*, pp. 185-186.

[27] *Politics*, Bk. I, Chap. 2, Sec. 5.

[28] *L'attelage et le cheval de selle à travers les âges*, pp. 123-124.

The events of the ninth and tenth centuries, therefore, the discovery of means by which animal power could be used to its full extent, divide the history of the western world into two distinct periods, the period of hand labor and slavery before the tenth century and the period after the tenth century when better animals, with better harnesses and vehicles, relieved men of their hardest work, initiating the movement which substituted serfage for slavery and, with the use of modern tools, ended by abolishing serfage. In this way, M. des Noëttes remarks, the brilliant invention of the modern harness by some unknown person or persons, made during the night of the dark ages, changed the face of the world and, by changing the means of production, effected a profound change in our social organization.[29]

One of the greatest discoveries made by man during the long course of human history was, therefore, according to M. des Noëttes, nothing more than to fasten on a horse the traces and shoulder-collar that enable him to draw his load! How does it happen that so simple an invention should be so long in coming? It is most extraordinary, as Mr. Gilbert M. Tucker once remarked, that man learned to forecast eclipses before he learned to harness a horse. Of the use of water and wind to turn the stones of a mill, Johannis Herengius remarked:

Res tam utilis et tam obvia, ad quam natura ipsa ducit, non potuit, non debuit diu quaeri.[30]

It surely should have taken neither long time nor great genius to discover anything so useful and so simple, but a water mill or a wind mill is a complicated piece of machinery when compared to the traces and breast-collar of a harness and, nevertheless, for the lack of these straps, mankind lived for centuries under the scourge of slavery and in fear of starvation.

[29] *L'attelage et le cheval de selle*, etc., p. 188.
[30] *De Molendinis* (Frankfort, 1625), p. 44.

50

It is evident that the mind of man turned very slowly to mechanical devices. Many stories are told of the ingenuity of Archimedes in the defence of Syracuse, and Caesar took great pride in the construction of a bridge over the Rhine, but centuries passed before the world learned the nature and value of physical science. In 1750, Dr. Samuel Johnson said:

The great praise of Socrates is that he drew the wits of Greece, by his instruction and example, from the vain pursuit of natural philosophy to moral inquiries, and turned their thoughts from stars and tides, and matter and motion, upon the various modes of virtue and relations of life.[31]

Over a century later, in 1860, it seemed to an observer well able to judge, a great change in accepted ways of thinking when "science is placed more on a par with poetry and philosophy,"[32] but science is a new-comer in the intellectual world. Recent years have seen a striking modification of man's outlook and, nevertheless, Dr. Johnson was not wholly wrong, for a strong moral fibre is the first condition of intellectual advance.

Had there been adequate means of communication—many good horses shod and harnessed so that they could draw well-built and well-loaded wagons—and had there been good roads for travel it might have been possible to carry food from any town which had more than it needed, if such towns ever existed, to another that was in want, but where all agricultural products had to be raised by hand labor, without chemical fertilizers, where reaping was done with the sickle and threshing was done by the ancient

[31] *The Rambler*, No. 24, June 9, 1750. See also *The Idler*, No. 88.
Macaulay (*Miscellaneous Works*, Essay on Lord Bacon, Vol. II, p. 412) says that Bacon has dropped hints from which it may be inferred that he believed that the prevalence of the opinion that philosophy should not be opifex instrumentorum ad usus necessarios "was in great measure to be attributed to the influence of Socrates." Possibly Johnson in the paragraph quoted was replying to Bacon.

[32] Beriah Botfield, *Prefaces to First Editions of Greek and Roman Classics* (Bohn, London, 1861), Introduction, page v.

methods, by roller or by treading out the grain with cattle, or later by the flail, there was never any satisfying margin of safety and a salable surplus was unusual. Moreover, all men could not give their time to farming, for stone masons, potters and artisans were needed. The women cared for the house and did what little cooking was necessary, giving the rest of their time to the spinning and weaving which clothed the family, with a total result that ancient life, so far as creature comforts are concerned, was not on a very much higher plane than the life of some savage tribes.

The decadence, then, of ancient civilization was largely due to the inadequacy of the means which mankind then possessed to supply the necessaries of life. Of the Roman Empire, Professor Gaston Bouthoul says:

This colossal State lived only upon the productions of hand labor. . . . The Romans who had created an Empire did not know how to create the tools required by so vast an organization. . . . Machinery was almost unknown and, worse still, the Romans did not know how to use draught animals. . . . The decadence of the Empire, it seems, is largely due to a lack of inventive genius among the Romans.[33]

In the absence of machinery, no great increase in the production of food was possible. Rome, by right of conquest, could buy and import foreign grain, but the lands from which this food was taken

---

[33] *La population dans le monde* by Professor Gaston Bouthoul (Payot, Paris, 1935), pp. 64, 65. *Peuples et civilisations* by Professor Gustave Fougères and co-authors (Alcan, Paris, 1926), pp. 404-405.

"Les Romains ne songèrent qu'au gouvernement des hommes, non à celui des choses." *La population dans le monde*, pp. 64, 65, 66.

"Rerum Naturae scientiam exosam omnino habuerunt." Bruyerinus Campegius, p. 3. Conf. *L'attelage*, by M. des Noëttes, p. 156.

"Excrevit autem mirum in modum istud malum, ex opinione quadam sive aestimatione inveterata, verum tumida et damnosa; minui nempe mentis humanae majestatem, si experimentis et rebus particularibus sensui subjectis et in materia determinatis diu ac multum versetur." *Novum Organum*, Francis Bacon, Pars II, Cap. LXXXIII.

Spinning Cotton

Spinning Wool

could ill spare what they lost[34] because hand labor could not produce it in sufficient quantity to keep the farmer alive and at the
same time to supply the many varied activities of a complicated
civilization. The civilization which hand labor supports is a simple
civilization. This is the secret of the 2300 years of what seems to
us like stagnation in the useful arts—a stagnation, if we may call
it so, which lasted from early history to the beginning of the nineteenth century. On this subject, Professor Grundy says:

Nearly all Englishmen and Americans know something of English history but their interest is apt to be directed by preference to stories of wars
and battles, and by compulsion to the growth of English law and the
British constitution. How many of them ever realize that in the period between the Saxon settlement and the first half of the 14th century not
merely thousands but hundreds of thousands of English people perished
of famine or of the terrible diseases which semi-starvation brought in its
train—and this in a land in which the percentage of productive area was
far greater than in the lands of the Mediterranean region, and where the
acreage under cereal cultivation was in the later centuries of the period
considerably greater than at the present day?

It is necessary to recognize brutal facts of this nature in order to realize
the conditions under which the ancient world lived. It is also necessary to
realize that variations in social and political conditions vary in direct
ratio to the extent to which the hardness of the conditions of physical life
can or cannot be alleviated. Poverty in the widest sense is an impediment
to the advance of civilization.[35]

We have, then, in this statement two important facts—that the
adequacy of the food supply depends upon the relation between
possible production and necessary consumption, and that the nature
of government reflects the adequacy or inadequacy of the food

[34] "The annual tribute of corn imposed upon Egypt . . . was applied to feed
a lazy and insolent populace at the expense of the husbandmen of an industrious province." Gibbon, *Decline and Fall* (Harper & Brothers, New York, 1905),
Chap. XVII, Vol. II, p. 265.
[35] *Ency. Brit.,* 14th ed., Vol. 10, pp. 779-780.

supply. Hard conditions make hard governments. These are simple principles, but they have cut a great, not always appreciated, figure in the development of human society, and it is intended in this book to deal with the history of both. It will be the story of Food and Freedom, taking first the subject of Food.

CHAPTER IV

HAND LABOR AND WANT

WE BEGIN in the ancient world with the population pressing upon the food supply under such conditions that all food was produced by awkward tools—ploughs and harrows difficult to use—and hand labor.[1] Of course, the quantity of food that can be raised in this way is small and, equally of course, it cannot greatly be increased, for hand labor is capable of producing just so much and no more and, in the absence of machinery, larger crops mean a larger number of laborers, all of whom must be fed, housed and clothed. Even of the quantity which hand labor could produce, indeed, the amount that can go to market is not very great, for approximately a quarter of the average crop must be kept for next year's seed and what remained would necessarily be used first of all to support the men who worked to raise it. After these needs had been met, there might be a surplus which ordinarily, except in favored places, would be small or there might be no surplus at all. Food supplies were, therefore, always very strictly limited.

On the other hand, the demand for food constantly increased since the supply, which was small at all times, tended to become proportionally smaller as population increased. Colonization was a temporary relief. War generally made a lessening of the demand

[1] "No increase in births will increase the numbers of the population without providing also the means of subsistence . . . Why else did the human race reach, three thousand years ago, as great a population as exists at present? Cities begin with a few inhabitants, increase to a certain point, but do not pass it." *Ragione di Stato*, Joh. Benesius Boterus (Venice, 1589), quoted in Hallam's *Literature of Europe*, Part II, Chap. IV, Sec. 42, 43.

for a short time only, and so there was steady, inevitable and continued want.

Comfort and hardship, nevertheless, are relative terms, and what would be luxury for one age or people would be deprivation for other ages or peoples. In a world where the diet was as restricted as in ancient Greece, a small addition to the food would naturally be received as a wonderful benefit and we are not surprised, therefore, to read Plutarch's statement that, if forefathers of the Greeks of his day could come to life and see what seemed to him the abundance of food then enjoyed, they would say to the men of his generation:

Oh, happy you, and highly favored of the Gods, who now live! Into what an age of the world are you fallen, who share and enjoy among you a plentiful portion of good things! What abundant supplies spring up for you! What fruitful vineyards you enjoy! What wealth you gather from the fields! What delicacies from trees and plants![2]

Plutarch often refers to feasting and, at first, it seems that he must have lived in an age of abundance, but the feasts were very simple: a soldier, it was said, could not be expected to care for the plain food of his native town "after his luxurious campaign fare." There must have been many in those days of whom it could be said, as Lucan said of Cato,[3] "huic epulae, vicisse famem"—to him it was a feast if he had conquered hunger. Moreover, even of the plain food procurable in Greece, the quantity was small for, in his *Symposiacs*, Plutarch debates in Question X whether the ancients who provided every guest at a feast his own mess did better than hosts in later times who set many guests to the same dish. Plutarch favored individual dishes for, he said, "snatching, contentions, shoving, and the like are not neighborly beginnings of mirth and jollity

[2] Plutarch, *Morals* (Little, Brown, & Co., Boston, 1883), On Eating Flesh, Vol. V, p. 4. *Ancient Greece at Work*, Gustave Glotz (Knopf & Co., New York, 1926), p. 261.

[3] *De Bello Civili*, Lib. II, line 384.

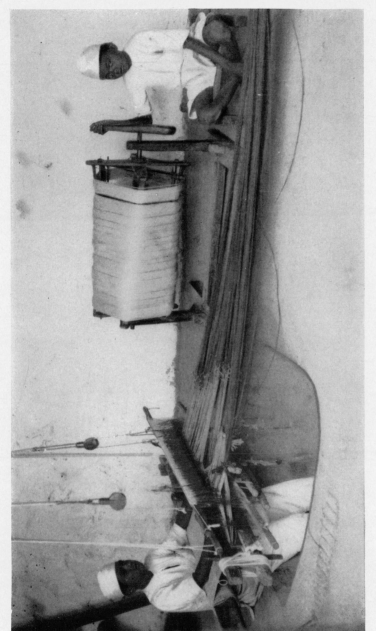

WEAVING

but they are absurd, doggish and often end in anger and reproaches."[4] Stuckius goes over the argument on both sides at great length, finally concurring in Plutarch's opinion which favored individual dishes and equal service for all guests of equal rank and honor.[5] Modern opinion would certainly favor this view, especially when we read that the use of a common dish sometimes led hungry guests to foul it in a repulsive manner so that they might have the whole to themselves.[6]

To important guests, however, a greater portion should be given,

Nam et Tydides carnibus et pluribus poculis honoratur,[7]

conduct which tells its own story of prevailing want, for, if all persons at the tables had had abundance, there would have been no honor in heaping the portions of favored guests. It is the fact of semi-starvation, as Professor Scott well remarks, which gives meaning to the strange kindness of Joseph, "when his bowels did yearn upon his brother . . . and he said, Set on bread . . . and he took and sent messes unto them . . . but Benjamin's mess was five times so much as any of theirs."[8]

It seems, therefore, that if the Greeks of Plutarch's time enjoyed

[4] *Morals*, Vol. III, p. 257.

[5] *Antiquitates Conviviales* by J. G. Stuckius (Tiguri, 1597), Lib. III, Cap. III, pp. 299-300b. See also *Antiquae Lectiones* by Coelius Rhodiginus, Lib. XIV, Cap. LV.

[6] *Morals*, Whether 'Twere Rightly Said, Live Concealed, Vol. III, p. 3. Athenaeus, *Deipnosophistae*, Bk. VIII, line 345; Bk. I, line 5.

"Zeno, when one snatched away the upper part of the fish at the very moment it was set before them, with a sudden twist snatched it away again himself. . . . And Socrates, seeing a man helping himself immoderately to the relish, said, 'Fellow-guests, who is it among you that treats bread like a relish, but a relish like bread?' " Athenaeus, *Deipnosophistae*, Bk. V, line 186.

[7] *Antiquitates Conviviales*, Lib. III, Cap. III, p. 300.

[8] Genesis, XLIII, 30-34. Paper on Modern Lessons from Ancient Forms of Government, read by Professor John A. Scott of Northwestern University before The Chicago Classical Club, May 7, 1938.

Antiquitates Conviviales, p. 300b.

better supplies than had been available to their forefathers, previous days must have lived on what our modern luxurious peoples would consider short rations. It was doubtless quite sufficient to many,

> So that thou have but a cake of the sorriest meal for sustenance,
> Kneaded by common hands in a cavernous trough of stone,
> And a little thyme and mint, with a morsel of salt to savour it,
> Sweeten'd, the poor man's way, and other seasoning none.[9]

There must, however, have been, for the comparatively small number of free citizens in ancient Greece, sufficient food to permit development of mind and body since, in the few years which constitute its best period, Greece not only produced many men of unsurpassed genius, but Greek troops were, in their day, the best in the world, and native Greeks were apparently a healthy, long-lived, handsome race. More than this, the average, both of looks and intelligence of the Greek people, must have been high for, where many examples of excellence show themselves among the leaders, it is evidence that a high level of excellence exists throughout all classes of the population.

Nevertheless, as Professor Scott says:

The first great problem in ancient Greece was the problem of food. Menelaus told Telemachus of his wanderings, how he had gone to Cyprus, Phoenicia, Egypt, Aethiopia and to Libya. The pyramids must have been as impressive then as now, but Menelaus never mentioned them. The one thing he saw which filled him with wonder and which he could not forget was that in Libya neither prince nor shepherd had any lack of cheese, of milk or of meat, and they had them all the year round. This seems a simple fare to us, but he always remembered that he had seen a land in which the people actually had enough to eat. . . . In Attica, want, if not starvation, was always a menace, so that the export of grain was prohibited. Ships must return with a cargo of grain and vessels that chanced to

---

[9] *The Poems of Leonidas of Tarentum*, translated into English verse by Edwyn Bevon (Clarendon Press, Oxford, 1931), p. 14.

58

anchor in an Athenian harbor must share with that city their supplies of food.[10]

Of conditions in Rome, Gibbon speaks in a way which suggests Plutarch's account of abundance in Greece;[11] but Gibbon was born in 1737, wrote his great history when he was less than fifty years old, and belongs to the period before 1800. To him, as to others of his time, grain or rice "constituted the ordinary and wholesome food of a civilized people."[12] In the great days of Rome little cooking was done, since the bread-cakes and the other simple foods on which Romans lived were easily made. Variety of food and the arts of cookery were unknown before the days of the Empire. During the reign of Tiberius and probably not far from the year 20 of the present era, Columella said that he had not only heard of schools which taught rhetoric, geometry and music, but he had seen them and, what was more astonishing, he had seen training places for the most contemptible arts of preparing delicate foods and setting luxurious tables.[13]

In the latter days of the Empire, Rome was weaker and the supply of foreign grain no longer to be depended upon, but it was still true for Rome in the time of the Emperors, as for Edward Gibbon in the time of the Georges, that the cereal grains were the staff of life. The training places of which Columella spoke did not furnish the food of the people.

That the supply of grain in former times was not equal to the needs is well shown by the excellent statement of Professor George Beard Grundy, in his article on Greece in the *Encyclopaedia Britan-*

[10] Modern Lessons from Ancient Forms of Government. See *Public Economy of the Athenians* by Augustus Boeckh, trans. from 2nd German edition by Anthony Lamb (Little, Brown, & Co., Boston, 1857), Chap. XV.

[11] *Decline and Fall* (Harper & Brothers, New York, 1905), Chap. II, Vol. I, p. 283.

[12] *Ibid.*, Chap. XXVI, Vol. III, p. 100.

[13] *De Re Rustica*, Lib. I, Cap. I. *Ency. Brit.*, 14th ed., Tit. Cookery, Vol. 6, p. 366, ranks the art of cooking as "to some extent" a decadent art.

nica.[14] As to the cause of the deficiency, however, there is much debate. Mr. Jules Toutain believes that the importation of grain by Rome destroyed the market for the Italian producer.[15] Professor N. S. B. Gras, with more reason, suggests that grain was imported because the inadequacy of Rome's local supply induced her to seek the next most accessible fields,[16] while Professor Grundy, who has given the best statement of the general condition of food resources of the ancient world, as compared with present times, attributes our modern abundance to "the introduction of steam power into communications by land and sea and to the invention of the telegraph,"[17] although railroads can only carry the food which agriculture has already produced and the fundamental trouble with the ancient food supply was nothing less than the inability of ancient agriculture with the means at its command to produce enough food to meet the needs of the population.

Like Plutarch, Ausonius also tells of feasts. We read of his table—mensa opulenta nitens; his letters speak of oysters, game birds and duck, while his poem on the Moselle River tells of many kinds of fish. It sounds more luxurious than in fact it was, and it is noticeable that Ausonius' correspondent, Symmachus, comments that, though he had often been at Ausonius' table, he had never found there such fish as were described in the poem.[18] Bread was the support of all classes of the population, and when Gildon made himself independent in Africa the interruption of the grain supply

[14] *Ency. Brit.*, 14th ed., Vol. 10, pp. 779-780.
[15] *Economic Life of the Ancient World* (Knopf, New York, 1930), p. 232.
[16] *A History of Agriculture in Europe and America* by Professor N. S. B. Gras (Crofts, New York, 1925), p. 70.
[17] *Ency. Brit.*, 14th ed., Vol. 10, pp. 779-780.
[18] "Atquin in tuis mensis saepe versatus, cum pleraque alia quae tunc in pretio erant esui objecta, mirarer, nunquam hoc genus piscium deprehendi. Quando tibi nati sunt in libro qui in ferculis non fuerunt?" *Quinti Aurelii Symmachi Epistolarum*, Lib. X (Paris, 1604), p. 6. Also to be found in *Mon. Germaniae Hist.*, edited by Otto Seek, Vol. 6, p. 9.

was severely felt in Rome. This interruption was the subject of Claudianus' poem where he described Rome praying at the threshold of Olympus for food:

> Let Porsenna bring back
> The Tarquins: renew the dreadful battles of the Allia,
> Turn the City over to the ruthless hands of Pyrrhus,
> To the fury of the Senones, or the flames of Brennus,
> All these things rather than hunger![19]

The resources of food at Rome were small, and a shortage of grain brought death.

There are stories of abundance in the middle ages, as Plutarch told of abundance in ancient Greece. References to books that give an impression of joyous living are mentioned by Mr. Albert Babeau[20] and Mr. Tighe Hopkins[21] and we find long lists of meats, fish and vegetables that have been well known and used for food whenever they could be had. Sir John Fortescue, for example, about the middle of the fifteenth century, said that in England:

They drink no water unless it be for that some by devotion and upon a zeale of pennance do abstain from other drink. They eat plentifully of all kinds of flesh and fish. They weare fine woolen cloth in all their apparell. They have also abundance of bed-coverings in their Houses and of all other woolen stuffs.[22]

It seems that there was generally somewhat less suffering in England than on the continent, and this may be the explanation of the happy appearance which Fortescue's native land presented to him on his return. Two hundred years later, Dr. Thomas Muffett said

[19] *In Gildonem*, lines 108 et seq.

[20] *La vie rurale dans l'ancienne France*, pp. 119 et seq. *Les voyageurs en France depuis la Renaissance jusqu'à la Révolution* (Librairie Firmin-Didot, Paris, 1885). *Le ménagier de Paris*, par un parisien bourgeois, written in 1392-1394, edited by M. Jérôme Pichon and published in Paris in 1846.

[21] *An Idler in Old France* (Hurst & Blackett, London, 1899), pp. 60 et seq.

[22] *De Laudibus Legum Angliae* (London, edition of 1660), Cap. XXXVI.

that the English meat supply was "the wonder of Europe, yea verily of the whole world."[23]

Nevertheless, Mr. Trevelyan says, "in every century before the eighteenth, the bread of a great majority of our ancestors had been rye, barley, oats or else one of these mixed with wheat; in England, as in all the lands of northern Europe, pure wheat bread had been regarded as a luxury proper to the rich. It was only under the Georges that wheat became the staple diet. That defiance of the natural economy of our climate was achieved by means of large farming and the application of capital and capitalistic methods to the cultivation of the soil. If England had remained a land of small peasants, she would not, any more than Germany or Scandinavia, have grown any large proportion of wheat."[24] Perhaps, however, even as early as Fortescue's time, there may have been a little more freedom in England than in France, for St. Anthony's fire, or ergotism, was common in France where rye was much used,[25] but is hardly mentioned in the English Chronicles. A popular derivation of the French word *baragouin*, which has found its way into English dictionaries, is that it was derived from the Breton words *bara* for bread and *gwenn*, white, and describes the expressions of astonishment used by Breton soldiers at the white bread which they first saw in England instead of the rye or other dark bread to which they had been accustomed. There was leprosy in England, of course, and Matthew Paris relates a conspicuous instance of its appearance;[26] but it seems to have been less common than on the continent and it may even be that the English people, being comparatively few in number, during the fifteenth century were a little better supplied with food than the peoples in Europe. Whatever the reason, Fortescue certainly found great satisfaction

[23] *Health's Improvement* (London, 1655), p. 50.

[24] *England under Queen Anne, Blenheim,* by G. M. Trevelyan (Longmans, Green & Co. 1930) pp. 10-11.

[25] *Social England,* Vol. I, p. 370.

[26] *Historia Anglorum* (Rolls Series), Vol. I, p. 201.

in England after his exile, and he spoke of what was abundance according to the standards of his time. Nevertheless, in reading such descriptions, it is well to remember that a poetic hue, as Sismondi says, still disguises ages which have only one lesson to teach us—that at all price we should avoid their return.[27]

Men of the modern world, comparing Fortescue's days with ours, would think the England of the 1400's neither free, rich nor comfortable, but Fortescue knew how men existed on the continent of Europe at that time, and he rejoiced in the things which England had to give.

People enjoy hearing and speaking of pleasant things. The poor old street fiddler in Mr. J. T. Trowbridge's moving poem, *The Vagabonds*, describing his life with his dog, could say:

> We know what comfort is, I tell you,

and so he spoke of comfort,—

> Plenty of catgut for my fiddle,
> This out-door business is bad for strings,
> Then a few nice buckwheats, hot from the griddle,
> And Roger and I set up for kings.

Nevertheless, they were not kings and the story misled no one. Even in present times, tales of comfort come from China and a native of China can write about happiness, the enjoyment of nature, the pleasures of the home and of living,[28] although for centuries China has been the dwelling place of famine and pestilence, as in recent years of war also. It is gratifying, however, to know that misery is not entirely unrelieved, and so we listen to the fiddler's story and the tales from China and we rejoice that such things can be said.

We must read Plutarch and Fortescue in much the same way, for

[27] *History of Italian Republics* (London, 1832—1 Vol.), p. 3.
[28] *The Importance of Living* by Lin Yutang (Reynal & Hitchcock, N. Y., 1937).

though they tell of many pleasing things, we know that the world has seen very little luxury and that comforts have been rare.

Of course, at all times many kinds of food were known.[29] Aulus Gellius gives a list of ancient dishes of great cost,[30] as also do Athenaeus and Petronius. We read of peacocks' tongues and of other extravagances in later times, but the world did not live on these rarities nor on Tartessian lampreys and brains of nightingales. Throughout the ages, man's companions have been Want and Dearness. Food in Europe, when there was food, has been very simple and limited both in kind and in quantity because, under the conditions which existed in Europe, enterprise and individual initiative were impossible. Food is the first need. Progress and education, the arts and sciences, are nothing to starving men.

It is interesting to notice how often and how casually old books refer to famine or scarcity, much as we speak of severe winters or dry summers, as though these things were occasionally to be expected and inevitable. Columella says that panic, ground and separated from the bran, and millet also, make a gruel which, in any time of scarcity, is not to be despised, especially when stirred with milk,[31] and that lupines also are a good defence against famine in any year of short crops.[32] Olivier de Serres, in 1600, describing the duties of a householder, mentions consideration for the poor, especially in time of famine and high prices.[33] Charles Estienne and Jean Liébault, in *L'agriculture et maison rustique* (1589), say that rice, beans and other legumes are not fit to make bread except in time of famine and when grain has given out or prices are very high.[34] To de Serres and to Estienne, therefore, Famine and High

[29] *Food in Early Greece* by Mr. Kenton Frank Vickery. University of Illinois Bulletin, Vol. XXXIV, No. 7, Sept. 22, 1936.
[30] *Noctes Atticae*, Lib. VII, Cap. XVI.
[31] *De Re Rustica*, Lib. II, Cap. IX.
[32] *Ibid.*, Lib. II, Cap. X.
[33] *Le théâtre d'agriculture*, Premier Lieu, Chap. VI, p. 25.
[34] Liv. V, p. 310.

Prices went together, as they have always gone together,—a fact which should be considered by every government before adopting a policy of high prices. Oats are not much better for bread than beans, and oat bread is not used except as a last resource in time of want.[35]

Modern conditions are so different from those which prevailed two or three centuries ago, or even two or three generations ago, that we read of times when people went hungry as though a very long period separated us from the days of such hardship. The fact is, nevertheless, that agricultural machinery, chemical fertilizers, improved seed and rapid transportation are very new influences in the world. As recently as 1844, an English writer, describing the conditions which then existed, said:

Full one-third of our population [in the United Kingdom] subsist almost entirely, or rather starve, upon potatoes alone, another third have, in addition to this edible, oaten or inferior wheaten bread, with one or two meals of fat pork, or the refuse of the shambles, per week; while a considerable majority of the remaining third seldom are able to procure an ample daily supply of good butcher's meat or obtain the luxury of poultry from year to year.

On the continent of Europe, population is still in a worse condition:— fish, soups made from herbs, a stuff called bread, made from every variety of grain, black, brown and sour, such as no Englishman could eat; olives, chestnuts, the pulpy saccharine fruits, roots, stalks and leaves and not infrequently the bark of trees; sawdust, blubber, train oil with frogs and snails, make up a good part of the food of the greater portion of the inhabitants of Europe.[36]

It is not easy to persuade people to talk of suffering and want, or to admit that the conditions of their early life were straitened. Most of all there is a disinclination to speak of going hungry, but

[35] *L'agriculture et maison rustique*, Liv. V, p. 314b.
[36] *Treatise on Artificial Incubation* by Mr. W. Bucknell, p. 36, quoted in *Dictionary of the Farm* by Mr. W. L. Rham (Charles Knight & Co., London, 1844), pp. 418-419.

there have been until recently in Europe, and perhaps still are, those whose memory goes back to all these things and who sometimes can be induced to talk of them—to tell even of using the bark of trees to make bread—and if such conditions existed when agricultural machinery was already beginning to make its way on farms in Europe as in America, we can easily imagine what the situation had been in previous ages when machinery was unknown.

CHAPTER V

WHAT WERE THE BANQUETS OF THE ANCIENT WORLD?

THE idea of a hungry world is so different from the impression we receive when reading accounts of the feasts of Lucullus, of Trimalchio's banquet and the descriptions which Seneca gives of Roman indulgence in the pleasures of the table, that it is well to reflect that scarcity never affects all persons in a population to the same degree. Voltaire gives a striking description of the European famine of 1691, when the French people suffered from lack of food while the kingdom resounded with Te Deums and rejoicings for military victories.[1] The world knows no equal distribution either of pleasure or of pain. Those who are well bear deprivation longer than those who are ill; the strong better than the weak; those with resources better than those whose resources are small or lacking. There have always been successful men in China and India although famine is ever present in both of these countries, and without successful men the suffering in both China and India would have been even greater than it has been.

So it was at Rome. There were those who, while their fortune lasted, enjoyed abundance, and there were feasts made notorious by excess, but abundance and excess were not the life of the world, for quite as striking as the descriptions of ostentatious waste are the descriptions of guests at such feasts who seem to have behaved as men or animals might behave who, living under the pressure of constant want, were occasionally placed where more than plenty

[1] *Siècle de Louis XIV* (Firmin-Didot, Paris, 1843), Chap. XXI, p. 237.

was before them.[2] The same thing was noticeable among American Indians who, living without an assured supply of food and frequently suffering great want, were, Parkman says, "often seriously injured by alternations of hunger and excess," so that they sometimes died from the effects of their feasts.[3] The mark which the primitive life of hunger and excess leaves upon a man can be seen also in the manners of Samuel Johnson who never, even in his days of plenty, forgot the want which he had endured in early life. "Whenever he was so fortunate," Macaulay says, "as to have near him a hare that had been kept too long, or a meat pie made with rancid butter, he gorged himself with such violence that his veins swelled and the moisture broke out on his forehead."[4]

Want, indeed, and excessive indulgence have been so closely related in human history that to understand the significance of indulgence we need to know also what hunger has been.

There is, in the Fifth Book of Taine's *Ancient Régime*, a famous and very terrible description of the conditions of want which ex-

[2] It seems that men were subject to this temptation in ancient days to a degree with which the modern world is entirely unacquainted. We never hear to-day from our severest critics such sermons on this vice as once were common.

"Cum ad mensam sederis, ne aperias faucem tuam super eam ut faucibus tuis illi inhies . . . Comede quasi homo ea quae tibi sunt apposita, nec te ingurgites, sive sis vorax . . . Cibos vorare, seque ingurgitare est belluinum, alienumque a natura hominis . . . Cum excessus nulla non in re sit vitiosus, tum in victu maxime suam naturam prodit dum liguritores et helluones ex hominibus in sues, aut canes, quo ad ingluviem, transformans, omnis honestatis in manibus, visu, esuque oblitos, tantam ipsis insaniam cupediarum amor gignit . . . Nam cum insatiabilis illa quasique lupina sive canina edendi cupiditas foedissima sit odioque hominum dignissima, cibi potusque modus est conservandus, et ubi expletum est naturale desiderium, desinendum, non quo inexplebilis rapit cupiditas progrediendum." *Antiquitates Conviviales*, by J. G. Stuckius, Lib. III, Cap. III, pp. 302b, 303b-304. The meaning of the foregoing text is that men should eat like men and not permit the sight of food to turn them into ravening beasts—wolves, dogs or swine.

[3] *The Jesuits in North America* (Boston, 1899), p. 29, note 1.

[4] *Ency. Brit.*, 9th Ed., Tit. Johnson, Vol 13, pp. 719, 721.

isted in France during the eighteenth century, but M. Taine's story is more than a chapter of French history,—it is a description of age-old sufferings projected from the past into sight and knowledge of modern times.

In the England of the eighteenth century, abolition of commons had already begun so that the food supply and the population of England were rising. In France the agriculture of the time was still the simple agriculture of the tenth century, bringing ancient want into an inescapable comparison with the better methods which even then were beginning elsewhere. Moreover, at this time, observers were many and printing presses everywhere, so that records were made and preserved which in previous ages would have been lost. M. Taine's book, therefore, forms a valuable introduction to the whole of European history and to the study of many previous ages.

Banquets there were, of course, among hungry peoples in France, in Rome and in other countries, as among the American Indians, but food seems to have been the great consideration, and companionship often a minor matter. "Feed and regard him not," said Lady Macbeth, and thus ancient banqueters commonly fed. To these gatherings came many guests from the outer darkness and hopeless conditions in the surrounding community. What must we expect from men so placed? Martialis satirizes a guest who took home food which he had concealed under the folds of his toga,[5] but taking food home was a well-known practice of which Stuckius says:

To departing guests, food was often given from the remains of the feast, and this liberality on the part of the host is praiseworthy, especially when poor and needy persons were among his guests. On the other hand, it is ungrateful boorishness on the part of guests who, not content with the generous feast of food and drink which they have received, take away what food they can lay their hands on, either secretly or openly.[6]

[5] *Epigrammatum*, Lib. II, No. 37. Coelius Rhodiginus, *Antiquae Lectiones*, Lib. XIV, Cap. LV.

[6] *Antiquitates Conviviales*, Lib. III, Cap. XXIV, p. 411b. In regard to stealing hand-cloths, see Martialis, *Epigrammatum*, Lib. XII, 29, De Hermogene fure.

There was an ancient saying that "fire in a kitchen betokens dinner."[7] About the entrance of a house, therefore, where smoke and odors told of coming food, a crowd would gather and wait, in order that when the door was opened for a departing guest, some might squeeze in to gather about the table where food was still to be had[8] and this was done not only by beggars but by friends. Pride and hunger do not live together, and many a man who was entitled to enjoy dignity had no hesitation to appear

> One bred of alms and fostered with cold dishes,
> With scraps o' th' Court.[9]

The tale of that waiting crowd, could it be known, would be a valuable foot-note to history through many centuries.

Plato in his *Symposium* speaks of a proverb,—Good men though not invited attend feasts of good men . . . for surely it would be not at all unseemly for any one to enter, especially if he be a person of standing, or a friend or connection. Beggars also who are forced to ask for money and victuals at private houses may come . . . for Homer taught that needy men intruding at our tables are not to be put out and unkindly treated but rather are to be given some portion of the food and drink.[10]

It is hard for us in modern times to understand all this or to realize conditions in a society where such conduct was tolerable. Hardest of all, perhaps, to understand is the action of a man in making an ostentatious waste of food in a world of want.

There were, however, two influences not often mentioned whose importance should not wholly be overlooked.

In the first place, with the abolition of the old Roman Republic and the establishment of the Empire, Roman citizens found their sphere of independent activity very much restricted. When political

[7] *De Conviviis* by J. C. Bulengerus, Lib. I, Cap. II, p. 4.
[8] *Ibid.*, Lib. I, Cap. XXV, p. 59.
[9] *Cymbeline*, Act II, Sc. iii.
[10] *Antiquitates Conviviales* by J. G. Stuckius, Lib. II, Cap. V, pp. 153-154.

70

advancement depended on the pleasure of the Emperor, and commercial or financial success attracted the attention of government, it seemed better to avoid conspicuous activity and to spend on pleasure the property which was held only by more or less insecure tenure. The pleasures, however, on which money could be spent were few. Great stories are told of ancient horse racing, but when the art of horse-shoeing was unknown, and racing horses had not yet been developed, hunting, riding and racing, as the present world knows these sports, were impossible. Yachting, of course, did not exist and travel was difficult, arduous and dangerous.[11] Moreover, in the absence of the sciences, and of mathematics based on the Arabian notation of figures, when there was no paper and when books were both rare and expensive, the world offered small resources for intellectual occupation. Costly dwellings and costly food furnished, therefore, the obvious interests for those who sought to fill with pleasure a life in which idleness was almost compulsory.

Pliny speaks, perhaps with a little irony, of nations which had been subjugated and whose citizens therefore were at liberty to turn their thoughts to the subject of cookery,[12] and Stuckius says that makers of fine dishes were found generally among the Macedonians, who "ob infoelicitatum urbium subiugatarum"[13]—on account of the unhappiness of their cities under the Roman rule—practised the art of making obsonia for banquets. Men had not turned to these things in the old days of freedom.

In the second place, banquets of the ancient world were in their origin not merely occasions of private pleasure, but were meetings

[11] *The Tourist in Antiquity* by Mr. F. W. Ogilvie. The Quarterly Review, Vol. 270, p. 264, April, 1938. Marco Polo's device for bringing home the wealth acquired on his travels is stated in *The Book of Ser Marco Polo*, edited by Sir Henry Yule (Murray, London, 1903), Vol. I, p. 5.

[12] *N. H.*, Lib. XVIII, Cap. 27.

[13] *Antiquitates Conviviales*, Lib. II, Cap. XIII, p. 191.

of religious significance and, in a way, of some public importance. There is no one, Stuckius says, who has even a slight acquaintance with ancient literature who does not know that feasts and sacrifices were very closely related, not only among the Jews but also among other nations, so that it was rare that a sacrifice was offered without a following feast, and on the other hand banquets, whether public or private and whether connected in some way with the temples or not, were almost always accompanied by religious rites and ceremonies.[14] In early times, therefore, cooks were priests, and the meat which was served at the banquet was that which had been cooked in the fire on the altar.

Mr. D. J. Medley in his article on *Anglo-Norman Social Life*,[15] speaking of the larger houses in England, says that seven hundred years ago—

In the ordinary kitchen built of timber, the fire would of necessity be in the middle of the room. Roasting would be a laborious though not an impossible process. But in any case, the greater part of the meat was boiled; for the kitchen seems also to have been the slaughter house, and the meat was either eaten in summer perfectly fresh from the knife of the butcher, or formed part of the store which had been salted down for winter use.

The same story is told also by other writers. "In a copy of the *'Forme of Cury'* now in the Bodleian Library, there is an interesting little woodcut of a fourteenth century kitchen in which the cook and the turn-broche are represented sitting on either side of a raised hearth in the middle of the room; the latter seeing to the roasting, the former superintending a number of little covered pots or casseroles, which are standing round the fire . . . In the more ancient dwelling-houses, the only fire-place, both in the hall and

[14] *Sacrorum Sacrificiorum Descriptio*, p. 1. Many of the feasts of American Indians, Parkman says, were feasts of sacrifice; *The Jesuits of North America*, p. 83, note 1.
[15] *Social England*, Vol. I, p. 379.

kitchen, was in the middle of the room, with a louvre or fumitory above it to let out the smoke, and these remained long in use, even after they had been supplemented by others with open chimneys at the sides. In the hall of Penshurst Place, in Kent, a perfect specimen of one of these central hearths is preserved."[16]

In the rural houses of antiquity, Stuckius describes the kitchen very much as Mr. Medley describes the old English kitchen. It was, Stuckius says, a large room having a high ceiling so that the floor above would be safe from danger of fire and where the family were able to meet together conveniently at every season of the year,[17]— a place which was both the kitchen and the room where the family and guests gathered about the hearth and the fire sacred to the household gods, the lares. The irons which supported the burning wood might well be regarded as an altar over which the cook as priest presided.[18] Cooks knowing the rites for sacrifices, wedding festivities and other occasions were of high value and authority among the Greeks. Among the Romans the censors, whose position was of the highest importance, dressed in purple and wearing ceremonial crowns, had the duty to strike down the victim with the sacrificial axe. Much was written of the honor and dignity of the ancient priestly cook, and none of the old poets, with the single exception of Posidippus,[19] ever ventured to present on the stage a cook who was a slave.

Immolating the victim, observing the sacrificial rites and cooking

[16] *Mediaeval Cookery*, The Quarterly Review, Vol. 178, No. 355, pp. 97, 98, January, 1894.

[17] *Antiquitates Conviviales*, Lib. II, Cap. XIII, pp. 193b, 194.

[18] "From pictures in the Bayeux Tapestry, we see that movable grates or grills, and movable hot plates, both resting on legs, like tables, were very early used for standing over the open hearths." *Mediaeval Cookery*, Quarterly Review, Vol. 178, No. 355, p. 97, January, 1894.

[19] Athenaeus, Lib. XIV, lines 658 et seq. On the general subject of Roman cooks, Miss Cornelia Gaskins Harcum submitted an interesting Dissertation at Johns Hopkins University in 1913.

the meat were only part of the duties of the cook, who was expected also to appear at the banquet table to carve the meat and to give to every guest his portion, observing always the rank and honor of the guest whom he served. This duty, which at first was performed by the cook, could also be performed by the host, or by any eminent guest, "nam Lysandrum, eo quandoque perfunctum munere, historia tradit,"—for history tells us, Coelius Rhodiginus says, that Lysander himself performed this duty of carving and distributing to each guest his portion,[20]—and it has been said that in this practice is to be found the origin of the phrase, the Lord is my portion and my cup, which in various forms is so often used in the Bible, as also the reference to the service of breaking bread to the hungry.[21]

When the food had been distributed and spirits of the company began to rise, the next important aspect of a banquet presented itself in the general conversation for, says Stuckius, if you will observe very closely the underlying meaning of Homer's story,[22] it was not a drug which Helen mixed with the wine, nor was it the Indian juice, but the opportunity for speech which turned the guest from thought of his sorrows to pleasure.[23] Of dinner table conversation, Stuckius says it may deal with everything in nature and even with things of which nature knows nothing, for "quales sunt convivae tales plerunque etiam illorum solent esse sermones conviviales,"—as are the guests so for the most part is their talk,—but always, he adds, conversation should be subject to the rule that

[20] *Antiquae Lectiones*, Lib. XIV, Cap. LV.
[21] *Antiquitates Conviviales*, Stuckius, Lib. III, Cap. III, pp. 194, 298, 298b.
[22] See *Odyssey*, Lib. IV, lines 221-230.
[23] *Antiquitates Conviviales*, Lib. III, Cap. XVII, p. 374b. Burton, *Anatomy*, Part II, Sec. IV, Mem. I, Subsec. III, Vol. II, p. 249, insists that there was a drug and that it was borage, a plant which it was thought had the property of strengthening the heart. Beckmann says, however, that the plant now so called was not known to the ancients. *History of Inventions, Discoveries and Origins* by John Beckmann (Bohn, London, 1846), Vol. II, p. 339.

anxious topics should be avoided and pleasant subjects sought.[24] In the simple days of Rome, when the party was about to break up, the tongue of the sacrificial animal was thrown into the fire and a libation was poured as an act of reverence to the gods, sometimes as a pledge that nothing said or done at the banquet would be spoken of later, and sometimes as a thank offering to Mercury for the free intercourse of speech.[25]

The ancient feasts were very frugal—nothing more, perhaps, than gruel with early fruits—but they were the more acceptable to the gods because they were simple. In this spirit, Horace calls his meals of garden vegetables the feasts of the gods:

> O noctes, coenaeque Deum, quibus ipse, meique
> Ante Larem proprium vescor, vernasque procaces
> Pasco libatis dapibus.[26]

O nights and feasts of the Gods, when I dine with my friends before my own Lares and leave the remains of our food to the familiar slaves as we make our final libation.

When the Empire of Rome began to bring great wealth to the City, luxury increased and banquets lost their simple character. Only after the conquest of Asia did the influence of eastern peoples and a softer life lead Romans to follow the practice of reclining at their meals,[27] a fashion of which Aldus Manutius says that it marked dissolute manners in the society where it prevailed, and in individuals showed a degree of absorption in pleasure hardly be-

[24] *Antiquitates Conviviales*, Lib. III, Cap. XVII, p. 377b. *Convivalium Sermonum Liber* (Basileae, 1541) by Joannis Peregrinus Petroselanus, is a collection of witticisms, and *Sermones Convivales* (Innsbruck, 1504) by Conradus Peutingerus discusses various subjects of early German history, neither book being necessarily concerned with table talk.

[25] *Sacrorum Sacrificiorum* by Stuckius, pp. 124b, 125. In later days banquets ended in no such sober manner. *Antiquitates Conviviales*, p. 412.

[26] *Satirarum*, Lib. II, No. VI, lines 65 et seq.

[27] *Virgilii Opera*, ad usum Delphini (Paris, 1675). Note by Carolus Ruaeus. *Aeneid*, Lib. I, line 702.

coming a serious man. It is true that serious men reclined, but at
least one man, Cato Uticensis, refused to do so.[28] When the old,
severe manners passed away and luxury came in, the banquet lost
its significance and the position of cook lost its dignity, so that
duties once performed by men of the highest rank were given over,
as Livy says,[29] to the meanest slave. Plautus in *Aulularia* tells how
cooks waited in the market to be hired by some person planning a
dinner party.

> After the host has bought his dainties and hired his cooks
> He hires his musicians here in the market.[30]

To which Ballio, one of the characters in Plautus' play of *Pseudolus*, adds:

> Those who call this a market-place of cooks, name it stupidly
> For this is a hiring-place of thieves, not of cooks.[31]

Besides the cooks who waited there for employment in private
entertainments or in taverns, there were also fishmongers, sausage-
makers, fishermen, dealers in unguents, millers, instructors in the
art of carving, and many others. All the luxuries, or what were
thought to be luxuries, were there for sale until Rome ceased to be
a place of wealth and the Empire ran its course through tyranny
back to a condition not very far from barbarism.

In mediaeval times the banquet in great houses, with the lord
and lady eating at the high table in the presence of retainers seated
at tables below the salt, was very ceremonious—and we may be
sure that what was done in great houses was followed in varying

[28] Dissertatiuncula IV, *De Accumbendi et Comedendi Ratione*, in *Novus
Thesaurus Antiquitatum Romanorum* of de Sallengre (Hague Comitum, 1716),
Vol. 1, col. 799.
[29] Lib. 39, Cap. 6.
[30] *Aulularia*, Act II, Sc. iv, lines 280, 281.
[31] *Pseudolus*, Act III, Sc. i, lines 790, 791.

degrees by houses of lesser dignity. Feudal service of the table was therefore elaborate.

When Stuckius wrote his book, these ceremonious fashions were declining. Population pressed upon the food supply, life was hard and work was the constant necessity for all but a few. When, therefore, the interval between courses was long, Stuckius said the delay was unpleasant to the guests and caused not only loss of time but sometimes an inconvenient interruption in one's private affairs. Guests were sure to reflect that their attention should be given to more serious and important matters, and so Stuckius said the practice had grown up among all European nations to put a whole course upon the table at once,[32] and with this practice "the principal duty of carving devolved upon the host and hostess, the honours of the 'side-dishes' being done by the guests before whom they were placed; the duty of the servants meanwhile consisting in handing plates and sauces, filling glasses, removing anything spilt, and putting the dishes straight when disarranged."[33]

Of the table manners of the times, Stuckius gives a vivid description which probably is as good for the days of old Rome as for the people in Europe at the time of the Reformation.

What is offered to you [he says] should be taken with three fingers or on the slice of bread which you use as a plate, since what cannot be taken with the fingers can be taken on bread. And if any one should offer you on a spoon something from the pie or from a stew, either take it on your bread or take the spoon and, having emptied it on your bread, return the spoon. If what is given is fluid, sip it and return the spoon well wiped off on the cloth. To lick your greasy fingers or to wipe them on your coat is not good manners,—it is better to wipe them on the cloth or towel. To put your hands into a dish with much gravy is a rustic way of doing

[32] *Antiquitates Conviviales*, Lib. III, Cap. I, p. 294b.

[33] *Mediaeval Cookery*, The Quarterly Review, Vol. 178, No. 355, p. 102, January, 1894. *Antiquitates Conviviales* by J. G. Stuckius, Lib. II, Cap. I, p. 290.

for it is better to use a knife or fork to take what is wanted. We take our food, therefore, with bare hands or using some utensil—a spoon, knife or fork or our bread—which is much the politer way.

The use of spoons—wooden, brass or silver—to help one's self to stew or a gruel is very frequent among Germans, though with the French, Italians and other nations, the bare hands are still employed, no spoon being used and gravy being taken up by soaking bread in it.[34]

Stuckius was a German and doubtless desired to present his countrymen in a favorable light, but forks were very little used in Europe in 1582 when his book was published, and even two hundred years later napkins and table-cloths were none too common.

In 1608 Thomas Coryat travelled from England to Italy and other countries and in regard to forks says:

Here I wil mention a thing that might have been spoken of before in discourse of the first Italian towne. I observed a custome in all those Italian cities and townes through which I passed, that is not used in any other country that I saw in my travels, neither doe I thinke that any other nation of Christendome doth use it, but only Italy. The Italian and also most strangers that are commorant in Italy, doe alwaies at their meales use a little forke when they cut their meat. For while with their knife which they hold in one hand they cut the meate out of the dish, they fasten the forke which they hold in their other hand upon the same dish, so that whatsoever he be that sitting in the company of any others at meale, should unadvisedly touch the dish of meate with his fingers from which all at the table doe cut, he will give occasion of offence unto the company, as having transgressed the laws of good manners, in so much that for his error he shall be at the least brow-beaten if not reprehended in wordes. This form of feeding I understand, is generally used in all places of Italy, their forkes being for the most part made of yron or steele, and some of silver, but those are used only by Gentlemen. The reason of this their curiosity is, because the Italian cannot by any means indure to have his dish touched with fingers seeing all mens fingers are not alike cleane. Hereupon I my selfe thought good to imitate the Italian fashion by this

[34] *Antiquitates Conviviales*, Lib. III, Cap. III, p. 303.

78

forked cutting of meate, not only while I was in Italy, but also in Germany, and oftentimes in England since I came home.[35]

It seems that the use of forks originated in Italy, as Coryat says, but it may have been adopted at so early a date by the scholars among whom Stuckius spent his life that it seemed to him a native German institution.

Napkins and table-cloths were slower in making their way. In 1762 Oliver Goldsmith remarked of the French:

They seldom spread a table-cloth before their guests: but in that I cannot be angry with them, since those who have no linen on their backs may very well be excused for wanting it upon their tables.[36]

To Arthur Young the common use of table napkins in France was a novelty as recently as 1787. Evidently they were not a daily necessity in England at that time, for Young makes the comment:

The idea of dining without a napkin seems ridiculous to a Frenchman.[37]

Martialis, the Roman poet, thought it undesirable to cover a table by a cloth which hid its beauties, for he said of a friend:

You set good tables, Olus, but they are covered tables.
How absurd! Mine would be as good, if never seen![38]

Cloths or towels, nevertheless, were used at the table in Rome[39] and Pliny tells of asbestos towels that could be cleaned by fire as well as they could be cleaned by water![40]

[35] *Coryat's Crudities*, p. 90.
Mr. D. J. Medley, in his article on Anglo-Norman Social Life—*Social England*, Vol. I, pp. 371, 381—in speaking of the period 1060-1216, says that "though forks were not unknown, fingers were invariably used." No authority is cited.
[36] *The Citizen of the World*, Letter LXXVIII.
[37] *Travels in France*, p. 277.
[38] *Epigrammatum*, Lib. X, No. LIV.
[39] *De Triclinio* by Petrus Ciacconius (Amst. 1689), pp. 28, 29. *De Conviviis*, Bulengerus, Lib. I, Cap. XXXVI.
[40] *N. H.*, Lib. XIX, Cap. IV.

Apparently, servants were always ready at an ancient banquet to pass ewer and towel to any guest who wished to wash hands or mouth and this may have been a frequent occurrence at every meal.[41]

Ursinus quotes Lampridius to the effect that the Emperor Elagabalus never used washed linen because he said beggars did as much.[42] Possibly mendicants of antiquity were more fastidious than those of the present day, or perhaps Elagabalus was himself inclined to underrate the merits of the laundry.

During the middle ages, the use of table linen was little known and indeed made its way into common practice very slowly. If, therefore, in the latter part of the eighteenth century table-cloths and napkins were not common in France and England, we may be sure that Germans were not wholly without excuse if, two centuries earlier, they were guilty of cleaning their fingers or spoons in the ways which Stuckius describes.

Forks were rare in Europe during the sixteenth century.[43] They are not mentioned in Erasmus' book on the manners of children and, though Henry III of France used forks, the practice was regarded as effeminate and was not followed by Louis XIV. Perhaps they were not as necessary in those days as they are to people of the present time, for much mediaeval food was chopped, ground or pounded in a mortar with a pestle until it was so soft and pulpy that it could easily be taken with a spoon. There are in the books occasional references to the fact that soft food can be eaten by those who are "edentuli"—persons who have few or no teeth[44]— and it is not impossible that the use of the fork marks a period of

[41] See Appendix by Fulvius Ursinus, p. 307, bound with *De Triclinio* by Petrus Ciacconius. *De Conviviis* by Bulengerus, Lib. I, Cap. XLI.

[42] Appendix by Fulvius Ursinus, p. 305, bound with *De Triclinio* by Petrus Ciacconius.

[43] See *Coryat's Crudities* by Thomas Coryat (London, 1611), pp. 90-91.

[44] See, for example, *De Re Cibaria* by Bruyerinus, Lib. VIII, Cap. II, p. 458.

improving health among European peoples, when their teeth lasted longer and could be used with more comfort. Furthermore, Baruffaldus says that the ancient spoon was probably pointed and could be used as a fork when such use was convenient.[45]

Conditions of life were very primitive two or three hundred years ago. The great forward movement which has created the new world of modern times had not begun and mankind was still struggling under the double burden of centralized government and lack of food.

It is shocking to think of the appearance which we imagine that men of great dignity—Erasmus or Sir Thomas More, Richelieu or Colbert—presented during a meal when the hand was to be used instead of a napkin, as Ovid advises:

> Ora nec immunda, tota perunge manu.[46]

We wonder, too, how Roman gentlemen and ladies lived in classic times and we are tempted to speculate as to what they would say were they seated at a handsome modern dinner table with ornamental silverware, sparkling cut glass and decorated plates. To put the hands into food seems to us so clearly barbaric that we hardly think another opinion possible. It is well to learn, therefore, that even in this matter there may be a difference of opinion among reasonable, well-informed persons, as is shown by the recent statement of a cultivated Hindoo Brahmin gentleman who had travelled much, who was intimately acquainted with the ways of our western world and who, after remarking that in India knives, forks and spoons are not used, even by the well-to-do, went on to say of western table manners:

[45] *De Armis Convivalibus* by Hieronymus Baruffaldus (Ferrariae, 1715), in *Novus Thesaurus*, etc., of de Sallengre, Vol. III, col. 742. See chapter on Forks in *History of Inventions, Discoveries and Origins* by John Beckmann, Vol. II, p. 407.

[46] *De Arte Amandi*, Lib. III, line 756.

I believe that owing to severe cold in the northern countries, people generally wear gloves on their hands and do not like to wash before and after meals. This must have been particularly so when there was no hot and cold running water such as is now found everywhere in America and Europe. The use of knives, forks and spoons must have begun in order to save the uncovering of hands and washing them often. In India we wash our hands and mouth just before and after meals.[47]

In cold climates people have to wear thick clothes in order to keep warm. Being piled up with clothing, they cannot sit on a carpet. So they have chairs and tables. In a warm climate like India, clothing is more an ornament than protection, the floors are never cold, and one can sit on a straw mat or a carpet with perfect ease.

It was not table manners, however, that troubled the mediaeval world. Their problem was maintenance of the food supply, and their most pressing business was to secure food at every opportunity and to store it safely.

The first duty of the head of a family, Stuckius says, is to see that pantry, cellar and store-rooms are well filled with food so as to supply those who are dependent upon him and to provide the means whereby he may entertain intimate friends and honored guests. Food and drink of every kind that will not spoil, from fields and flocks, orchards and gardens, he should with all diligence collect, store and keep. Whatever he does not raise himself, he should buy whenever the price makes it possible to do so, and should make it his first business to put it away where it can be had when necessary for his own household, his intimate friends or his guests. And, as in the invitation of persons to a banquet and in the buying of food, the master of the house should consider the numbers and habits of those for whom he must provide, he must bear these considera-

[47] Marco Polo relates as a matter of interest that Indians in the Province of Maabar touched their food with the right hand only, reserving the left hand for less cleanly uses, and that in drinking they never permitted the vessel to touch the mouth. *Book of Ser Marco Polo*, edited by Sir Henry Yule, Vol. II, p. 342.

tions in mind as he uses his stores, taking care always to keep on hand a safe provision of food for future needs.[48] Dinner companies, therefore, could not be casual entertainments on the spur of the moment. They must be carefully planned and must be supplied out of stores laid by for future use. Guests could be invited only when the store is sufficient to provide for present and future wants, always remembering, as Cato says, how long the winter is.

[48] *Antiquitates Conviviales*, Lib. II, Cap. XII, p. 189.

CHAPTER VI

THE FOOD OF OUR FATHERS. PORRIDGE. BREAD. ACORNS AS A SOURCE OF FLOUR. "DISTRESSFUL BREAD."

BREAD in the old days was truly the staff of life. It holds "the first rank among the things which give nourishment to men." Of all other foods we become tired, but bread "is the last appetite lost in case of illness and the first recovered in convalescence."[1] The life of man consists in the use of bread above all other foods.[2]

It was, certainly, a very different life from that of modern times which men led in those long ages when dry bread was the chief food—when, indeed, bread by itself made a sufficient meal, all that was asked or expected—and when white bread was a luxury. "We all live on bread and water," said St. Jerome, "a familiar and common practice, and we do not think it fasting."[3] Men of the present world would call such a diet prison fare, regarding it as a great hardship. Nevertheless, we need not go back to the times of St. Jerome, nor to periods earlier than those which history considers very recent, in order to find a sufficient diet of bread a privilege of

[1] *De Re Cibaria*, Bruyerinus, Lib. VI, Cap. VI, p. 391.

[2] *L'agriculture et maison rustique*, Estienne and Liébault (Paris, 1589), p. 315. *The Bread of Our Forefathers* by Sir William Ashley (Oxford, 1928), a very interesting and scholarly work. In Greek the word for bread was artos, but Homer used the word sitos for bread, from whatever grain made, as distinguished from meats, and man in the common phrase was designated the bread eater, *Odyssey*, Bk. IX, lines 89, 191, Bk. VIII, line 222; *Iliad*, Bk. VI, line 142, Bk. XXI, line 465. See *Les céréales dans l'antiquité grecque* by M. Auguste Jarde (Bocard, Paris, 1925), pp. 1-2.

[3] Letter LII, ad Nepotianum, Presbyterum.

the fortunate ones of earth, and of this food, in 1896 or 1897, Oscar Wilde wrote:

Some six weeks ago I was allowed by the doctor to have white bread to eat instead of the coarse black or brown bread of ordinary prison fare. It is a great delicacy. It will sound strange that dry bread could be a delicacy to any one. To me it is so much so that at the close of each meal I carefully eat whatever crumbs may be left on my tin plate, or have fallen on the rough towel that one uses as a cloth so as not to soil one's table; and I do so not from hunger—I get now quite sufficient food—but simply that nothing should be wasted of what is given to me.[4]

In this way bread has been eaten and enjoyed through many ages of human history.

And what kind of bread was it? The best bread was made from fine wheat flour,[5] but wheat was often expensive, and on the continent of Europe rye was very generally used. There is a question when this grain was first planted as a farm crop. Bruyerinus doubts that rye was known to men of the ancient world,[6] but long before

[4] De Profundis by Oscar Wilde (Putnam, New York, 1905), pp. 79, 80.

[5] Pliny, N. H., Lib. XVIII, Cap. XXVII. De Alimento by Franciscus Bonamicus (Florence, 1603), p. 380.

[6] De Re Cibaria, Lib. V, Cap. XVII, p. 355. Diaeteticon, Ludovicus Nonnius, p. 20. Essai historique, by Count Henri Grégoire, printed as an Introduction to the edition of Le théâtre d'agriculture by Olivier de Serres, published at Paris in 1804, p. cxxxix. Both Jean Mathias Gesner, who edited in 1735 an edition of Latin writers on agriculture, and Saboureaux de la Bonneterie, who in 1771 translated this edition into French, believed that the grain which in Gesner's edition of Columella's book was called hexastichum (Lib. II, Cap. IX), was in fact rye. In the edition published by Joannes Hervagius at Baslé in 1535, the word hexastichum does not appear but in its place is alicastrum. Facciolati defines hexastichum as 6-rowed barley and alicastrum as March wheat—i.e., wheat that is sowed in March and reaped in summer. Pliny (N. H., Lib. XVIII, Cap. XL) mentions secale as deterrimum et tantum ad arcendam famem utile. Facciolati says that Pontedera suspects that Pliny's secale was none other than Columella's hordeum hexastichum, adding, however, "suspicatur, inquam, nam certi nihil statui potest." See Origin of Cultivated Grains by Alphonse de Candolle (Int. Sci. Ser., Appleton, N. Y., 1902), pp. 370-373; also The Bread of Our Forefathers by Sir William Ashley, pp. 68, 160-161.

the sixteenth century rye was well known and commonly used. Moreover, as need arose, bread was made from barley, millet, oats, buckwheat, rice, vetch, beans, peas, lupines, lentils,[7] the bark of trees and from whatever could be had and used. In the Cevennes mountains, Le Grand d'Aussy says, bread was always rare, so that even persons in comfortable circumstances lived for the most part on chestnuts, having bread on holidays only[8]—and there doubtless were many other places besides the Cevennes mountains where grain was not easily raised and where, in consequence, bread was not often to be had. Malthus tells of the use in Sweden during the summer of 1799 of bread made of the inner part of the fir and of dried sorrel without any mixture whatever of meal.[9]

For many years Romans lived chiefly on the cakes or gruel known as puls, not what modern times would call bread.[10]

Ausonius, who lived in the fourth century A. D., says of the old times:

Gruel was our food and diluted with water was our drink,[11]

and it may have been partly because of the use of puls that there were no bakers in Rome until some time after the year A. U. C. 800—that is, perhaps, until after A. D. 47. Pliny's statement, which is much quoted on this subject, adds the comment that before that time bread was made by native Romans, being there, as in most countries, the work of the women.[12] One can imagine the primitive puls or sitos, cooked with little attention and much economy

[7] De Alimentis, J. D. Sala (Pavia, 1628), p. 13. De Re Cibaria, Lib. VI, Cap. IX, p. 410.

[8] La vie privée des Français, Vol. I, p. 3.

[9] Essay on the Population, Bk. II, Chap. II, p. 173. See De Alimentis by J. D. Sala, p. 7.

[10] Pliny, N. H., Lib. XVIII, Cap. XIX. "Puls simplex ex farina tritici, saepius crassiore rarius tenuiore et sale et aqua." Antiquitates Conviviales, Johannis Guilielmus Stuckius (Tiguri, 1597), Lib. I, Cap. XXI, p. 58.

[11] Technopaegnion, Sec. IX, De Cibis.

[12] Pliny, N. H., Lib. XVIII, Cap. XXVIII.

of fire-wood, as not very different from the staple food of the Iroquois Indians, which Parkman says consisted of cakes of corn "cooked without salt in a variety of ways, each more odious than the last."[13] Possibly, as the *Encyclopaedia Britannica* suggests, "the art of cookery is to some extent the product of an increased refinement of taste consequent on culture and increase of wealth" and "to this extent a decadent art,"[14] but if so the writer of the article in the *Encyclopaedia* would rank ancient culture "to this extent" as not far above the culture of the Iroquois Indians.

Besides the grains mentioned, other materials were used to make bread or gruel as necessity required. "I shall not speak of acorns," Sala says, "for there is no person at this time who would not willingly give them to the swine, although I know that in Switzerland and elsewhere peasants make bread from acorns ground into flour."[15]

There are, however, two kinds of acorns, the bitter and the sweet. Possibly the bitter kind was better known in northern Italy, while the sweet kind was abundant in Switzerland and other countries north of Italy. If this were the case, Sala's objection to the use of acorns as a food would be explained, although even in his time acorns were often used in Italy to make bread. "It is possible," Mr. J. Russell Smith says, "that the human race has eaten more of acorns than it has of wheat, for wheat is the food of only one of the four large masses of humans, the European-North American group. The other three groups, the Chinese-Japanese, the Indian (Asiatic), and the tropical peoples pay small attention to wheat; hundreds of millions of their peoples have never heard of it. Meanwhile those humans (and possibly pre-humans) who dwelt in or near the oak forests in the middle latitudes—Japan, China, the Himalaya moun-

[13] *The Jesuits in North America*, p. 16.
[14] *Ency. Brit.*, 14th ed., Tit. Cookery, Vol 6, p. 366.
[15] *De Alimentis* by J. D. Sala, p. 11. *De Re Cibaria* by Bruyerinus, Lib. IX, Cap. XLII, p. 656.

tains, West Asia, Europe, North America—have probably lived in part on acorns for unknown centuries, possibly for thousands of centuries."[16]

There is no written history of the various European peoples north of Italy before the arrival of the Romans, but we have every reason to believe that, occupying countries covered with immense forests, they lived on game, on such grain as they could raise, and on the wild fruits of trees, especially on the acorns of the different kinds of oak which were common. The especial respect which they paid to this tree, the imposing ceremony with which the High Priest came every year to cut the mistletoe, indeed the very name Druid, derived from the Indo-European word meaning oak, all seem to show the importance of the tree to the early Gauls.[17] Idolatry, Le Grand d'Aussy adds, has not always begun in fear. With most peoples it has been an act of gratitude.[18]

According to Virgil, agriculture did not arise until the supply of acorns ran short.

> Prima Ceres ferro mortales vertere terram
> Instituit, cum jam glandes atque arbuta sacrae
> Deficerent sylvae et victum Dodona negaret.[19]

> First Ceres taught the Ground with Grain to sow,
> And arm'd with Iron Shares the crooked Plough;
> When now Dodonian Oaks no more supply'd
> Their Mast and Trees their Forrest-fruit deny'd.[20]

[16] *Tree Crops, a Permanent Agriculture* by Mr. J. Russell Smith (Harcourt, Brace and Company, New York, 1929), p. 150.

[17] *La vie privée des Français* by Le Grand d'Aussy, Vol. I, p. 8. Nevertheless, when Montesquieu in 1748 published his book, *L'esprit des lois*, he was unacquainted with the use of acorns as food in France, and referred to oaks as "barren trees" (Liv. XVIII, Ch. 9),—so quickly is lost the memory of the conditions of life out of which mankind has arisen.

[18] *La vie privée des Français*, Vol. I, p. 251.

[19] *Georgics*, Lib. I, lines 147-149,—as though Ceres had herself supplied early man with iron ploughs!

[20] Dryden's translation, *Georgics*, I, lines 219-222.

Of the life of savage man in the infancy of agriculture, there is a good description by Mr. J. S. Newberry in an article on *The Food and Fibre Plants of the North American Indians*, published in the Popular Science Monthly for November, 1887.[21] Game and fish were not always to be had, maize was never very abundant, so the Indians were great berry eaters, using, besides wild strawberries, huckleberries, and blackberries, such fruits as service berries, cranberries, elderberries, etc., when in season. Then too, there were nuts—chestnuts, hickory nuts, walnuts and butternuts, roots and fruits, and finally acorns, which were a great reliance both in Europe and America.

In primitive ages, Plutarch says, when men "had by chance tasted or eaten an acorn, they danced for joy about some oak or aesculus, calling it by the name of life-giver, mother and nourisher. And this was the only festival that these times were acquainted with; upon all other occasions all things were full of anguish and dismal sadness."[22]

Ovid gives a similar account, for man's first food, he says, was supplied by green herbs until the acorn was found, and thereafter all was well since the hard oak furnished immense wealth.[23] Man, of course, used all the food he could find, including other tree fruits besides nuts and acorns,[24] but acorns had the double advantage that they kept well when stored and were available in large quantities. Sir James G. Frazer says that great stores of acorns have been found buried in prehistoric village sites of northern Italy and Switzerland.[25]

In Greece, the Valonia oak forms considerable forests, especially

[21] Vol. XXXII, p. 37.
[22] *Morals*, On Eating Flesh, Vol. V, p. 5.
[23] *Fasti*, edited by Sir James G. Frazer (Macmillan, 1929), Lib. IV, lines 395 et seq., and note, Vol. III, p. 265.
[24] *De Re Cibaria* by Bruyerinus, Lib. XI, Cap. XLII, p. 656.
[25] *Fasti*, Lib. I, line 676, and note, Vol. II, p. 259.

on the lower slopes of Taygetos and on the island of Crete. Its acorns, which are large and variable in shape, are one of the common articles of trade in the bazaars and are eaten either raw or cooked,[26] as doubtless they were eaten in prehistoric times. The acorns most palatable to man are those of the ilex Ballota of the Iberian peninsula and northern Africa, the quercus Aegilops of the Orient, the quercus Emoryi of southwestern United States and northern Mexico and quercus Michauxii of southeastern United States, although the American Indians, like the rest of the hungry world, used the acorns of many other species of oak when better was not to be had.[27] For the use of acorns by Indians of New England, Mr. Sargent gives two interesting references.[28] The first is from Roger Williams:

These akornes also they drie, and in case of want of corne, by much boyling they make a good dish of them; yea, sometimes in plentie of corne do they eate these akornes for a novelty.[29]

The second is from John Josselyn's *New England Rarities Discovered*, p. 48, a book published in London in 1672. Josselyn says:

And out of the white Oak acorns (which is the acorn Bears delight to feed upon): the Natives draw an Oyle, taking the rottenest Maple Wood, which being burnt to ashes, they make a strong Lye therewith, wherein they boyl their white Oak acorns until the Oyl swim on the top in great quantity; this they fleet off, and put into bladders to anoint their naked Limbs, which corrobarates them exceedingly; they eat it likewise with their Meat, it is an excellent clear and sweet Oyl.

Mr. Newberry says that in California the acorns of quercus lobata and quercus agrifolia are much used for food by the Indians.

[26] *Silva of North America* by Mr. Charles Sprague Sargent (Houghton Mifflin Company), Vol. III, p. 8.
[27] *Ibid.*, Vol. III, p. 3.
[28] *Ibid.*, Vol. III, p. 8.
[29] *A Key into the Language of America* by Roger Williams. R. I. Hist. Soc. Coll., i. 90.

The acorns are long-elliptical in outline, an inch and a half in length by half an inch or more in diameter. The kernel is sometimes rather bitter, but more palatable than that of any of our Eastern oaks and quite nutritious. In the region where the tree abounds, the Indians in former times were in the habit of collecting acorns in large quantities, and storing them for winter and I have seen nearly a hundred bushels in one wigwam. They are prepared for eating by grinding the kernels to a kind of coarse flour; this is mixed with water to a thick paste; a circular depression with raised edges is made in the sand, into which this paste is poured. A fire is then built over it and it is half-baked, half-steamed, to the Indian taste. This treatment takes the bitterness from the acorn and the resulting cake, though according to our notions somewhat lacking in cleanliness, is well-flavored and wholesome.[30]

The oak has the disadvantage that it affords support to a much larger number of insects than any other genus of trees whose insect enemies have been studied,[31] but its fruit, unless the crop is interrupted by pests, is valuable as food for domestic animals and thus indirectly as well as directly is useful to mankind.[32] Moreover, Mr. Merriam says the California acorns make a rich gelatinous food containing from 18 to 25 per cent. of nut oil having nutritive value. Acorn flour, too, is easy to work and a good binder, holding together several times its bulk of corn meal or other coarsely ground material.

Former times knew little of the art of cookery. It is possible, by an ammonia process or by washing, to remove the tannin from acorns, and it is reported that in Mexico a good bread is made containing acorn flour which American travellers like. It is also possible, by mixing acorn flour with milk so as to make a paste, to remove all bitterness by fermentation,[33] a method that has the ad-

[30] *Food and Fibre Plants of the North American Indians*, Popular Science Monthly, Nov. 1887, Vol. XXXII, p. 37.

[31] *Silva of North America*, Vol. III, p. 10.

[32] *The Acorn, a Possibly Neglected Source of Food*, by Mr. C. Hart Merriam. National Geographic Magazine, Vol. 34, p. 129, August, 1918.

[33] *Foods, their Origin, Composition and Manufacture* by William Tibbles (Baillière, Tindal & Cox, London, 1912), pp. 683-684.

vantage of saving nutritive qualities that are lost by the washing process. Of these things the middle ages knew nothing, and so the methods of making bread from acorns and other substitutes in time of need is given by Segni[34] as follows:

On Increasing the Quantity of Bread with Acorns. The oak gives a sweeter nut than any other; it is bigger and more abundant and easier to eat. The nut of the beech tree also is very sweet and has much nourishment. To use these in time of necessity they are to be treated, carefully, in the manner hereafter stated, if we wish to increase the volume of ordinary bread.

Take fourteen pounds and a half of acorns, putting them into a kettle, and over the fire with so much water that all the acorns will be well covered and, when the water is nearly boiling, begin with a ladle, with holes in it, to lift the acorns out, putting them on the ground and crushing them under foot, or in any other way, until they break and lose both of their shells. The water in the kettle must not boil because if the water boil over the acorns will not cook. But the water must also be hot, so that the acorns may lose their shells, and as soon as the shells have fallen off, throw the acorns into a kettle of cold water and then put it on the stove again, allowing it to stand four good inches under water, adding to it a handful of ashes which are as big as an egg. When the water barely covers the acorns, remove the kettle from the fire, drain off the rest of the water, remove the ashes and put the kettle on the fire again with as much water as before, adding to it a kind of sachet in which have been put half a loaf of bread, four cloves of garlic, the meat of ten or twelve nuts, two ounces of yeast, four sprigs of sage, or of laurel. And when the water has boiled down, as above, change the water and repeat the above operation, leaving the sachet in it, however, until the acorns have lost their bitterness and acid taste. At the end a little salt can even be added, perhaps about an ounce, but this must not be put into the sachet so that the acorns will not become too hard, for salt seems to make cooking acorns difficult.

When all this is done, and the water has been drained off, as above, and the acorns have been allowed to cool, work it with the hands until

[34] *Carestia e Fame* by Giovanni Battista Segni (Bologna, 1602), pp. 151-155.

it becomes a dough, and pass it through a sieve, and it goes through very rapidly, for in one hour you can pass three measures of it, or at least two. And when you have made the yeast in the usual way, add it to the acorn dough that you have passed through the sieve, and add twelve pounds of flour, because we presume that one half a pound of flour was used in making the yeast. And so this bread is made, after allowing it to rise, in the usual manner. In this way the quantity of bread can be increased, even when it is being made in a hurry. If anyone should think that the expense of making this bread is great because of the amount of fire necessary, it can be made with less fire and with a little more time; and the acorns can be prepared even better in the following manner.

After the acorns have been treated as described above, that is, after they have boiled the first time and the ashes have been removed and they have been returned to the kettle with the sachet filled with the abovesaid spices, and after it has boiled for half an hour, and the water has been drained, then throw the acorns with the sachet into a tub of water which has a hole in the bottom, filling the tub so as to cover all the acorns; in short, following the method that is given above, and which is used also to remove the bitterness from olives. Then it will be enough to change the water only once a day, continuing this until it has lost its bitterness. This can be done in six or eight days, more or less, according to the quantity of acorns. For this reason it is very wise always to keep a large quantity in these tubs because the softer they become, the more perfect they become, and I can even say that then, bread can be made with a great deal less flour. And, if the acorns are very slow in losing their bitterness, they can be spread on a board and allowed to dry in the oven, very carefully. The oven must be just a little warmer than the sun. In this way they can be made into flour, and can be used with the method described above, and it cannot fail to be a success.

Two Other Refuges for the Rich and the Poor. There are two other refuges in time of want; one for the rich citizens, the other for the poor and wretched.

For the rich: When this great lack of grain is upon us and we cannot continue to get white bread made with the best of flour for our rich citizens, then remove only the bran, or actually make bread of whole wheat. When there is even greater want of wheat, barley of every kind can be used ground whole, afterward making bread of it as the Jews are in the habit of doing according to history; or, perhaps, with rice mixed with wheat, as is the custom in the greater part of the Orient, in all India and in the island of Japan, because this bread gives fine nourishment and it increases the quantity greatly. One can make good and digestible bread from buckwheat, and this was done before we had wheat-bread. It is for this reason that the Romans called flour farina from farro, meaning wheat. Bread is made from broom-corn or rye, or from Indian corn as is the custom in Germany.

Galenus and Oribasius make mention of the fact that, in time of want, bread was made from oats and millet. Bread has been made from all vegetables, horse-beans, chick-peas, white beans, sow thistles, lentils, peas, pure vetch, which can be mixed with other flours, according to their abundance. God revealed to Ezekiel these different breads by saying to him: Take grain, barley, horse-beans, lentils, millet, vetch, these six things, and make bread from them which may last all the time that you shall sleep. Bread can be made from millet, from chestnuts, dried and pulverized, mixed with decoctions of pumpkins, turnips or apples, along with wheat. The provision and the conservation of these things will be good in any event, and the prudent man must respect them.

In Piacenza, people eat spaghetti which has been boiled in water and strained and then put into wine. They practically drink this spaghetti, and they get from it great vigor and nourishment. In time of want, one can have polenta for bread because it is very satisfying. This polenta can be made from the milk of any animal, from hot broths, from any kind of flour we have described above, from vegetables, from chestnuts, flavored with fresh butter, with cheese made of mare's milk, cow's milk, buffalo's milk, goat's milk or sheep's milk.

Polenta can also be made from cow beef meat, buffalo and any other animal like these. It can be prepared in loaves and then dried, salted and pulverized, mixing with them a little pepper or saffron. Then, cook this pulverized meat in broth or wine or vinegar, or must of wine, or water, with the above spices to the amount of one spoonful for every person, which will be enough to sustain the person for one day. This has more nourishment than milk when it is mixed with flour of vegetables or with chestnuts.

When there is an abundance of meat, it can be made into bread, after

94

removing the bones and the tendons. Use one-third of flour and two of meat and boil this with wheat, salt, anise seed to taste, and cook it all very well. One can also make bread from fish, as they do in Scotland and in India by the people of Sora, by cooking the fish in the sun and then pulverizing them into flour. Finally, the rich can provide for a multiplication and increase of bread by the method pointed out above since by adding three pounds of rice to thirty pounds of wheat flour, there is an increase of six pounds for every ten pounds of flour combined with one of rice. Buckwheat gives almost the same increase, if one pound and a half of rice is added to every ten pounds of buckwheat flour.

Pulverized horse-beans of a suitable kind give a reasonable increase; so do chick-peas, beans, especially the white beans, and peas, all of which increase the quantity of bread and the weight of wheat flour. Flour made from chestnuts increases the amount greatly, especially when one adds to these mixtures apples, turnips, pears, pulverized pumpkins which have been passed through the sieve with a little salt, anise seed, fennel to keep it from blowing away. These are enough suggestions for the help of the rich.

For the poor: Now, for the poor and miserable people, so that they can nourish themselves at little expense and keep themselves alive, let them always be sure to have good yeast of wheat-flour so as to make wholesome bread, for, otherwise, the bread would not rise and unleavened bread is very bad. Let them have always some goat's milk cheese and bran and keep this in batter as long as possible, so that it will easily be made into flour, and when it is wet it can be used so much more easily to make bread. They should gather all of the dog's grass that they can, and after washing it and drying it thoroughly in the oven, they should make it into flour, leaving only the hay and the straw for animals. They should put in a supply of dried acorns and chestnuts and millet flour, panic grass, buckwheat, vetch, lupines, ervum and rye. They should keep for themselves the mixtures of all wheats which are generally given to chickens and mix these with pumpkins, barnacles, cooked melons which have been put into the oven with the seeds in them, with their rinds cut into four parts, for all this makes good food and helps us to fight the rage of hunger.

One can make bread from the fine sawdust of young trees, such as pear trees, cherry trees and their barks, after they have been dried in the oven and pulverized. One takes as much of this powder as of prepared dog-

grass, and the same amount of groats, and a kettle full of pulverized turnips, all this passed through the sieve with fennel, after all this has been
fermented. This bread is very good when cooked for the sustenance of
the poor.

Another kind of bread can be made from twigs if they are picked when
green, dried and pulverized. These twigs are from chestnut trees or oak
trees. They can be added to every sort of grain and of vegetables, in equal
quantities, with a kettle full of pumpkins which have been kneaded and
fermented and thoroughly cooked. Bread can be made from the roots of
herbs, like artichokes, sow thistles, cyclamen, sword-grass, the roots of
cabbage, all well washed and dried, with as much bran, or groats, or
flour made from vegetables, or wheat. All of this, when well cooked, is
very sustaining.

With acorns, chestnuts, lupines, and dried, powdered roots, along with
a third of flour made from vegetables or from wheat, a third part fruits
or acorns, the other third of dog's grass, bran or groats, this always added
to a kettle full of turnips, apples, pears, buckwheat, dried figs, cabbage
roots, dried grapes, with two or three ounces of salt, four ounces of fennel, or cumin seed or anise seed for every hundred pounds of mixture,
cooking the bread thoroughly but not allowing it to get too hard, man
has prepared himself valiantly to fight Hunger and Want.

Sir Hugh Platt in his *Sundry New and Artificial Remedies
against Famine, Written upon the Occasion of the Great Dearth in
the Year 1590,* gives an account of substitutes which may be
used in place of grain. His recommendations are like those given
by Segni but have their own interest as telling of resources likely to
be available in England during a period of want. Sir Hugh says:

**How to take away a great part of that rank and unsavoury taste
of Beans, Pease, Beechmast, Chestnuts, Acorns, Vetches and such
like.** Boyl your Beans, Pease, Beechmast, etc. in fair Water, and if they
be not yet pleasing enough, Change your Water again, and at the second
or third boyling, you shall find a strange Alteration in Taste, for the
Water hath sucked out and imbibed the greatest part of their rankness, then
you must dry them (and if you think good you may also hull them, according to the manner set down hereafter in the Abstract of Anchora

Famis, etc.) or else you may grind them unhulled, and then make bread there of, either simply of it self, or with the Addition of some third or fourth part of other Wheat-flower; or else for better Expedition at the least in drink, if not in bread, you may take the ground Meal of them, and infuse warm Water thereon, and as it beginneth to cool, dreyne the same away, and re-infuse fresh warm Water till the taste please you: Then dry up the Meal, and make bread thereof either simply, or compounded as before. And as concerning the Chestnuts, we have the Experience of France therein already, where in great abundance they are spent and consumed in their usual bread in divers parts of that Country.

The Beechmast doth yield a most sweet and delicate Oyl, and every way comparable with the Nut it self, and therefore it is very probable that it will make an excellent bread with a very small correction: and if there might be some easie way or manner found out for the ready husking or hulling of them (which seemeth no matter of any great difficulty), then I durst promise a most rich and plentiful Oyl of our own growing, and serviceable for many uses. But if notwithstanding my former Preparation of Beans, Pease, etc., the Meal thereof do not yet content you, then work it into Past, with a liquor first strengthened with some bruised Aniseseeds, licoras, or sweet Fennel seeds, or with the seeds themselves incorporated in the Past, or for the avoiding of charge with Pepperwort, Thime, Winter-savary, Penniroyal, etc. For if you can but deceive the Taste, you shall find the bread very harty, wholsome and nourishing. And whatsoever is here spoken of Beans, Pease, etc. May be generally understood of all other Grain, Seeds, Plants, Pulse, Roots, etc.

. . . .

How to make an excellent Bread of the Roots of Aaron called Cuckowpit, or Starch Roots. The making thereof is set down by a late Writer in this manner. First the roots that are large must be cleansed from all skin and filth, and then cut into small and thin slices, the thinner you make them the sooner they are prepared, seeth them in boyling water, so long as you find the water hot and biting, and till the Roots begin to wax sweet. Then change your water and pour fresh water unto them, and so continue boyling until the water become sweet, and that the roots have lost all their acrimony. Then take them out, and lay them abroad upon Canvas, supported with frames, and being dry grind them with hand-

97

mills, and they make a most white and pure meal, which either of it self or by the mixture of one third of wheat meal with it, maketh a most fair and savoury bread. This carrieth some good sence and liklyhood of truth with it, for we find by daily experience, that it maketh as fair, if not a fairer starch, than our wheat. And therefore it were to be wished that some good husbandry were used in the planting and multiplying of these Roots, observing the nature of such soil and place wherein they most delight. And though it should fail us in this kind, yet we shall find our labour richly requited, if we convert them into starch only. But here it is to be remembered, that the root must be gathered when it is plump full, and in his pride, which is about the latter end of March, and all April: For when it beginneth once to spire, and that the sap is run up into the leaves, then the root shrinketh and also loseth much of his vertue. Here a just occasion is offered to practice the like upon the turnep, whereof there are both good store and the price of them likewise very reasonable.

Bread and other food made of Pompions. This food being both cheap, and great, doth also make a very savoury bread if a little meal be mixed therewith, yielding food to a great number with a small charge. And if you bestow sugar, and other sauce upon it, it may also pass for a delicate dish. The manner of making the same is thus described by Porta: Choose the greatest and ripest Pompions, cut them into thin slices, and take away the hard crust or coat, and the inner marrow or softness, seeth them in boyling water, and bring them to a pulp or pap, and then strein it, adding thereto a third part of meal or flower and make it up into bread, the fresher you eat the same, the more pleasant and delicate you shall esteem it. But with mine Authors favour: I think you will find it in his best forme, and of farthest extention, when it is in his pap or pulp, for his Body is exceeding waterish, and vanisheth away to a small substance if you seek to dry it. This I write by mine own trial, yet peradventure the Goord of Naples, which he calleth Cucurbita, may be of a differing nature from our Pompions.

In 1772, M. Antoine Augustin Parmentier produced a *Mémoir* on substitutes which might, in times of scarcity, be used for ordinary foods. This *Mémoir*, which was crowned by the Academy of Besançon, was expanded into a book published in Paris in 1781, of which an English translation appeared in London in 1783.

This book dealt chiefly with the use of potatoes, then little known in Europe, but there were many other vegetables, farinaceous seeds and roots which are listed, and the methods by which they can be prepared and used are given (p. 65).

M. Parmentier on Foods Available in Times of Scarcity. Take any of the roots listed hereafter, when ripe, strip them of their skin, divide them by a grater, pour water on the grated mass, which, as it passes through a close searce, will carry along with it a matter that will deposit itself gradually at the bottom of the wooden or earthen vessel set to receive it: after some time, pour off the liquor, and wash the deposited matter repeatedly with fresh water till it becomes perfectly insipid; then expose it to the most gentle heat; as it becomes dry, it turns white, and presents a friable matter, without colour, taste or smell, exhibiting all the characters that distinguish starch.

Of all the plants mentioned below, the root or its bark are the only parts proper for the object in view: it should be gathered in autumn, should be chosen fresh and succulent, cleared from its hairy filaments and its coloured coats; it should also be cleaned and washed till the water appears quite transparent and colourless.

As all the bitterness of the horse-chestnut, the asperity of the acorn, the causticity of the arum and ranunculuses, the burning acrimony of the bryony, etc. remain in the water employed to separate and wash the starch, it is proper to use wooden instruments to stir the mixture, as the hands might suffer.

The starch separated from the seeds and roots, when well washed and dried, is perfectly identical: but it is not sufficient to separate it from the substance in which it is contained; it is moreover requisite to give directions how to convert it into food. It may be introduced, either alone or mixed with the pulp of Potatoes, into the dough of various grains, to make an addition to the quantity of bread. Bread may be made without flour of any kind, by the process described above; but if the Potatoe should also fail, the pulpous fruits of the cucurbitaceous family, such as the pumpkin, which are sometimes added to wheaten dough in various proportions, may be substituted; lastly, should every other resource fail, the starch representing flour would still serve for food; it would be sufficient to dilute it in some vehicle, in order to obtain a very nutritious broth or jelly.

I have used the several starches extracted from the following plants, without distinction, nor was it possible to tell from which it had been procured; when there is a light difference perceptible in the taste, smell or colour, it should be attributed to the number of washings rather than to any essential difference of nature.

Among the plants and fruits which M. Parmentier lists are the horse-chestnut, the acorn and many roots, among them the roots of the common burdock, deadly nightshade, common elder, flag and meadowsweet. Among farinaceous seeds and roots which may be used entire for food are wall-barley, cocks-foot, panic grass and darnell, while the plants which may be substituted for pot-herbs include milk thistles, globe thistles, march thistles, canterbury bells, orchis and others.

The work of grinding grain in ancient days was done by the mistress of the house, but later, in Rome, it was given to slaves who, for some fault, had been thrown into chains and put to grinding, as Milton represents Samson Agonistes, which was in itself, when done with large stones for protracted periods, a sufficient punishment. In the country asses were often used for this work and later horses and cattle were sometimes used.[35]

Dr. Savoy, on the authority of an article by M. Lindet in Revue Archéologique[36] gives a good description of the development of the ancient mill. The best documents on the subject which we possess, he says, are the Roman mills which can still be seen in the ruins of Pompeii and of which some can be used to-day. Roman grain-mills, according to the size of the stones and the amount of force required, were turned either by animals or men, the force

[35] Appendix by Fulvius Ursinus to De Triclinio by Petrus Ciacconius (Amstel. 1689), p. 318.

[36] Vol. XXXVI, p. 19. See chapter on Corn-Mills in the History of Inventions, Discoveries and Origins by John Beckmann, Vol. I, p. 147.

most commonly employed being that of slaves or condemned prisoners. Mills built by the Romans can still be found in different places in France.

Mills in Gaul were appreciably smaller than those in Italy, for they could be carried from place to place. The use of hand-mills must have spread rapidly thoughout the country about the commencement of the Christian era, beginning with those peoples which had been brought under Roman power and passing quickly to all who felt the Roman influence.

Water-mills were invented about a hundred years before Christ. Mr. Rudolf P. Hommel, in his interesting book, *China at Work*,[37] quotes Mr. B. Laufer[38] as saying that water-mills were first mentioned in Chinese writings during the first century of the present era—just the time when they were introduced by the Romans into Europe. The Romans may have invented these mills or they may have found them operating in western Asia, whence the knowledge that water power could be used for grinding grain spread both to the east and west at the same time. In the fourth century after Christ, many water-mills were constructed in Italy on streams and aqueducts.[39]

Bruyerinus says that flour made in mills worked by slaves and condemned criminals was not very good, for "who, indeed, with his feet bound, with criminal hands and a branded face would be expected to make good food?"[40] Pliny was born in the year A. D. 23, about the time when Romans began to pass from the use of bread made by the women to the use of baker's bread, and this may have something to do with his statement that in Gaul and Spain bread was lighter than elsewhere, a fact for which he accounts

[37] (The John Day Company, New York, 1937), p. 121.
[38] *Chinese Pottery of the Hans Dynasty* (Leyden, 1909).
[39] *L'agriculture à travers les âges* by Dr. Emile Savoy (Paris, 1935), Vol. 2, p. 263.
[40] *De Re Cibaria*, Bruyerinus, Lib. VI, Cap. II, pp. 378-379.

by saying that bread in those countries was made with ferment skimmed during the process of beer making,[41] possibly not unlike the use of the dregs of beer—lie de bière—which Le Grand d'Aussy mentions,[42] a practice still occasionally found in the Province of Quebec.

Millers carried a bad reputation for many centuries. Chaucer in *The Reeve's Tale* describes an English miller:

> A theefe he was for sothe of corn and mele
> And that a sly and ussunt for to stele.

Bruyerinus, who was himself a Frenchman and whose book was published at Lyons in the year 1560, says that in his time the work of grinding grain was given to more honest hands than those of Roman slaves, but that very oddly, French millers—and this may include bakers, for during many years bakers ground their own flour and Bruyerinus uses the same word, pistor, for both trades[43] —were in the common speech of his day known as "thieves."[44] Willichius seems to class pistores and cooks together and adds that "if anything was missing it was common to say the cook took it,"[45] an amiable view, of which it seems that there is a surviving trace in the French use of the word "coquin" to mean a thief.

Some of the bakers who have little conscience (and we have found many such) put in lime or ground earth or chalk. Sometimes they fill

[41] Pliny, *N. H.*, Lib. XVIII, Cap. XII. *De Re Cibaria*, Lib. VI, Cap. VI, p. 391.

[42] *La vie privée des Français*, Vol. I, p. 63.

[43] This was also the ancient use of the word. See Pliny, *N. H.*, edited by Joannes Harduinus (Paris, 1723), Vol. II, Lib. XVIII, Cap. XXVIII, p. 113, note 1.

[44] *De Re Cibaria*, Lib. VI, Cap. II, p. 379; Bruyerinus may himself give the explanation of this term for he says, on page 407, that bakers by their intolerable avarice made bread that it was not safe to eat,—"Dum enim pondus quaerunt, vitas hominum perdunt."

[45] *Ars Magirica*, Cap. I. See Livy, Lib. XXXIX, Cap. VI. "Coquus vilissimum antiquis mancipium."

THE MILL.

the flour with tares and bran and with dross to make it have a larger weight. We must see to it that the baker does not make badly risen bread on purpose so as to deceive us on the weight, for this bread has made thousands of people die . . . and note well that when he throws water into the dough, if he has put in lime you will see the dough fume and you will smell it.[46]

Notwithstanding the severity of the criticism to which bakers were subject, the best French bread seems long to have maintained its reputation, for Voltaire spoke highly of it in the 1700's and Mr. James Paton of Glasgow, in his article written for the *Encyclopaedia Britannica*, said in 1875 that Parisian bakers excelled all others in the quality of their bread, adding that it was noteworthy that they used leaven, not yeast. According to the *Encyclopaedia*, "the use of yeast appears to have died out in France but was revived again toward the end of the seventeenth century, when its re-introduction was violently opposed by the Faculty of Medicine of Paris. Yeast is now used by Parisian bakers for fancy bread and pastry only."[47]

Bread of the middle ages and much later was, however, very different from modern Parisian bread. For the most part, of course, bread on the continent of Europe was made from rye flour. On fertile land wheat can be raised as easily as rye, but chemical fertilizers were unknown, cattle were few, fertility was low, and in poor land wheat will not grow as well as rye. Wheat bread was therefore an expensive luxury, and rye or other kinds of bread was the food of the people. What it was like we can only imagine. Mr. Albert Babeau describes bread as the principal food of the French peasant, or indeed, he adds, "one might say the principal food of the French people," but while the bread of the townsman was made of wheat and was of good quality, that of the peasant

[46] *Carestia e Fame* by Giovanni Battista Segni (Bologna, 1602), p. 147.
[47] *Ency. Brit.*, 9th ed. (1875), Tit. Baking, Vol. 3, p. 253. *La vie privée des Français* by Le Grand d'Aussy (Paris, 1782), Vol. I, pp. 61 et seq.

was coarse, ordinarily of a grey or black color, with barley, rye, oats, chestnuts or peas entering into its composition, according to the district where it was made.[48] During the famine of 1709, Voltaire says, for several months the people of Paris had only the hard bread known as pain bis, probably a kind of brown bread, and that "many families, even in Versailles, lived on oat bread, Madame de Maintenon setting the example."[49] Bruyerinus says that in his time the size of a loaf of the best bread at the Court, and at Paris and in the other chief cities of France, was such that two loaves a day, that is, one at each meal, would satisfy the heartiest eater, even when the top crust was taken off, as was done in the houses where provision was most abundant (in familiis lautioribus), and given to the ladies, some of whom in Paris soaked it most daintily in their broth.[50] In another place, Bruyerinus is more specific, giving the weight of bread commonly allowed to each person as follows:

Loaves of the best bread are in Paris of the size known as three-quarters, that is weighing twelve ounces each, and these are given, one apiece, to the guests both at mid-day and in the evening, and it has been observed that no person leading a more liberal life, not being engaged in heavy physical labor and having only two meals a day, can eat in one day more than two loaves of bread. Often, indeed, at the tables of the nobles and the rich the crusts are removed from the white bread, reducing the weight not a little. The schools inflate with yeast the smaller breads which weigh less, but generally the scholars are satisfied with one loaf. I know that some persons are bigger eaters by nature and some by habit, but those who are moderate, as are almost the majority, are content with one three-quarters loaf, Roman weight [9 oz.]. But as the proverb says, all men cannot wear the same shoe, so all are not content with the same weight or the same measure of food.[51]

[48] *La vie rurale dans l'ancienne France* (Paris, 1885, 2nd ed.), pp. 102-103.
[49] *Siècle de Louis XIV* (Firmin-Didot, Paris, 1843), Chap. XXI, p. 230.
[50] *De Re Cibaria*, Lib. VI, Cap. IX, p. 415. *La vie privée des Français*, Vol. I, p. 89.
[51] *De Re Cibaria*, Lib. VI, Cap. VI, pp. 394-395. See ante, note 18, p. 17.

Bread could be good when fresh, but when dried it became hard. It was, therefore, the practice to use a slice of bread, the tranchoir, as a plate on which food was placed, to be softened and flavored by the sauce and juice of whatever food might be placed upon it. This was the custom to which the harpy Celaeno referred when she threatened the invading Trojans that, before they could build their city, hunger would compel them to eat their tables![52] It is from this custom also that the word trencherman and other compounds of this sort, trencher-bread, trencher-friend, etc., have come into the English language. This use of bread, it appears, prevailed among high and low, rich and poor, having a place even as part of the ceremonies and pomps attending the coronation of a king in France.[53]

In Auvergne loaves of bread were made weighing twenty or thirty pounds, which kept for a month in winter. In Dauphiné it was the practice to bake bread twice a year and the loaves kept for a year and a half. The boys who went to school at Embrun took a six months' supply of bread with them, which it was necessary to break with a hammer and soak before it could be eaten.[54]

It seems, however, that a diet founded upon bread alone was not entirely wholesome. It may well be, indeed, that the greatest disease of the middle ages was neither leprosy, as Dr. Charles Creighton thought,[55] nor St. Anthony's fire, as Mr. D. J. Medley suggested,[56] but the constantly sluggish condition of bodily metabolism due to a diet too largely made up of bread, a condition which may cause not one simple disease, but may, in Schoockius' phrase, bring whole armies of diseases—quasi integra agmina morborum.[57]

[52] *Aeneid*, Lib. III, lines 255 et seq.
[53] *La vie privée des Français*, Vol. I, pp. 60-61.
[54] *La vie rurale dans l'ancienne France* by Albert Babeau (Paris, 1885), p. 104.
[55] *Ency. Brit.*, 9th ed., Tit. Leprosy, Vol. 14, p. 468.
[56] *Social England*, Vol. I, p. 370.
[57] Conf. Herodotus, Bk. II, Chap. 77.

Shakespeare refers to the man who "gets him to bed, crammed with distressful bread,"[58] and Bonamicus says that a hearty meal of bread is too nourishing and "clogs the system," if that be intended by the phrase "implet admodum vasa."[59] Bruyerinus says that bread made with milk causes obstructions and kidney stones,[60] and many statements may be found showing the prevalence of "black bile"—melancholy—and rheumatism. It is sometimes useful, therefore, it was said, to roast bread in thin slices, making what to-day would be called Melba toast, while for invalids Estienne and Liébault describe "washed bread."[61] If bread were thrown into water, they say, it would swim like a cork, but when taken out of the water and, we must suppose, drained, its lightness was astonishing for half its weight had been lost. The explanation offered is that the washing had taken away its thickness and "viscosité terrestre," or in other words, that the water dissolved something out of the bread.

Many persons who are old enough to have attended the Centennial Exhibition at Philadelphia can well remember the interest aroused when "Vienna bread" first became known to the American public in 1876. It would probably now be called French bread, but it was introduced to the French people by Marie Antoinette, and in her time made as much stir in Paris as later it made in America. French bread, before the days of Marie Antoinette, was probably

[58] *King Henry V*, Act IV, Sc. i. Conf. *Diaeteticon*, Ludovicus Nonnius, 1627 ed., p. 185. "Alimenti omnis repletionem esse pravam, panis autem pessimam."

[59] *De Alimento*, F. Bonamicus, p. 380. *L'agriculture et maison rustique*, Estienne and Liébault, p. 315. *Diaeteticon*, Ludovicus Nonnius, p. 10. Salt was used in bread to correct this tendency. *Le gouvernement nécessaire à chacun pour vivre longuement* by La Framboisière (Paris, 1601), p. 51. *La vie privée des Français* by Le Grand d'Aussy, Vol. I, p. 86.

[60] *De Re Cibaria* by Bruyerinus, Lib. VI, Cap. III, pp. 385-386. *Diaeteticon* by Ludovicus Nonnius, p. 10.

[61] *L'agriculture et maison rustique* by Estienne and Liébault, p. 317. *De Alimentis* by J. D. Sala, p. 15. *De Re Cibaria* by Bruyerinus, Lib. VI, p. 399.

much like some of the bread now to be found in the French provinces, but it would be hard to find bread out of which half its
weight could advantageously be washed. Nevertheless, the bread of
the middle ages was to men of the time a wonderful benefit of
nature, endowed with all the flavors which arouse appetite and invite to the use of any food.

It was not only in the middle ages, however, that mankind lived
on grains in the form of bread or porridge. This was true also in
the ancient world. Facciolati defines the Latin word "obsonium"
as meaning anything provided to go with bread and wine, giving a
little variety to the meal. In the Roman world, this would generally
be fish, but no obsonium was necessary. The bread and wine of the
Lord's Supper are not merely a symbolic meal—we can look upon
it as the food set before men at any ordinary meal of the ancient
world.

CHAPTER VII

DIFFICULTY OF PROCURING MEAT.
WILD ANIMALS, MEAT OF CARNIVOROUS ANIMALS.
FOOD FROM MARKET GARDENS

THE very interesting and suggestive cook book with the rather forbidding title of *Ars Magirica*, written by Jodocus Willichius—Willich or Wilcke—of Rössel in East Prussia and published at Zurich in 1563, says of meat that in the housewife's storeroom it claims the place of second importance, coming next after bread.[1]

Animal Food. Of the different kinds of meat, Willichius passes rather quickly over beef and mutton as not very healthful and productive of "black bile." Bishop Isidore of Seville, who lived in the seventh century, did not include oxen among meat animals. Strictly speaking, he says, the term domestic animals is applied to two classes of creatures, first those which are fit for human food, as the sheep and swine, and second those which are convenient for man's use, as are horses and oxen.[2] The labor of cattle indeed was so valuable and necessary that men in former days could not afford to use their best draught animals for meat. Barnaby Googe speaks of the ox as "a good Plowman and a faithful servant," so essential to human welfare that Hesiod, "the gravest Author of our profession, af-

[1] *Ars Magirica* by Jodocus Willichius Resellianus (Zurich, 1563), p. 38. Burton, *Anatomy of Melancholy*, Part I, Sec. II, Mem. II, Subsec. I (London, 1896, Vol. I, pp. 247 et seq.), gives a good summary of the opinions of different writers as to qualities of various meats and other foods. See also *Antiquitates Conviviales* by J. G. Stuckius, Lib. II, Cap. VIII.

[2] Isidore, *Etymologiarum*, Lib. XII, Cap. I, Sec. 5.

firmeth that the family doth consist of the Husband, the Wife and the Oxe."[3] Varro speaks of the ox as "the companion of man in rustic labor and the servant of Ceres. The ancients wished so to protect this animal from violence that they decreed capital punishment for any person who wilfully killed an ox."[4]

In other words, the ox, like farm horses of the days before tractors, was necessary in order to raise crops, and to such an extent was the companion of mankind that there had been a time when the wilful slaughter of an ox was a capital offence. Vegetius tells us the whole story when he says that without the ox the ground could not have been cultivated nor the human race fed. The crops which kept the Roman world alive were produced by the ox and the plough. All other animals, including poultry, derived their food from the labor of cattle. "Whence," says Vegetius, "could the genius of the master provide barley for horses, food for dogs, or nourishment for swine unless it had been raised by the labor of the ox? . . . Among some peoples mules, among others, camels, among a few, elephants, have been used to a small extent, but no nation could exist without cattle."[5]

Ultimately cattle were used as food, when their laboring days were past; the females, too, furnished milk in excess of the requirements of their calves, but both meat and milk were entirely secondary matters. The breeding and rearing of cattle for the primary purpose of furnishing meat or milk are very modern developments

[3] *The Whole Art and Trade of Husbandry* (1614), p. 120.

[4] Lib. II, Cap. V. See Pliny, *N. H.*, Lib. VIII, Cap. XIV; Aelianus, *De Nat. Animal.*, Lib. XII, Cap. XXXIV. Pausanias' *Description of Greece*, tr. Prof. J. G. Frazer, see comment on text of Bk. I, Chap. XXIV, 4, in Vol. II, p. 303.

[5] *Artis Veterinariae Prologus*, Lib. III.

"C'est donc avec raison qu'on a dit: sans bétail point d'agriculture. Du bétail et beaucoup de bétail, c'est le grand, le seul moyen d'accroître nos produits en raison des besoins croissants de la consommation, et d'en abaisser en même temps le prix de revient." *La connaissance du boeuf* by Moll and Gayot (Paris, 1860), Introduction, p. viii. See, however, post, pp. 150, 188-189, and The Ultimate Stage of Agriculture, post, pp. 222-223.

in the western world. In the middle ages, as in the ancient world, cattle were draught animals and beasts of burden.[6]

Goat meat, Willichius says,[7] is neither pleasant nor good. Mule foals, deer, poultry, birds and fish are mentioned, but the best of all is the pig.[8] All meat, of course, was hard to get and expensive, but we can readily see that the spring pig could make a poor living for itself during the summer and in the fall could be killed and salted for the year's supply. Raised in this manner, the pigs probably resembled what are known in the southern States as razorbacks, fleet of foot and hungry enough, almost, to make credible the story which Gerald de Berri tells of the piglet which sucked a hunting dog and, when grown, excelled the hounds themselves for hunting purposes.[9]

Le Grand d'Aussy cites Strabo for the statement that the Gauls were great meat eaters, especially fond of pork.

> Their pigs are left out in the fields night and day and are of extraordinary size, strength and speed. It is as dangerous to meet one as to meet a wolf.

According to Varro, the principal trade which the Gauls had with Rome was in hams and salt pork. Indeed, the immense forests which covered their country enabled them easily to raise, without expense, a large number of these animals, and probably this fact had something to do with the religious respect which they paid to the oak. Every consideration which led the Athenians to honor the olive tree, which by its oil and fruit enriched their sterile territory, led the ancient Gauls to do the same for the useful tree which, having fed the Gauls themselves, fed also the animal which had become

---

[6] *Breeding Profitable Dairy Cattle* by E. Parmalee Prentice (Houghton Mifflin, 1935), pp. 110-111.

[7] *Ars Magirica*, p. 38.

[8] *De Re Cibaria* by Bruyerinus, Lib. XIII, Cap. I, p. 683.

[9] Geraldus Cambrensis, *Opera* (Rolls Series, London, 1868). *Itinerarium Kambriae*, Vol. VI, pp. 27-28.

their principal meat and their chief wealth. It is probable that all the northern tribes raised swine in their woods, for the forests gave food, the pigs required little care and they were very strong and fertile. And so, Le Grand d'Aussy says, common people and soldiers ate pork while men of means—bishops, nobles, the king himself— kept pigs to supply their own table and as a source of revenue. On St. Martin's day or at Christmas it was the custom of persons in comfortable circumstances to kill and salt a pig to provide meat for the following year, and many who could not afford the expense alone joined with others to put up salt pork for the winter. In the thirteenth century, English pork had a continental reputation, and we can be confident that wherever mast was found, pigs were kept.[10]

Of course, at a time when mankind was short of food, domestic live stock had to go hungry—or worse, to starve. "To feed them in Winter-time is the Thing dreaded," as Noël Chomell said.[11] No grain was available for animals or poultry, and since hay seed had not been separated at this time and native grasses furnished the only hay known, the winter feed for cattle was inadequate. The Atinian elm, Columella says, yields a leaf that is sweeter than the leaf of the Italian elm and more agreeable to cattle.[12] For this reason, he advises the planting of Atinian elms as far as possible. Dried leaves are surely a poor substitute for hay or even for straw, but for starving animals no other food could be had. The surplus production of food, therefore, over and above what was required to supply the barest necessities of life was small, and whenever this surplus ran low, suffering began. Refrigeration as a means of preserving food was unknown, and meat that could not be eaten at the

[10] *La vie privée des Français*, Le Grand d'Aussy, Vol. I, pp. 250 et seq.

[11] *Dictionnaire oeconomique*, tr. and rev. by Professor R. Bradley (Dublin, 1727), Tit. Cattle.

[12] Columella (*Libri De Re Rustica*, Joan. Hervag. Basileae, 1535), Lib. V, Cap. V, pp. 118 et seq.

time was salted. The first business of the farmer, therefore, when pasture gave out in the fall, was to slaughter and salt the animals which could not be kept over winter. It was important, of course, that some breeding cattle be saved, as also cattle for the next year's ploughing, and for them, besides the small quantity of pasture hay that may have been secured, there would be some straw and, with the straw, Cato says:

Give the cattle elm, poplar, oak and fig leaves as long as these leaves hold out . . . and remember how long the winter is.[13]

Animals could not, therefore, be carried along and killed from time to time during the winter. Under these circumstances, as Mr. Hallam observes, "when no alternative was offered but these salted meats, even the leanest venison was devoured with relish."[14] Of course, hunting had the attraction of a sport, but it was also a means of obtaining fresh meat—a food not otherwise easily to be had. These facts, then, explain the great interest which was taken during so many years in hawking and hunting, as they also give an excuse—such as it is—for the severity of the laws relating to the preservation of game. The amount of meat that could be procured by these methods was small, but Le Grand d'Aussy makes it very clear that hunting was not merely a pleasure as it is to-day. It was also a means of getting food so that all the animals killed were eaten, even such birds as herons, bitterns, cormorants and others which he describes as tough and not easily digested.[15] Bitterns, cranes, curlews, sea-gulls and herons are all mentioned in Robert May's book, *The Accomplish't Cook*, published in London in 1660, with receipts for proper cooking and seasoning. Cranes were considered delicacies by the Romans,[16] and apparently the stork was

[13] *De Re Rustica*, Cap. XXX.
[14] *Middle Ages*, Chap. IX, Part II (Murray, London, 1853), Vol. III, p. 311.
[15] *La vie privée des Français*, Vol. I, p. 310.
[16] Horatius, *Sat.*, Lib. II, No. 8, line 87.

accepted at the same time, although Count Grégoire says that it is detestable.[17] Symeon Sethus says that cranes when eaten induce melancholy, adding, however, that some think their marrow taken mixed with olive oil helps the memory,[18] which can easily be believed for such a dish at a modern table might well prove unforgettable. These birds, he says, should hang a couple of days before being eaten.

The author of *Le ménagier de Paris*[19] writes as though the Paris markets in his time were always well supplied with the best kinds of food, but it is noticeable that among table fowl (Vol. 2, p. 181), he includes cranes, bustards, bitterns, cormorants and storks of which, as of all such water-fowl, Bruyerinus says that the meat is tough and, while it can be made tender by hanging a few days,[20] nevertheless some of these birds are not only offensive to the taste but a source of illness if eaten freely.[21] In times, however, when the taste of tainted or otherwise unpleasant meat was disguised by spices,[22] the objections to the taste of these water-fowl were not as strong as they would be at a modern table. Mr. Simmonds, in his interesting book, *Curiosities of Food*, says that "according to Vauban, Bossuet, and La Grange, the richest and most comfortable nation is that which eats the most meat,"[23]—

[17] See *Le théâtre d'agriculture*, Olivier de Serres, Paris edition of 1804, *Essai historique*, Vol. I, p. cxxxv.

[18] *De Facultate Cibariorum* by Symeon Sethus (Basle, 1538), p. 134.

[19] Written about 1392-1394 by a citizen of Paris. Edited by M. Jérôme Pichon and published for the first time in 1846 (Chapelet, Paris).

[20] *De Re Cibaria*, Lib. XV, Cap. LIX, p. 818.

[21] *De Re Cibaria*, Cap. LXVI, p. 826.

[22] Of the use of spices to cover unpleasant flavors, see *La vie privée des Français* by Le Grand d'Aussy, Vol. II, p. 163. "The absolute necessity of spices to season food in an age when there were no vegetables to speak of made the spice trade the most profitable thing of the time." *Social England*, Vol. III, p. 131. *Town Life* by C. R. L. Fletcher. *The Influence of the Spice Trade on World History* by General Sir Percy Sykes, Nineteenth Century and After, April, 1933, p. 479.

[23] *Curiosities of Food* (Richard Bentley, London, 1859), p. 2.

an opinion which reflects the very human longing for that which it is difficult to get. Such a statement would hardly be made to-day when so many persons could well reduce the proportion of meat in their diet, and it is not probable that at any time it was intended to advocate unrestricted use of salt meat, for salt is easily taken in excess. Hird, therefore, well said that "milk and vegetable food," that is, of course, when they could be bought, "had the great advantage over animal food that in using them the juices of the body are not overloaded with salt"—

Lac, et cibus vegetabilis, carni et cibo animali, hoc praecipue praestat; quod illo utendo, succi nimiis salibus non adeo onerentur.[24]

Fresh meat, however, was not always wholly unobtainable. Apparently men of former times used nearly all the meats, vegetables and fishes that we have to-day[25] and in addition used many articles which we would regard with aversion.[26] Sala says that when food was dear men took whatever they could get, and apparently there was put into the stew almost everything that grew, including some things which no one before had ever tasted. Of what they could eat, they did eat until hunger was satisfied, with the result that

[24] *Inquisitio de Lactis Natura et Usu* by Gulielmus Hird (Edinburgh, 1751), p. 61. Bruyerinus has a chapter on Thirst at Night, Lib. XVI, Cap. III, p. 848.

[25] *De Facultate Cibariorum* by Symeon Sethus. *De Re Cibaria* by Bruyerinus. *Diaeteticon* by Ludovicus Nonnius. *De Alimentis* by J. D. Sala. *Traité des aliments* by Louis Lémery (Paris, 1702).

[26] For example: "Cossi sunt vermes sub arborum corticibus, quos etiam gula Romana altiles facere docuit, et mensis apponere lautioribus, teste Plinio." *De Re Cibaria*, Bruyerinus, Lib. XV, p. 834. These cossi may have been not unlike the large grubs found in the dwarf gum trees and eaten by New England savages (Malthus on *The Principle of Population*, Bk. I, Chap. III) or like the worms "thick as a man's finger" which live on reeds and were much thought of in India. *De Alimentis*, J. D. Sala, Cap. II, p. 9. As to cats and dogs, see *De Re Cibaria*, Lib. XIII, Cap. XXXVI, XXXVII, pp. 726-727. *Diaeteticon*, Ludovicus Nonnius, Lib. II, Cap. VII, p. 210. Pliny, *N. H.*, Lib. XXIX, Cap. XIV and note by Joannes Harduinus.

many persons suffered great and serious disorders.[27] Of meat, Sala says:

Carnivora in the extreme lack of other food now are much in use, and I think were in ancient times for Galen calls those men leonine who eat lions' flesh; some men eat bears, badgers and foxes; a few eat cats, both the domestic and wood cats, fewer eat wolves, dogs and mice; some like new born kittens in place of a crab. They take field rats as well as mountain rats [possibly marmots], but these, that they may be fatter for this doggish appetite, they prefer to have fed on fruits. They take also porcupines, hedgehogs and that little pig called Indian (perhaps a kind of mouse) from which we do not abstain. Foxes at the time when they feed on grapes are thought quite a delicacy and therefore among the Greeks, Galen says, they were commonly eaten.[28]

These carnivorous animals, which Sala describes as "digitata" —having claws—were not pleasant food, and did not often reach the table,[29] but in times of want there was no choice.

Of course, when there was no refrigeration, no rapid transportation, and when the need of sterilizing utensils had never been conceived, food must have been used that to-day would be considered uneatable. Receipts for bringing back tainted meat can still be found. Robert May, for example, in a well-known cook

[27] De Alimentis by J. D. Sala, Cap. XII, p. 62.
[28] Ibid., Cap. V, p. 27. De Re Cibaria, Lib. XIII, Cap. XXXIII, XXXIV, pp. 724-725. Bromatologia, J. J. Plenck, p. 212. Mr. F. E. Beddard, in his book on Mammalia (Macmillan, 1900) says that glis myoxus which occurs in the south of Europe, "was the fat dormouse of the Continent" (See Varro, Lib. III, Cap. XV), and Cuvier in his book, The Animal Kingdom (Bohn, London, 1863), p. 99, said that in his time it was still eaten by Italians. Nonnius scorns the house rat, see Diaeteticon, p. 226, but the passage quoted from Sala shows that men fed on other glires besides glis myoxus. Like Friar Tuck in the opera, Robin Hood, they took what they could get. The "little pig, called Indian" was the guinea pig which was introduced into Europe about the year 1580, soon after the conquest of Peru. Bromatologia, J. J. Plenck, p. 208. See The Guinea Pig or Domestic Cavy by Mr. C. Cumberland (Charles Scribner's Sons, New York, 1901).
[29] De Alimentis by J. D. Sala, Cap. XII, pp. 68-69.

book[30] which is strongly marked by mediaeval tradition, at the same time that it shows the beginning of modern cookery, gives as a method to preserve tainted venison:

Bury it in the ground in a clean cloath a whole night and it will take away the corruption, savour and stink. [p. 214.]

As a preservative sauce for tainted venison:

Boil water, beer and wine vinegar together, and some bay leaves, time, savoury, rosemary and fennil, of each a handful, when it boils put in your venison parboil it well and season it as aforesaid. [p. 214.]

The meat is to be baked as follows:

Bone and lard the meat with great lard as big as one's little finger and season it with two ounces of pepper, two ounces of nutmeg and four ounces of salt; then have a pye made and lay some butter in the bottom of it, then lay in the flesh, the inside downward, coat it thick with seasoning, and put to it on the top of the meat, with a few cloves, and a good store of butter, close it up and bake it. (p. 213.)

The pastry should be made of rye meal "coursely searced" and the pie should be baked "the space of eight or nine hours." How any taste of meat, good or bad, could survive such treatment, it is hard to see.

It is easy, however, to see good grounds for the statement that those who make their meals with other foods than bread have always "l'haleine puante."[31] Bruyerinus says that he was personally acquainted with a man of distinguished learning who ate much meat and little bread, with the result that his breath was most objectionable.[32] Burton, in the *Anatomy of Melancholy*,[33] quotes Neubrigensis (William of Newbury) as saying that Philip, the

---

[30] *The Accomplish't Cook*, London, 1660.
[31] *L'agriculture et maison rustique*, Estienne and Liébault (Paris, 1589), p. 315.
[32] *De Re Cibaria*, Lib. VI, Cap. I, p. 377.
[33] Part III, Sec. II, Mem. V, Subsec. III.

French King, sent away his newly married queen, daughter of the King of Denmark, "post unam noctem . . . propter foetentem spiritum"—or for some other reason.[34]

Burton also quotes Peter Matthaeus as criticizing the English Chronicles for saying that Margaret, daughter of the King of Scotland, was rejected by Louis XI "ob graveolentiam oris." References to bad breath appear also in classic times.[35] Bruyerinus says that fennel can be used to sweeten the breath,[36] a purpose for which cloves also are useful,[37] and galangal, an aromatic stimulant formerly well known,[38] and laurel leaves[39] of which Virgil says:

> . . . animas et olentia Medi
> Ora fovent illo, et senibus medicantur anhelis.[40]

In English prose this means that the Medes used the laurel to cure unpleasant odors from the mouth and to sweeten the breath of old people. Doubtless, diligent search would produce other so-called remedies besides those mentioned above. It is not impossible that in former days, when men lived chiefly on bread or gruel,

[34] *Historia Rerum Anglicarum* by William of Newbury (Neubrigensis), Lib. IV, Cap. XXVI.

The story of the marriage of Philip Augustus of France to Ingeborg, the sister of the Danish King Canute III, is given in Southey's *Naval History* (Philadelphia, 1835), pp. 161-163, where, however, nothing is said of such matters as those mentioned in the text, supra. See Chevalier, *Répertoire des sources historiques du moyen âge* (Picard, Paris, 1907), Vol. 2, col. 3627-3629. Marco Polo says that the Great Kaan, in order to be sure that candidates for his favor had sweet breath, etc., required them, before acceptance, to procure approval of certain elderly ladies. *The Book of Ser Marco Polo*, edited by Sir Henry Yule (London, 1903), Bk. II, Chap. VIII, Vol. I, p. 357.

[35] See Martialis, Lib. IV, No. IV.

[36] *De Re Cibaria*, Lib. VIII, Cap. XXVIII, p. 489.

[37] *Ibid.*, Lib. X, Cap. XI, p. 565.

[38] *Ibid.*, Lib. X, Cap. XIV, p. 567. See *The Book of Ser Marco Polo*, edited by Sir Henry Yule, note 5, Vol. II, p. 229.

[39] *De Conviviis* by J. C. Bulengerus (Lugduni, 1627), Lib. II, Cap. XXXIX.

[40] *Georgics*, Lib. II, lines 134-135. See note on this passage by Carolus Ruaeus in Delphine edition, Paris, 1675.

they were more sensitive to unpleasant odors of this sort than we are in modern times when meat is so much used. The statement has been made that to Japanese, as to some Africans who use little meat, the people of our western nations are characterized by unpleasant odors.

When bread could be had, however, bread was sufficient, and of it Sala says:

Far the greater part of mankind live on bread alone, and of the rest of our race who have other things, it is the settled practice to eat two or three times as much bread as of anything else.[41]

To the same effect was the statement made by Bruyerinus seventy years earlier, that the greatest part of mankind live on bread or porridge alone, some either dipping the bread in wine or broth or taking it with salt pork, beef or fish, a radish, garlic, onions or pickles to provide a flavor,[42] to which La Framboisière adds that all these other foods, however well they may taste, are neither pleasant nor wholesome unless eaten with bread.[43]

Food from Market Gardens. One of the great sources of food for modern times is in the vegetables which come to us from market gardens and which constantly occupy an increasingly important place in our diet. With the exception of potatoes, maize, Jerusalem artichokes, lima beans, squash, tomatoes and chocolate, which came from America, most of our vegetables were known to the ancient world and to the middle ages.

Before Linnaeus, however, there was no systematic botany and ancient names are often so vague that it is impossible accurately to identify the plants to which they refer. By continued culture, too, through many ages and in many countries, new varieties have

[41] *De Alimentis*, Cap. XVIII, p. 111.

[42] *De Re Cibaria* by Bruyerinus, Lib. VI, Cap. VI, pp. 392, 396.

[43] *Le gouvernement nécessaire à chacun*, etc., by La Framboisière, pp. 48-49.

from time to time arisen and old varieties have been lost, or superseded.

It is certain that many old plants have in this manner been banished from our gardens. . . . Thus have common alexanders (Smyrnium olusatrum) fallen into neglect since celery was made known by the Italians, about the end of the seventeenth century; and so at present has the cultivation of winter-cresses (Erysimum barbarea), bulbous-rooted chaerophyllum (Chaerophyllum bulbosum), rocket (Brassica eruca), and others, been abandoned since better vegetables have been obtained to supply their place.[44]

Thus, though we know that the Latin brassica is cabbage, we cannot be sure that we still have the variety which the ancients ate raw to prevent intoxication, while on the other hand it seems that the modern red cabbage was unknown to Greeks and Romans. This is a matter of interest to Mr. Beckmann, a good German who —since as Bruyerinus says, "consuetudinem in cibis plurimum valere,"[45] taste is largely a matter of habit—goes carefully into the red cabbage question. He says:

We nowhere find any trace of that excellent preparation of cabbage called by the Germans sour kraut, though the ancients were acquainted with the art of preparing turnips in the same manner.[46]

Spinach is modern,[47] being first mentioned about the year 1351 as of Spanish origin, whence its name, olus Hispaniense or, as the Moors called it, hispanich. Cauliflowers came about the end of the sixteenth century from the Near East to Italy.[48] Many other improved forms of ancient vegetables can be found, but much of the change in food is due to alteration in human habits, for not

[44] See chapters on Kitchen Vegetables and on The Artichoke, in *History of Inventions, Discoveries and Origins* by John Beckmann, Vol. I, pp. 212, 217, Vol. II, p. 336.
[45] *De Re Cibaria*, Lib. I, Cap. XXII, p. 73.
[46] *History of Inventions, Discoveries and Origins*, Vol. II, p. 341.
[47] *De Re Cibaria* by Bruyerinus, Lib. VIII, p. 474.
[48] *History of Inventions, Discoveries and Origins*, Vol. II, p. 342.

only is our cooking better than the cooking of previous ages, but we know more about the needs of the human body and the means of supplying them. The vegetable sources from which we draw our supplies have, however, for the most part long been known to the human race.

Some of these foods, moreover, notably beans and peas, had the advantage that they could be dried and kept as a supply of food to be used at any time during the year.[49] It is surprising, therefore, to find that garden vegetables, of which the world was not without knowledge, were comparatively little used as food in previous ages, while bread, salt meat and fish occupied so great a place in the diet.

The Romans were well acquainted with gardens from very early days. According to Martialis,[50] Romulus fed in Heaven on the turnip which he so enjoyed on earth, and Martinus Schoockius refers to Suetonius as authority for the statement that the Emperor Augustus was fond of asparagus, that Domitianus liked truffles,[51] and, indeed, Schoockius, a Dutchman who was evidently interested in the occupations of his countrymen, had the notion that in all ages mankind had greatly valued the garden vegetables. Pliny says that Roman kings worked in their gardens[52] and great Roman families, the Fabii, Pisones and Lentuli, preserved in their names the value to the Roman people of some of the foods which to-day are garden vegetables, but which in Roman times were part of the usual rotation of crops on the farm.

Romans had learned that the cereal grains grew better after a leguminous crop and so we have beans, peas, lupines, and vetch as farm crops. It would be unsafe to say that no Roman families took their names from plants that belonged distinctively to the

[49] In regard to beans, see Pliny, *N. H.*, Lib. XVIII, Cap. XXX.
[50] Lib. XIII, No. 16.
[51] *De Butyro: De Aversatione Casei* (Groningae, 1604), p. 195.
[52] *N. H.*, Lib. XIX, Cap. XIX.

garden, but, except the Lactucini and the Valeriani, named from the lettuce and the valerian plants, no family names taken from the garden suggest themselves.[53]

Apparently, therefore, the Romans were more interested in agriculture than in horticulture[54] and made a distinction in dignity between the vegetable garden and the farm—a distinction which it is not easy for the modern world to understand, since garden culture has no small dignity in our present world and, when food supplies begin to run short, we resort at once to gardens, as was the case in 1917-1918 during the Great War. What is the reason that this means of getting food, which to men of modern times is so prompt and effective, was so little regarded by previous generations?

It does not fully satisfy modern readers to say that former ages thought vegetables a poor source of nourishment, since we rely so much upon them for our daily food that such an answer would be unintelligible to us. Nevertheless, we read that:

Stalks and field herbs are entirely of unwholesome juice; they furnish

[53] A similar tendency appears among English names—Pease, Bean, Wheat, Corn, Flax, Oates, Froment and Rice come from cereals or legumes; Rye, Clover and Barley are not unknown as family names, and the name Wheaton may possibly have its origin in the name of the cereal. There seem to be, however, few names of English origin which come from garden vegetables, though the name Onion is known, Garlick and Leek are to be found in some city directories and possibly a complete catalogue of vegetables could be made by careful search. There seems also to be a tendency to use names derived from medicinal herbs, as in Fennell, Basil, Dill, Sage, Savory, Cresse, Annis, etc. Some of these names doubtless are translations from, or originate in, other languages. The Romans did not object to many names that modern use does not favor—as, for example, the names Asinius and Asina. Plutarch, in his *Life of Poplicola*, calls attention to the fact that Romans did not hesitate to name their sons Suilli, Bubulii, Caprarii, and Porcii. The names of Verres and Scrofa were also known. Peculia, however—i.e. property in cattle—were wealth in ancient days, and these names may have had a substantial sound which Romans liked. The use of fish names—Muraena and Orata—arose from the practice of building private fish-ponds.

[54] *De Re Cibaria* by Bruyerinus, Lib. I, Cap. I, pp. 1, 2.

slight nourishment, and indeed, all vegetables are of this character. Wherefore we should be moderate in their use, nor should we think that they provide much food.[55]

The value of common vegetables which have long been cultivated in gardens is well known, but even these vegetables bring some difficulties. Pork and peas were at one time a favorite dish at the royal table[56] and it is interesting to observe that due recognition is given to a dish well known to-day—pork and beans[57]—though in ancient days this was regarded as food better for farm hands than for others of less active life. We find, however, when vegetables are discussed, vivid descriptions are given of flatulence which seems to have been great and painful, also of "obstructions," kidney-stones, "black bile," colic and sometimes of impaired eyesight.

Possibly we may get some clue to the cause of part of this trouble in Pliny's statement that the chief thing which in former times made men fond of the garden was that among its products were many that could be eaten without cooking, as Plutarch says of Cato that he was "content with a dinner cooked without fire,"[58] making in this way an economy of fuel and of labor. Moreover, what Romans called "acetaria"—salads and pickles—were easy of digestion, they gave no sense of repletion and created no desire for bread—an additional economy not to be overlooked when bread was not too plentiful.[59] They should be used moderately,

[55] *De Re Cibaria*, Lib. VIII, Cap. III, p. 457. "Olera omnia parum alunt," *Diaeteticon* by Ludovicus Nonnius, p. 37.

[56] *La vie privée des Français* by Le Grand d'Aussy, Vol. I, p. 130. *De Re Cibaria* by Bruyerinus, Lib. VII, Cap. II, p. 433.

[57] *De Re Cibaria* by Bruyerinus, Lib. VII, Cap. II, p. 430.

[58] *Life of Cato.* Bruyerinus quotes a letter from St. Jerome to Marcella in which, among the benefits derived from gardens, it is noted that many vegetables need no cooking and save the expense of fuel. *De Re Cibaria*, Lib. VIII, Cap. I, p. 453.

[59] Pliny, *N. H.*, Lib. XIX, Cap. XIX. *De Alimentis*, J. D. Sala, p. 12.

however, Bruyerinus says, and not so much as a food as for a medicine.[60]

Some further light on the question why garden vegetables were so little used in former ages may be had by going over the lists of garden products in Pliny and Columella, for there, though we find some very useful foods, cabbages, turnips, radishes and onions, we are quite overwhelmed with the mass of flavorings and medicinal herbs, sage, thyme, helenium, pepper-weed, wild marjoram, rue, coriander, sweet basil, anise, mustard, water parsley, alexander, mint, savory, cumin, garlic, leeks, skirret, caraway seed, poppy seed, hemp seed and other plants little used to-day.

We find these herbs also in Pliny's book on Gardens, and elsewhere with directions for compounding medicines from herbs, vegetables and trees, and altogether Pliny gives not less than 1600 or 1700 different remedies which can be made from plants for the cure of diseases.

Plautus repeats in his play of *The Captives* a very enlightening conversation on the subject of vegetables as food. Hegio has invited Ergasilus to dinner, adding, however, that his fare is rough. "Why," said Ergasilus, "you don't dine on thorns!" "No," said Hegio, "but I will give you many vegetables from the garden." To which Ergasilus replies, "Use them to cure your sick at home."[61]

Evidently, then, so far as concerned Ergasilus and the audiences for whom Plautus wrote, garden vegetables made a poor substitute for the bread and obsonia to which they were accustomed and which they liked. Garden vegetables could be used for food, of course, and there was an old saying that the garden is the pro-

[60] *De Re Cibaria*, Lib. VIII, Cap. II, p. 454.
[61] *Captivi*, Plautus, Act I, Sc. ii. See Romans, XIV, 2,—qui infirmus est, olus manducet.

123

vision store of the poor,[62] but the phrase suggests that it was not the provision store for persons who were not poor.

The subject is also mentioned in Plautus' play, *Pseudolus*, where one of the characters says:

> It is on account of these remedies which do not remedy
> But like harpies eat out the bowels of living guests
> That men on earth cultivate so short a life—
> Remedies terrible not only to take but even to mention.
> Men, indeed, feed upon plants that cattle refuse.[63]

Plautus' criticism may have had some foundation, for very many years later Bruyerinus, writing of lupines, said that, though hunger might compel men to use them, he would consider a person crazy who took lupines when anything else was to be had and, nevertheless, he remarks:

> There are writers who say that lupines taken rather often with food raise a person's color, a remedy which some of our fine ladies greatly need, for at times they have so little color in their faces that they seem like persons who are half dead.[64]

The reader's sympathy will surely go out to the ladies who looked so pale. How they could look otherwise on a continued diet of bread with salt meat or salt fish for obsonia, it is not easy to see. La Framboisière says that physicians of the Court advised the use, at the beginning of a meal, of bread made from bolted rye flour which, when well cooked and fresh, has a laxative effect. Some persons, he adds, thought that the use of this bread in the Lyonnais, Auvergne and Champagne made the women of those

[62] *Ars Magirica*, Jodocus Willichius (Zurich, 1563), p. 63. *Diaeteticon*, Ludovicus Nonnius, Lib. I, Cap. XI. Pliny, *N. H.*, Lib. XIX, Cap. XIX.

[63] *Pseudolus*, Plautus, Act III, Sc. ii.

[64] *De Re Cibaria*, Bruyerinus, Lib. VII, Cap. VI, p. 443. See Pliny, *N. H.*, Lib. XXII, Cap. LXXIV. Professor Henry D. Wild suggests that Thomas Dekker may have had such practices as this in mind when he wrote of ladies who "diet their faces."

provinces good looking and gave them excellent color.[65] Apparently, also, endives help the complexion, for Bruyerinus says, "I know that ladies make a drink from the wild endives which they are persuaded gives a stylish and cheerful color to the face."[66]

Good natural color, if we only knew the facts of the matter, is probably one of our pleasantest modern improvements, coming much more easily and lasting longer with a little of the meat, potatoes and other vegetables now available than any color which could ever be obtained by the use of lupines or endives. Only in recent years has it been possible to keep vegetables well more than a short time. Modern methods of preserving in cans or glass jars or of freezing and holding at low temperatures, so that the fresh flavor of new vegetables can be kept with little impairment throughout the year, were unknown. Beans and peas could, of course, even in old times, be dried and held almost indefinitely; fall squashes could, Sala says, be cut into small pieces, dried and kept into winter,[67] a process which Galen did not mention, as Sala notes; to which Plenck adds that some greens can be dried in a warm stove for winter use—"Sunt oeconomi qui folia viridia in furno tepido torrefaciunt et in usum hyemalem servant."[68] This refers to spinach, and probably as well to lettuce, cabbage and other green plants. Columella also describes the method of preserving garden products by pickling in brine.[69] Turnips, beets, carrots, radishes and parsnips could be kept fresh for a while and cabbages for a short time, but many other vegetables could not be kept at all and must therefore be used when fresh.[70] Add to this

[65] *Le gouvernement nécessaire à chacun pour vivre longuement en santé* (Paris, 1601), pp. 49, 50. Conf. *De Re Cibaria*, Bruyerinus, p. 357. *Maison rustique*, Estienne and Liébault (Paris, 1589), p. 316. *La vie privée des Français*, Le Grand d'Aussy, Vol. I, p. 101.

[66] *De Re Cibaria*, Lib. VIII, Cap. V, pp. 461, 463.

[67] *De Alimentis* by J. D. Sala, p. 11.

[68] Plenck, *Bromatologia*, pp. 72-73.

[69] *De Re Rustica*, Lib. XII, Cap. VI, VII. *De Alimentis*, Sala, p. 12.

[70] *De Re Cibaria* by Bruyerinus, Lib. IV, Cap. I, p. 236.

that very little was known about proper methods of cooking and that ignorance, united with a desire to save the cost of fuel and labor, led men to eat vegetables raw, and we have an explanation for much of the dislike for garden products.

It seems, however, that complete as this explanation may be, there was another reason stronger still—that garden products in such quantity as would make a defence against hunger were not to be had.

Pliny said, in the first century of our era,[71] and Bruyerinus repeated the statement fifteen hundred years later,[72] that care of the garden was a responsibility which belonged to the women.

The first and most imperative demand of the human race was for the cereal crops. Puls or pulmentum or bread, as the case might be, must be provided and, with the tools which were available, the work of raising cereals and providing the grain which was needed was a task of overwhelming labor which laid upon the men all that they could do and more. Other labor fell upon the women—the care of the family and of the house, cooking, with some limitations however, spinning, weaving, often the care of the dairy when there was such a thing, the care of poultry and cultivation of the garden, again with limitations, for there were plants and times when a woman's touch would be injurious,[73] and, as all this was far beyond human strength, the women, like the men, had to give their attention to what seemed most important and the rest was left undone.

The Romans took seriously their religious obligations to refrain from certain kinds of work on holidays, but there were no holidays for horses, mules and asses unless they were a part of the farmer's establishment (nisi in familia sunt),[74] and gardeners apparently

---

[71] *N. H.*, Lib. XIX, Cap. XIX.

[72] *De Re Cibaria*, Lib. VIII, Cap. I, p. 452.

[73] Columella, Lib. XI, Cap. III. Plutarch's *Roman Questions*, edited by Frank Byron Jevons (David Nutt, London, 1892), Introduction, p. lxxvi.

[74] Cato, *De Re Rustica*, Cap. CXXXVIII. Columella, Lib. II, Cap. XXII.

fared no better than hired horses, for gardens seem to have been regarded as drug stores which should always be open, and so there were no restrictions on garden work—in horto quidquid olerum causa facias, omne licet.[75]

During the early centuries of the Christian era, when conditions permitted, gardens were cultivated by the Moors in southern Spain. Later they were cultivated in northern Italy and later still by Flemings and Dutch in the Low Countries. The rest of the world got along with comparatively little help from garden vegetables.

At a recent exhibit in New York of vegetables obtainable out of season, there was, for comparison, an exhibit of four models, with this explanation:

These small prototypes of our common peas, beans, beets and leeks were the only fresh vegetables in common use in twelfth century England.

Supplies, however, were not quite so limited for our ancestors had also, when in season, cresses, common alexanders which served for celery, and some plants which they used as greens.[76] Apparently, however, vegetables were little used in England for, in the days when rent was payable in kind, Mr. Garnier says that he has found the terms of tenancy to include pepper, poultry, honey, salt, etc., but never vegetables.[77] If any vegetables other than peas, beans, beets or leeks had been wanted, it would have been necessary to import them and perhaps even these four vegetables were not always easy to find, for Thomas Fuller, as late as 1662, describes peas as "imported dainties for great ladies."[78] It was not until the seventeenth century that market gardens be-

[75] Columella, *De Re Rustica*, Lib. II, Cap. XXII.
[76] *History of Inventions, Discoveries and Origins* by John Beckmann, Vol. II, p. 354.
[77] *The Introduction of Forage Crops into Great Britain* by Mr. Russel M. Garnier, Jour. Roy. Ag. Soc., Vol. 57, 3rd Series Vol. 7, p. 77. March, 1896.
[78] *History of the Worthies of England* (1840 ed.), Vol. III, p. 200. See letter of Madame de Maintenon, May 10, 1796, cited by Count Grégoire in *Essai historique* (*Théâtre d'agriculture* by Olivier de Serres, Paris ed. of

came established in England when, as Thomas Fuller says, they "crept out of Holland to Sandwich in Kent,"[79]—an important event for, in England, it was one of the early steps toward the plentiful and varied food of the present day. Apparently, France was not much ahead of England in the use of vegetables, for La Framboisière, in 1601, gives lettuce the first place in his discussion, regards cabbage as a source of bad juice, says that spinach is "venteux" and speaks of borage, buglos and the flavoring and medicinal herbs very much as Pliny had spoken of them long before.[80]

The potato, as is well known, is a native of South America. Early explorers in Peru and Chile learned its use, found it an agreeable addition to their diet and, returning home, took it with them.

Apparently there were at least two independent introductions of the potato into Europe, one by way of the British Isles and the other by way of Spain.

It is the ancient tradition that it was brought to the British Isles by Sir Francis Drake and Sir Walter Raleigh and though this has been denied,[81] nevertheless Dr. Salaman believes that this tradition "though not proven, cannot lightly be dismissed."[82] Drake

---

1804, Vol. I, p. cli). *La vie privée des Français*, by Le Grand d'Aussy, Vol. I, p. 131.

[79] See article on *The Cultivation of Hops, Fruit and Vegetables* by Mr. Charles Whitehead. Jour. Roy. Ag. Soc., Vol. 39, 2nd Series Vol. 14, 1878. Chap. III, p. 749-483 treats of Vegetables.

[80] *Le gouvernement nécessaire à chacun*, etc., pp. 82 et seq.

[81] *The Potato of Romance and Reality* by Mr. W. E. Safford. Journal of Heredity, Vol. XVI, pp. 113-120 (1925). See *Origin, Introduction and Primitive Culture of the Potato* by Mr. W. F. Wight, printed in Proceedings of Third Annual Meeting of Potato Association of America, 1916, pp. 35-52.

[82] *The Potato in its Early Home and its Introduction into Europe* by Redcliffe N. Salaman. Jour. Roy. Hort. Soc., Vol. LXII, pp. 61, 111, 153, 253. (1937)

had brought Raleigh's colonists back from Virginia in 1586 and it is possible that the planting of the potato in England and Ireland began at that time.[83] John Gerarde mentioned it in the catalogue of plants growing in his garden at Holborn, published in 1596, and described it in his Herbal published the next year, 1597. Falstaff's exclamation, "Let the sky rain potatoes," in Act V, scene v, of *The Merry Wives of Windsor*,—a play which appeared about the time that Gerarde published his Herbal and ten or twelve years after Drake's return,—suggests that during this interval potatoes had been cultivated in England enough to make such a reference intelligible to an English audience.

Dr. Thomas Venner, an English physician at Bath, said of potatoes, in his book published in London in 1650:

Potato-roots are of a temperate quality, and of strong nourishing parts: the nutriment which they yeeld is, though somewhat windy, very substantiall, good and restorative, surpassing the nourishment of all other roots or fruits . . . They are very pleasant to the tast, and do wonderfully comfort, nourish and strengthen the body.[84]

In 1655 Dr. Thomas Muffett spoke of "potadoes" among other well known foods,—artichokes, carrots, radishes, etc.

Apparently, therefore, the potato had come into general use both in Ireland and England at an early day, so that when in 1664 John Forster published his pamphlet, *England's Happiness Increased by a Plantation of Potatoes,* he could say of this vegetable:

These roots, although they came at first from the Indies, yet thrive and prosper very well in Ireland, where there is whole Fields of them; from whence they have been brought into Wales, and into the North parts of England, where they likewise prosper and increase exceedingly. They are in quality temperate, very agreeable and amicable to the Nature

[83] *The Potato in its Early Home,* etc., pp. 61, 253. *Origin, Early History and Development of the Potato* by T. P. McIntosh, Gardeners' Chronicle, Series 3, Vol. 79, pp. 49, 85, 120, 159, 178, 279.

[84] *Via Recta ad Vitam Longam* (London, 1650), pp. 188-189.

of Man, and of a good and strong nourishment. In substance they are brittle and mealy, and therefore very fit to be put into Bread, and to make divers kinds of wholesome Meats. . . .

The potato evidently, by this time, had become an accepted food among the people of the British Isles.[85]

On the continent of Europe the potato came into use before it was known in England and Ireland. The conquest of Peru took place between the years 1531 and 1541, and it is probable that the potato was carried to Spain by returning vessels not long after the latter date.[86] What vessel carried this valuable cargo or when the importation into Spain was made, we do not know, but the subsequent history of the potato in Europe is fairly complete. Dr. Salaman, in his very illuminating article on this subject, after quoting the *Historia Plantarum* of Clusius, adds:

From this we learn that prior to 1588 the tuber was an established garden vegetable in certain parts of Italy, which implies that it must have arrived there from Spain at least five or more years earlier, and that it could not therefore have reached Spain much later than 1580. This, however, is but guessing and till now 1588 has been our earliest fixed date.

It gives the writer great pleasure to state that, with the help of Professor E. Hamilton, he is able to improve on that date by fifteen years. In his book (*American Treasure and the Price Revolution in Spain*, 1501-1650. Harvard Economic Series, Vol. XLIII, p. 196, note, 1934) Hamilton mentions that the account books of the Hospital de la Sangre at Seville show that they bought potatoes as part of their normal housekeeping in 1576. Recently Professor Hamilton has written that he found mention of such a purchase in the fourth quarter of 1573, and thinks there may be still earlier ones.

It is interesting to note that prior to 1584 the hospital bought its potatoes by the pound, but that at the later date they were purchased by the arroba (a unit of 25 lb.); moreover, all the purchases took place in the

[85] Conf. *Agriculture from the Restoration to Anne*, by Mr. G. E. Fussell. *The Economic History Review*, Vol. IX, No. I, pp. 68, 72. November, 1938.

[86] *Origin, Early History*, etc., by T. P. McIntosh, Gardeners' Chronicle, Vol. 79, p. 49.

fourth quarter of the year, which is good evidence that they were grown in Spain and eaten freshly harvested. They were probably regarded as luxuries up till 1584.[87]

The story of the extension of potato growing from Spain to Italy, thence to the Low Countries, from the Low Countries in sequence to Austria, Germany, Switzerland and France is most admirably told by M. Ernest Roze.[88] Toward the end of the sixteenth century, M. Roze says, the cultivation of the potato had been introduced not only into Franche-Comté, but generally throughout the Vosges district. The plant was not mentioned by Bruyerinus, whose book on Foods was published at Lyons in 1560, nor by Estienne and Liébault, whose book was published in 1589, but in 1600 it was well described by Olivier de Serres under the name cartoufle.[89] Parmentier believed that the plant which de Serres had in mind was the Jerusalem artichoke,[90] but M. Roze refers to de Candolle as authority for the statement that the Jerusalem artichoke was not known in France until the year 1616. Apparently a knowledge of the potato had made its way from Switzerland down the eastern provinces of France until it came to the country with which de Serres was acquainted.

M. Roze says (p. 106), moreover, that in 1620 the potato was carried from England to Flanders where its use spread slowly, but where it was cultivated on a large scale after 1704. It was cultivated in Saxony after 1717, and in Prussia in 1738 (p. 105). Thereafter the knowledge of the potato steadily made its way throughout Europe.

Of the method of cooking the potato Sala gives a description

[87] *The Potato in its Early Home and its Introduction into Europe.* Jour. Roy. Hort. Soc., Vol. LXII, p. 254.

[88] *Histoire de la pomme de terre* (Paris, 1898), a book which Dr. Salaman describes as "a magnificent classic."

[89] *Le théâtre d'agriculture*, 6me Lieu, Chap. X.

[90] See note, Vol. II, p. 279 of the Paris 1804 edition of de Serres' book.

which makes the reader hungry. It was roasted, he says, under the ashes and then eaten with a little pepper, as we might well expect in times when all food was spiced, or being cut into small pieces was eaten with gravy poured over it.[91]

In 1749 de Combles described the potato[92] under the name truffe. In Italy the potato had been known as tartuffalo. In France, among other names, the second syllable of the Italian name had been used, while in Germany, and probably in Switzerland, the potato had been called erdtoffeln and cartoufeln. Of this plant de Combles said:

> This is a plant of which no writer has spoken, being restrained probably by the contempt which has excluded it from the list of kitchen vegetables, for it has been too long known and too widely cultivated to have escaped attention. It would be wrong, however, to omit mention of a vegetable which is food for a large part of the people of all nations . . . not only for the lower orders and country folk . . . but even for persons in comfortable circumstances.

Long before the middle of the eighteenth century, therefore, the potato had become a common food for laborers, in many of the European nations, who lived where they could have a garden, and for many persons in country districts. These people evidently had learned the value of the new vegetable and the knowledge that the potato was easily cultivated, pleasant to eat and a great protection in times of want, had spread throughout a widely scattered population in a large territory. Such knowledge did not travel fast in those days, and it seems that general use of the potato among the poorer people of France must have begun about 1700, or perhaps earlier. It was the townspeople and persons of substantial means who were slow to accept it. For a short time, about 1740, the potato became popular even among townspeople. Physi-

[91] *De Alimentis* by J. D. Sala, p. 13.

[92] *L'école du jardin potager*. In the 1752 edition, this description is in Vol. II, Chap. LXXIX.

cians advised its use and writers praised its virtues, but Le Grand d'Aussy says that this favor was undeserved. The potato might please the poor but it could not satisfy the taste of those who could afford other food.

The pasty taste, the natural insipidity, the unwholesome quality of the food which, like all unfermented starch, is windy and indigestible, has caused it to be rejected by careful households and sent for consumption to those whose gross taste and strong stomachs make them satisfied with anything that will appease hunger. The potato can be raised with little care, it produces much food at low cost and is a valuable supply for the class of persons mentioned, and even as a general resource in time of want.[93]

It appears, therefore, that the potato in those days was a food of the poor and of country folk. It is not, however, a poor food. What reason can be given, then, for its rejection during so many years by townspeople and persons of means? There are probably two explanations of this curious fact.

In the first place, in a society where spiced foods had corrupted the taste, the mild flavor of the potato lacked quality, as Dr. Thomas Muffett thought melons, pears, apples and plums insipid,— "tasting just of nothing."[94] Ireland was a poor country and the Irish, like poor people in other countries, were unable to buy spices, and consequently were able to enjoy the potato. In Ireland, therefore, and among many people in England and France, the potato won its way on its merits,[95] wherever men were found to agree with Bruyerinus that "the choicest foods are those whose natural flavor is most pleasing."[96]

[93] *La vie privée des Français*, Vol. I, pp. 111-112.
[94] *Health's Improvement* by Dr. Thomas Muffett (London, 1655), Chap. V, p. 40.
[95] *Introduction of Forage Crops into Great Britain* by Mr. Russel M. Garnier, Jour. Roy. Ag. Soc., Vol. 57, 3rd Series Vol. 7, p. 77, March 1896.
[96] *De Re Cibaria*, Lib. X, Cap. VIII, p. 563.

Besides this, there is also a second possible explanation for the fact that the value of the potato was so slowly appreciated, in that Europeans had not yet learned the best ways of preparing it for the table. Popular habits are hard to change. At the present time Ireland may be called the land of the boiled potato and France the land of the fried potato. If by some sudden change, it became impossible to boil potatoes in Ireland and to fry them in France, the popularity of the potato would decline greatly in both countries. It might be difficult to persuade Frenchmen to eat boiled potatoes or to induce the Irish to fry them. Two hundred years ago, mankind had so long lived on bread that there was a strong tendency to value possible foods by their suitability for bread. If judged in this way, therefore, potatoes must be good for bread or good for nothing.

Another instance of failure to use a food for the purpose for which it is best suited is found in the case of oats, which make an excellent porridge, both agreeable and satisfying. Oats, however, make a very poor bread and so, because oatmeal porridge was not to be considered, we have the picture of Madame de Maintenon eating oat bread at Versailles as an example to all French people of her willingness in times of want to submit to common hardships, when in fact her oat bread was a conspicuous example of the slow development of human ideas. Had Madame de Maintenon introduced oatmeal porridge into common use, she would have done more for the French nation than had been done by many victorious French generals.

The history of this misuse of oats resembles the history of potatoes in Europe. Sala had told the world that baked potatoes and gravy were good to eat, but the world had not been accustomed to eat baked potatoes and gravy and would not do it. Parmentier well said that "the vegetable kingdom affords no food more wholesome, more easily procured or less expensive than the

Potatoe,"[97] and he advised the use of boiled potatoes. The world, however, was not prepared for anything so simple. What was wanted was bread and so, a hundred and fifty years after Sala's book, Parmentier published receipts for the making of potato bread. Nevertheless, potatoes did not make bread which was acceptable to people of those times and, used in this way, potatoes were not liked. The great discovery of their intrinsic value was slow in coming, and the man who did most to bring the potato, cooked in practical ways, into the use of townspeople of France, was Antoine Augustin Parmentier, who was able in 1781 to say:

At present there is scarce an elegant repast where Potatoes are not used in various disguises; and their great consumption in the Capital proves that they are no longer despised there.[98]

This statement, like all other statements of times past, must be read with an understanding of conditions then existing, as we take the statements of Plutarch and Fortescue in regard to abundance prevailing long ago in Greece and England. Great and small are relative terms. Potatoes were coming into use when Parmentier wrote and he welcomed them, but they came so slowly, and apparently disguise was so necessary, that in 1827, forty-six years after Parmentier's book, the *Encyclopédie moderne*, speaking of the improvement of agriculture by crop rotation, said:

Two plants, hitherto much neglected, have in this way become capable of cultivation on a large scale. I speak of maize and potatoes. The cultivation of the latter has increased greatly since the Germans have shown how to distill spirits from it, using the residue as food for domestic animals, and since chemistry has shown how potatoes can be used for making flour, starch and syrup.[99]

[97] *Observations on Nutritive Vegetables* (London, 1783), p. 7.
[98] *Observations on Nutritive Vegetables*, p. 8.
[99] "Deux plantes, auparavant fort négligées, ont pu, par ce moyen, être cultivées en grand. Je veux parler du maïs et de la pomme de terre. La culture de cette dernière a pris des développements d'autant plus considérables que les

The potato, then, must to a considerable extent be regarded as an addition made since the beginning of the nineteenth century to the food resources of townspeople in all the nations of Europe.

Garden vegetables, however, began to take their place in common use during the seventeenth century, as also did coffee, tea and chocolate.[100] The many cook books of the period show that there was at this time a great improvement in domestic management. Obviously, so far as increase of possible food supplies was concerned, the seventeenth century was such a period as the world never before had seen in all its long history, and this period has continued, with constant increase of comforts and luxuries, to the present time.

Allemands nous ont appris à en extraire de l'eau-de-vie en augmentant les moyens de nourriture des bestiaux, et que le chimie nous a fait connaître les autres propriétés de ce tubercule, soit comme farine, soit comme fécule, soit comme sirop." *Encyclopédie moderne*, 2nd ed. (Lejeune, La Haye, 1827), Tit. Agriculture, Vol. I, p. 231.

[100] *La vie privée des Français* by Le Grand d'Aussy, Vol. III, p. 97. Robert Burton, *Anatomy of Melancholy*, Part I, Sec. II, Mem. II, Subsec. III, mentions as a remarkable thing that in the Low Countries men feed on roots,— meaning, doubtless, turnips, beets, parsnips, etc.,—a comment which suggests the remark made eight years earlier by Bishop Goodman, that "the poore Dutch men, like swine, digge up the rootes; and the gentleman-like Italian . . . feeds upon Sallads. The poore people of England are usually kept with their oates, which here we give to our horses. . . ." *The Fall of Man* by Godfrey Goodman (London, 1616), p. 80.

This last statement may have been in Dr. Johnson's mind when he described oats in his Dictionary.

CHAPTER VIII

THE EFFECT OF WANT ON THE HUMAN MIND

THE great stages of man's progress, the barbaric, pastoral, agricultural and industrial, are marked by constantly increasing ability to supply human wants. There was an increase of population when a people passed from the barbaric to the pastoral era, a second increase when they entered the agricultural era, and a great increase when they entered the industrial era.[1]

Human history, however, in the Mediterranean basin from the beginning of the agricultural era long before Christ, to the beginning of the nineteenth century after Christ, covers a very long period during which progress was small.[2] What is the explanation of such delay?

It is hard for persons living under modern conditions to realize even inadequately what life was when the population pressed upon the food supply during those long ages when want was universal. Virgil, in the sixth book of the *Aeneid*, describes the gates of Hell where, among others of man's enemies, are Malasuada Fames— Hunger, the Evil Counselor—and Pestilence, War, the iron couches of the Furies, and insane Discord.

Famine, War and Pestilence—the world knows them well, these three, and knows that they come not singly, one by one. Where there is Want, Pestilence makes her home and War is not far distant. Professor F. York Russel says that historians, from Thucyd-

---

[1] *Mankind at the Crossroads* by Professor Edward M. East (Charles Scribner's Sons, New York, 1923), p. 151. *Man, Bread and Destiny* by Professor and Mrs. C. C. Furnas (Reynal & Hitchcock, New York, 1937), pp. 280 et seq.

[2] *Ante*, pp. 31 et seq.

137

ides to Niebuhr, have remarked on the demoralizing effect of a great pestilence. Of the pestilence in the seventh century, Bede says that it caused the East Saxons to relapse into heathenism "and it can hardly be doubted that the desolation of Britain, and of all Europe shortly before, little as it bulks in the annals, was one of the chief reasons why the centuries following were emphatically the Dark Ages."[3]

Dr. Caspar Hoffman made a striking statement three hundred years ago[4] when, after saying that fresh olive oil can safely be eaten with bread, he adds that butter cannot so be eaten because, among other things, it tends to produce leprosy. The explanation for this remarkable idea is, probably, that much of the butter to be had at that time in towns and cities was rancid, and that leprosy, a great disease of mediaeval Europe, as Dr. Charles Creighton says, "was commonly supposed to come from bad food—semiputrid fish or flesh."[5] Matthew Paris says that there were about 19,000 leper-houses established in northern Europe, of which 2,000 were in France, and that there were 95 such houses of the first class in England, besides others in Scotland and Ireland,[6] surely enormous figures for the small population of those days. Apparently, the name leprosy was applied to a number of different diseases which, under the circumstances of the times, were commonly serious, sparing neither high nor low, rich nor poor. Baldwin IV, King of Jerusalem from 1173 to 1183, was a leper of whose condition Matthew Paris gives a shocking account.[7]

Leprosy, however, was but one of the great plagues. In addition to the diseases included under this name, there were constant visitations of epidemics—the Black Death, typhus fever, the sweat-

---

[3] *Social England* (Putnam, New York, 1901), Vol. I, p. 175.
[4] *Institutionum*, etc., *Epitome* (Paris, 1648), Lib. V, Cap. XIII, Sec. 4, p. 433.
[5] *Social England*, Vol. I, pp. 369-370.
[6] *Ency. Brit.*, 14th ed., Tit. Leprosy.
[7] *Historia Anglorum* (Rolls Series, London, 1866), Vol. I, p. 429.

ing sickness, dysentery, plague of the throat, malaria and others—and with them was almost constant war and brigandage, one evil producing another, as M. Luchaire says.

Great as these plagues were, however, there was one other that was greater than all these, and the source of many—famine—of which Professor Sergius Morgulis says:

Famine is not merely destructive of health and physique, it is in a still greater degree a disrupter of morale and character. In the sharp struggle to maintain life all scruples are overcome, neighbor is against neighbor, and the strong are ruthless towards the weak. With wonderful force of simplicity does a thirteenth century Russian chronicle relate the horrors of the famine in the Novgorod province: "We were all in a fury of irritation; a brother rose against his brother, a father had no pity for his son, mothers had no mercy for their daughters; one denied his neighbor a crumb of bread. There was no charity left among us, only sadness, gloom and mourning dwelt constantly within and without our habitations. It was a bitter sight, indeed, to watch the crying children, begging in vain for bread, and falling dead like flies."

Still more appalling, however, is the aftermath of famine. Little actual information can be gathered of the after-effects. Prugavin tells of the many thousands of peasants afflicted with scurvy, typhus, spotted fever, influenza and diarrhea in the terrible famine which spread over the central provinces of Russia in 1898. Even long after the famine nearly all children suffered from various skin eruptions, rickets, diarrhea and purulent inflammation of the eyes. The doctors who went into the pestilential districts to offer succor to the famine victims have noted the unusually large number of people with severe diseases of the eyes. The great Irish famine of 1848 likewise left a trail of blind men and women in its wake. Dr. Emmet reports that the number of blind increased from 13,812 in 1849 to 45,947 in 1851. . . . This is a specific effect of certain kinds of inanition and is invariably met with in every instance of malnutrition.[8]

[8] *Fasting and Undernutrition* by Professor Sergius Morgulis of the University of Nebraska (Dutton, New York, 1923), Introduction, pp. 15-16.

"The people here are more poor, and therefore more destitute of humanity," Peter Heylin's description of the Island of Jersey. See *Two Journeys* (London, 1656), p. 303. Misery may love company—but chiefly when troubles are not overwhelming. See answer of Psammenitus, Herodotus, Bk. III, Chap. 14.

It is not surprising that, in a world where such experiences were common, human sympathies should be dull and hard to arouse. We wonder, indeed, that any Roman who enjoyed the spectacles of the amphitheatre could say that cruelty did not please him, although Cicero quotes this very phrase from Piso, and we are perplexed that Francis Bacon, who attended the torture of Peacham, reporting Peacham's conduct before, during, between and after his sufferings, could speak of pity as the tenderest of human affections. Perhaps to modern readers there is hardly another scene in history which so arouses admiration and contempt as that which contrasts Peacham's courage with Bacon's suppleness, but it must be remembered that both men were of the former age and that, if want led to callousness and hardness, it also strengthened the hearts of men to endure as few can who know only the easy ways of life.

Upon the intellectual life also, want had its inevitable effect. Progress makes little headway among needy men and it is, therefore, surprising to find that among the men living in those days there was at least one who looked to mankind for intellectual advance and who, finding none, sought for the delaying cause.

Four hundred years ago, in 1538, an Italian, Oddo degli Oddi, who wrote in Latin under the name Odus de Odis, considered this very question:

I have often turned it over in my mind, why it is that although the world is the same as it was of old, nor is there any change in the revolution of the sun or other stars, nevertheless, it is exceedingly rare that a person is born in these times who can make any advance in the useful arts —no one, indeed, seems now to stand forward as in ancient times did Phidias among sculptors, Appelles among painters, Plato and Aristotle among philosophers or Hippocrates and Galen among physicians. This, I say, greatly perplexes me, especially since the approach to useful arts is made easy for us by the writings of the ancients, so that knowledge which they acquired only by earnest vigils and labor, we can acquire very quickly.

And when I considered the cause of this thing, it occurred to me, after some study, that Galen had given the solution by his statement that a right use of food and drink produces not only a good condition of the body, but renders also the mind more vigorous, while a bad use of food and drink not only impairs bodily health but destroys the good habits of the mind and distracts the intelligence from its proper duty. When men therefore in that ancient fortunate age established for themselves right conditions of living, they created healthy conditions both for mind and body.[9]

Into Odus' further discussion of hygiene, it is not necessary to go, but it is interesting to know that, during these long ages of retarded development, the world was not entirely unaware that normal growth had been interrupted, and that at least one writer associated the interruption in some way with the question of food.

The modern world, with its abundant information as to the importance of regular nourishment, both good and varied, needs no argument to prove that those who suffer want are held back from progress. "Hunger," Segni said in a book first published in 1591, during a period of great want in Italy, "torments our vital spirits, stunts our growth, weakens our perceptions and alters our intellectual life."[10] In Cowper's phrase, men

> . . . inured to drudgery and distress
> Act without aim, think little and feel less.

It is easy for us to see also that man cannot do his best on a cereal diet alone. Puls or sitos, porridge or bread, cannot by itself maintain men's full activity, and when even bread and porridge were reduced so that famines were of frequent occurrence for the

[9] *De Coenae et Prandii Portione*, Odus de Odis (Lyons, 1538), Dedicatory Epistle.

[10] *Carestia e Fame* by Giovanni Battista Segni, p. 2.

141

great majority of the race, intellectual progress was necessarily very slow.

It was inevitable, then, that political progress also should be slow, for free government, always a difficult government to maintain, is exposed to its greatest dangers among a populace that lacks food.

Hunger and cold, it is said, deliver a man up to his enemies, and so it happened in Rome where, by the distribution of bread, Augustus, according to Gibbon, "artfully contrived that in the enjoyment of plenty, the Romans should lose the memory of freedom."[11] Popular want, in whatever form it may exist, or even discontent, justifiable or not, is so easily used for purposes hostile to popular welfare that the republic of Sparta punished Agesilaus for sending to every veteran an ox as a reward of his fortitude, and the reason given for the punishment was that "by this means he won too much upon the people and made the commonwealth wholly serviceable to his private interest."[12]

Lucan says of Curio that he was

Gallorum captus spoliis et Caesaris auro,[13]

caught by Gallic spoils and Caesar's money, and so—or by hope of spoils and money which they saw scattered so generously—were many of Caesar's party which destroyed the old Roman republic. In the Life of Coriolanus, Plutarch quotes the statement that "the person who first began to give treats and largesses to the people, was he that first deprived them of their power."[14]

The want, therefore, which was so wide-spread during the mid-

[11] *Decline and Fall*, Chap. XVII, Vol. II, p. 265.

[12] Plutarch, *Morals*, Of Brotherly Love (Little, Brown, & Co., 1883), Vol. IV, p. 64.

[13] *Pharsalia*, Lib. IV, line 820.

[14] *Lives*, Vol. II, p. 154.

dle ages not only stunted growth and weakened perceptions, but besides this it made many persons willing to be

> . . . bred of alms, and fostered with cold dishes,

like the crowd, described by Stuckius, that waited outside a house of feasting. Free democracy is impossible in a population where this class of persons is large.[15] Democracy came with machinery and plenty.

Over a hundred and fifty years after Odus de Odis, the subject of food and progress was mentioned in casual but illuminating fashion by Jonathan Swift in his *Tale of a Tub*, Section VII. The seventeenth century had been a period of great advance, both in the intellectual life and in the physical conditions amidst which life was lived. Introduction of what was called Dutch agriculture, with clover in the rotation had, it was said, brought enough wealth into England to pay the losses of the civil wars, and prosperous farming meant increased food supplies of beef and mutton. Market gardens had made their way into England and all this change was included by Dean Swift in a reference to "the late refinements of knowledge running parallel to those of dyet in our nation."

The difference of outlook between Odus de Odis in 1538 and Swift in 1696 is striking, for the Italian writer, being conscious that human knowledge was making little progress, and having no reason to think that there could be an increase in the quantity of food produced, sought to explain retarded development as caused by failure to put available food to the best use, while Dean Swift in 1696, observing the great improvement of his day, both in food and in knowledge, rightly referred to progress in one field as parallel with progress in the other field,—and, nevertheless, the progress that had been achieved at that time was not great. There

[15] *Public Economy of the Athenians* by Augustus Boeckh, 2nd ed. tr. by Anthony Lamb (Little, Brown, and Co., Boston, 1857), Donations to the People, Bk. II, Chap. XIII, p. 300.

were good observers, as late as the middle of the eighteenth century, to whom it seemed that knowledge had gone as far as the mind of man could penetrate. In 1751, nearly sixty years after Dean Swift's statement, Dr. Samuel Johnson quoted La Bruyère that we are come into the world too late to produce anything new; that nature and life are preoccupied and that description and sentiment had long been exhausted.[16] It is the present state of the skies and the earth, he said, on which plenty and famine are suspended, and on which millions depend for the necessaries of life. Man, then, could do nothing and progress was impossible. To La Bruyère and to Samuel Johnson, if we can judge their considered opinions by their statements here quoted, civilization had not paused,—it had completed its course. And notwithstanding all this, as the modern world well knows, great advance was even then just beginning.

Seventy years later, Mr. Henry Hallam, writing on *The Middle Ages* in 1818, deals with the idea of progress, for several parts of his work, notably Chapter IX, show that he had in mind the same subject with which Odus de Odis had dealt, and to which Dean Swift had so briefly and luminously referred, but to Hallam the matter presented an aspect a little different from that which it had borne for the earlier students of this subject, since men of his time and situation were already beginning to rely upon an assured supply of food. They expected enough to eat as a matter of course and, moreover, the idea of advance in human knowledge had for them lost its first appearance of novelty. Hallam's form of the question, therefore, was the form which belonged to his generation—why had not progress come sooner? Mr. Hoskyns, a little later still, presented this question in very emphatic form. "When we consider," he said, "the duration of the recorded period of man's occupation of the earth, and contrast it with the

[16] *The Rambler*, No. 143, July 30, 1751.

dates from which hang all that we name our greatest discoveries, in the nature and powers of the elements around us, there is hardly a reflecting mind which does not feel that amongst all the wonders of advanced or advancing science, the greatest wonder is its own infancy."[17] Apparently, to Mr. Hoskyns it was a question why progress had ever stopped. Later years seem to have assumed that the history of civilization had been a slow but continuous rise from earliest conditions of savagery. Progress, it was said, is the law of man.

Continuous progress, nevertheless, has not been the law of man in past ages. On the contrary, progress has been rare and periods of great advance have been followed by long stagnation.

Peoples have moved up from barbarism to pastoral life and, this step being taken, have continued long ages to live with their flocks and herds.

Similarly, the peoples who developed agriculture, having reached this level, dwelt there until the coming of the wonderful century eighteen hundred years after Christ. The civilization which hand labor supports is a simple civilization, and the inadequacy of the supplies which could be produced by hand labor was its limiting factor.

It may be, therefore, that the industrial era having placed civilization on a new level, if the population shall now rise to press upon the supplies possible under present conditions, there will be another pause, and progress will no more be the law of man in the future than it has been in the past. Progress is not a necessary evolution. It is a result of conditions which in man's history have been rare—the exception, not the rule. Progress, therefore,

[17] *An Inquiry into the History of Agriculture* by Mr. Chandos Wren Hoskyns (London, 1849), pp. 94-95. "It is the most striking circumstance in the literary annals of the dark ages, that they seem to us still more deficient in native than in acquired ability." *Literature of Europe*, Hallam, Part I, Chap. I, Sec. 11.

145

has been rare, and if the forward movement we now see about us is to continue, indeed, if we are even to hold the position we have achieved, we must maintain the conditions out of which freedom, safety, ambition and progress arise.

Of course, every step forward which mankind has made was the result of an effort to supply some need, but the greatest progress does not come where the need is greatest, else, as Professor Bouthoul well remarks, both India and China would live in a flowering of unceasing invention. In fact, both in modern times and in antiquity, the larger part of the inventions have come from smaller towns or countries not densely populated. Too large a population hinders advance, as can be seen in China which, at first, showed marked spirit of invention but ended in a stagnation which grew as her great population increased. Europe to-day, Professor Bouthoul says, is threatened by the same danger, for in a dense population there is an irresistible movement hostile to invention, to machinery and to culture itself.[18]

The world is developing the power of producing food and other supplies in great quantities, but by the irony of fate the popular movement tends toward inefficient methods and in some countries the use of agricultural machinery is restricted, so easily do men forget the past.

Learning, when planted in any country, is transient and fleeting,[19]

and so it happens that to many of Professor Bury's readers his statement that the idea of progress is of very recent origin came as a surprise.[20]

[18] *La population dans le monde*, Professor Gaston Bouthoul, pp. 125, 126.

[19] *An Inquiry into the Present State of Polite Learning in Europe* by Oliver Goldsmith, Chap. 11.

[20] *The Idea of Progress* by Professor J. B. Bury (Clarendon Press, 1928), p. 6—a subject which had long interested French writers, to whom Professor Bury refers. See also *The Idea of Progress* by Dr. W. R. Inge, Outspoken Essays, Second Series (Longmans, Green & Co., 1926), p. 158.

We are not now concerned with the philosophical aspect of the subject in which Professor Bury was chiefly interested. The physical impediments to progress were quite sufficient to account for all the delay that had occurred. Starving men do not meditate upon the arts and it was lack of food, among other things, which prevented progress.

And all through those millennia of suffering, man was ready and able to move ahead. He had the intelligence that he has now. What he needed was freedom to use that intelligence. When governmental restraints were removed, when the right to enjoy private property was established and protection given from confiscation, from invasion of personal rights and from excessive taxation,—all the rest came very quickly. Human history is not merely the tale of 2300 years of pause and 139 years of activity. It was first and foremost the tale on the one hand of 2300 years of various ways of living in which man was never fully his own master, and, on the other hand, 139 years of freedom.

Mediaeval history, therefore, is an impressive demonstration that by wrong policies governments can reduce mankind to want and can bring civilization to the verge of extinction. Policies which deprive the farmer of independence in the use of land, which restrict cultivation or destroy what has been produced, are farming for famine, and the same can be said of debasing the currency in order to raise prices. Penkethman said of the famine of 1124 in England, when "everywhere in cities, villages and cross-roads lifeless bodies lay unburied," that one of its contributing causes was that "by means of changing the coins all things became very deere."

If food and other necessaries of life are adequate in quantity and variety, and if men are free, there will be industry. If savings are secure from confiscation and debasement, there will be thrift; and an industrious, thrifty people make a prosperous and rich nation.

147

CHAPTER IX

THE HISTORY OF THE MILK INDUSTRY

THE modern world has two sources of food supply of which, in former times, men were able to make but comparatively little use,—the dairy industry and the poultry industry. These subjects have now become so important that their history demands special attention if we are to understand why such great resources were so little used in a starving world. They demand attention also because, being fruits of recent progress, their continuance depends upon the continuance of the conditions out of which they arose.

Milk is not a pleasant food for everybody. Many grown persons and children do not like milk and so, apparently, it has always been. Sala said, long ago:

Antiqui lac melle et sale corrigebant, tantum mellis miscentes ut nauseam non excitaret, tantum salis ut saperet.[1]

That is, the ancients flavored milk with honey and salt, using enough honey to prevent nausea, and enough salt to give the milk a taste. Even to-day, there are many persons who demand a flavor to disguise the natural taste of milk. The number of those who do not care for cheese is large, and even larger perhaps is the number of those who would be willing to accept in place of butter some of the many substitutes that are wholesome, palatable and nutritious, and whose use is limited by adverse taxation. The dairy industry does not live on any universal delight in the taste of its

[1] *De Alimentis*, pp. 48-49.

148

products, but upon its ability—so far as such ability exist—to compete successfully with many other foods that are cheap, abundant and good. Should this ability decline, the dairy industry must decline also, for the competition is inevitable. Housekeepers are continually compelled to look more and more carefully into the qualities of the many foods from every climate which rapid transportation and new methods of preserving offer to them, and in this way, as a recent publication of the League of Nations says, "A more scientific appreciation of nutritive values has been spreading throughout the world."[2] There is good ground for Mr. Rudolf A. Clemens' statement:

The rewards of the future will go to the most scientifically managed food industry.[3]

The dairy industry faces a new competition with fruits and vegetables from all parts of the world and with foods which chemists are beginning to produce from plants without the intervention of animals. To this competition dairymen must direct their best efforts, reducing the price and improving the food value of their products.

The art of dairying had its beginning almost as soon as man began to lift himself above brute creation. It has grown in importance with the increase of human knowledge, and as our means for carrying it on have grown, but it never was a great source of food until very recently when milk and its products have become a daily requirement of immense populations, valuable as nourishment for the support of life, and even more valuable as a source of elements necessary for maintenance of health. It is well worth our while, therefore, to consider the history of this great industry, to know what it has done for mankind and to learn something also

[2] League of Nations, Economic Intelligence Service, Fifth Year, 1935-36, p. 115.

[3] *Ency. of Soc. Sci.* (Macmillan, 1933), Vol. 9, p. 551.

about the possibilities of good which it holds out to the modern world, both to those who want milk as a food and to those who depend upon the production of milk as the occupation which provides their livelihood.

It is sometimes said that civilization began with the plough. Measured by this test, the dairy industry may be older than civilization, for it seems that in some countries men learned to use milk before the plough was invented.

In the ninth book of the *Odyssey*, Homer describes the Cyclops, a pastoral people who, according to Pope's translation, were

> . . . a savage kind
> Nor tamed by manners nor by laws confined;
> Untaught to plant, to turn the glebe and sow
> They all their products to free nature owe.

This savage race, nevertheless, pastured sheep and goats, and it is related that one of them kept his flock at night in a cave where were

> Full pails and vessels of the milking trade

and where also were

> The bending shelves with loads of cheeses pressed.

To such people, and to all those of the white race who follow a pastoral mode of life, milk is an important article of diet. That the Chinese should not consider milk fit for human food seems strange to us at first, particularly since their neighbors, the Mongols on the north and the Thibetans on the west, have used milk and milk products from time immemorial. It is obvious, however, that conditions of living among these peoples are very different, for China is densely populated, as neither Thibet nor Mongolia is, and where food is short and space is limited animal food is a luxury. Men may prefer milk but they can live on bread. When peoples become crowded, therefore, they shift to a cereal diet ex-

150

cept so far as meat can be produced on uncultivable grazing land, or swine can be raised without consuming food which starving men could use.[4] Milk cannot be produced on rough pasture throughout the year and like meat, therefore, it is a luxury of which the consumption tends to decrease as a growing population begins to crowd.[5] This has probably been the history of milk in China, where the population has become so crowded that even the memory of using milk as a food is lost. There may be a similar explanation for the objection to milk which has existed also among peoples in Borneo, Java and some native tribes of Africa. The ancestors of European races, undoubtedly, hunted before they domesticated live stock, but by the time they reached a pastoral stage of existence the milk industry had been born.

It is the history of all white peoples who have had to do with milk while it is fresh and good, that they have almost invariably considered it a pleasant, wholesome, satisfying food, and many references to this fact can be found in the rural history of European nations.[6] Plutarch, in his *Rules for the Preservation of Health*,[7] advises that milk should not be taken merely as a drink to satisfy our thirst but should be regarded as a food. In his *Life of Pelopidas*, nevertheless, commenting upon a present of four score cows and herdsmen to care for them, given by the Persian king to

---

[4] *Man, Bread and Destiny* by Professor and Mrs. C. C. Furnas (Reynal & Hitchcock, New York, 1937), pp. 302, 303.

[5] *Mankind at the Crossroads* by Professor Edward M. East, p. 161.

[6] "Elle fut le premier des mets de l'âge d'or,
Et malgré notre luxe, elle a son prix encor."
L'agriculture, Rosset, Chant Cinquième (1774), p. 199.
Evidently milk was no luxury to M. Rosset!
"Lacte mero veteres usi memorantur et herbis."
Ovid, *Fasti*, Lib. IV, line 369.
De Re Cibaria, Bruyerinus, Lib. XIV, Cap. I, p. 738. *Disquisitio de Lactis Natura et Usu*, Gulielmus Hird (Edinburgh, 1760), p. 63.

[7] *Morals* (Little, Brown, & Co., Boston, 1871), Vol. I, Chap. 19, p. 269.

Timagoras, the Athenian envoy, Plutarch suggests that the king must have thought that Timagoras "wanted milk for some distemper."[8] Apparently, Plutarch was in as much perplexity how milk should be used, whether as a food or a medicine, as Timagoras must have been to discover how he could get the feed for eighty cows.

Varro, who lived in the first century before Christ, says that of all our foods, the most nourishing liquid is milk. The written history of Europe, north of Italy, begins with Caesar's *Commentaries*, and there, in describing the Germans, he says that they did not practise agriculture but found the greater part of their food in milk, cheese and meat. Tacitus gives a little fuller information in his famous statement that the Germans took the fruits of the field, fresh game and curdled milk to satisfy hunger, but that they were not so abstemious about their drink.[9] Peter Mundy, in the account of his *Journey Overland from Constantinople to London*, in May-September, 1620, says that "milke sweete and sowr, fresh cheese, butter, etc.," were offered to his party in Bulgaria,[10] a statement that has much present interest because of the benefit which, in recent years, it has been found can be derived from lactic acid in milk containing the Bulgarian bacillus.

Louis Liger, in 1713, spoke of northern countries where many persons lived on bread, butter and cheese, while in northern Holland and Friesland many peasants have been content with whey for their drink, and he says that they kept wonderfully well.[11]

Bruyerinus said in 1560 that it was common for young ladies

---

[8] *Lives*, Vol. II, p. 320.

[9] *De Moribus Germanorum*, Cap. 23.

[10] *Travels of Peter Mundy* (Cambridge, 1907), p. 77.

[11] *Le nouveau théâtre d'agriculture*, p. 197. *Compendious History of the Goths*, etc. by Olaus Magnus, Archbishop of Upsala (London, 1658), Chap. VII, p. 157.

to soften their rye bread in milk,[12] which they might well do, for rye bread that is not fresh can become very hard and, as he says rather vividly, "mandendo lentorem dentibus repraesentat"—that is, makes a tough morsel for the teeth.

Professor Gamgee of the Veterinary College in Edinburgh, in his book on Dairy Stock published in 1861, quotes (p. 290) the *Narrative of a Walking Tour in Brittany*, in which the writer, Mr. Jephson, tells of seeing peasants in a country inn break buckwheat pancakes, hot from the griddle, into basins of milk which had been placed on the table for all guests. In another place Professor Gamgee quotes (p. 292) the account given by an Englishman of his visit to a Breton farmhouse of the better sort where "a massive table seemed to groan under the weight of huge rings of bread and large basins of milk." It is very likely that this milk was boiled before being put on the table for it is common in Brittany at the present day to avoid the use of raw milk, and the practice of boiling was wide-spread. Le Grand d'Aussy tells of a drink called sarat which was made in Normandy by boiling milk with garlic and onions and used when sour. In Provence milk was warmed over a slow fire and, the foam being skimmed off from time time with a spoon, was eaten with powdered sugar.[13] In the Grimm brothers' *Household Tales*, the story of Mrs. Fox tells of the Wolf who called on the Cat and, finding her in the kitchen at work, asked:

What is that you are cooking so nicely, I pray?

to which she replied:

O, that's bread and milk for my dinner to-day.

Plainly, that milk was boiled, and indeed, when notions of hygiene were rudimentary or non-existent, when sterilization was unknown

[12] Lib. V, Cap. XVII, p. 357.
[13] *La vie privée des Français* (1782), Vol. 2, p. 51.

and diseases both of men and animals common, it is not surprising that men discovered that raw milk was a dangerous food. How they discovered that boiling made it safe, we do not know.[14]

Many farmers in America and elsewhere who give their principal attention to other branches of agriculture—poultrymen, market gardeners, and others not a few who have a bit of land and an interest in animals—still carry on the non-commercial kind of dairying with cows or goats to provide milk for household needs, as also do those who keep cows to provide milk for a boarding-house or to supply tourists.

It has, therefore, always been known, in the ancient as in the modern world, that at its point of origin milk was good for human consumption. Fluid milk, however, soon spoils unless very carefully handled and promptly cooled. As late, indeed, as 1877, the *Encyclopaedia Britannica*, in the article on Dietetics, stated that fresh milk had long had a bad popular reputation as occasionally carrying fever. It is, in fact, an excellent culture medium in which germs of typhoid fever, diphtheria, septic sore throat and many other diseases thrive, so that few persons to-day would dare to use raw milk were it not for the care which is now exercised in its production and marketing. Even under present conditions, there were in New York State, during the ten years from 1925 to 1935, seventeen epidemics of septic sore throat attributed to raw milk.[15] Pasteurizing is necessary for the milk provided in cities, but in former times nothing was known about the ways in which disease was carried, nor how it could be prevented, and it is likely that the first definite knowledge that milk might be a vehicle of contagion came with the publication by A. Hutchinson

[14] Nevertheless, the importance of boiling is ancient knowledge. Herodotus says that, wherever the King of Persia traveled, he took with him his drinking water ready boiled for use and stored in silver flagons. The History of Herodotus (Tudor Co., New York, 1932), p. 70, Bk. I, Chap. 188.

[15] 24th Annual Rep. Intern. Assoc. Dairy & Milk Inspectors, Oct. 1935.

Smee in 1875 of his work on *Milk in Health and Disease*. That there was danger in the use of milk, nevertheless, was understood, and so at a distance from its point of origin milk was not considered fit for human consumption. A striking instance of this view is found in a letter written by the Superior of the Carmelites in Blois to a lady in Paris during the famine of 1662, in which, after giving many distressing particulars—the eating of flesh of animals that had died in the fields and other details still more unpleasant— the Superior goes on to say:

Many honorable families suffer hunger and are ashamed to disclose their need. Two young ladies whose want was not known, were discovered eating bran soaked in milk and the person who surprised them was so touched by the situation that she mingled her tears with theirs.[16]

Clearly the use of milk as food at that time was, even in a great emergency, regarded with such aversion as, for example, many persons would now have for the meat of iguana lizards or other animals not commonly used for food in northern countries—with this difference, however, that the milk which the young ladies took so unwillingly was probably, if judged by modern American standards, quite unfit for human consumption.

Moreover, milk is not a food which agrees with all adults and this is probably the explanation of Burton's statement that "milk, and all that comes of milk, as butter and cheese, curds, etc., increase melancholy (whey only excepted which is most wholesome); some except asses milk."[17] Even under the most favorable conditions and when cooled without delay, milk keeps only long enough to supply those markets to which it can be carried quickly. Until very recently, however, there were no methods generally available by which milk could be promptly cooled, and there

[16] *Vie de Colbert* by Pierre Clément, Chap. III, p. 118.
[17] *Anatomy of Melancholy*, Part I, Sec. II, Mem. II, Subsec. I.
"Le laict de vache . . . est oppilatif et venteux," La Framboisière, p. 65.

was no rapid transportation whatever by which it could be taken quickly to market. In the ancient world, as until very recently in the modern world, a large trade in fluid milk was impossible.

Butter was well known in many parts of Europe and Asia in prehistoric times. Pliny says that some persons knead their dough with eggs or milk and that there are peoples who, being pacified, as the Romans termed a state of subjection, and being free, therefore, to turn their attention to cookery, have followed a practice of putting butter into their bread.[18] Dr. Thomas Muffett in his book, *Health's Improvement*, written about the year 1600, says (Chapter XV) that in Iceland such a quantity of butter was made that, having neither earthern vessels nor casks to hold it, fir chests were constructed thirty feet long and five feet square which were filled every year with salt butter and buried in the ground where it was left until needed. Both on the continent of Europe and in Great Britain there have been dug up from bogs a number of deposits of what originally was butter. These deposits obviously have been buried many years, and among them it is not impossible that some date back to very remote periods. Pliny says of butter that it is the most luxurious food of barbarous peoples, where its use marked a man as rich. It is probable, however, that even at the point of origin the art and means of making butter were so primitive that the product was often not edible. Dr. Muffett expresses surprise that butter could ever be regarded as a desirable food, for in England, he says, in Holland and in all the northern countries, it was eaten only by the poorest people, though Ford's remark in *The Merry Wives of Windsor*, Act II, Scene ii, that he would not trust a a Fleming with his butter, suggests that butter was as well liked in England by persons of substantial means as in Flanders and seems inconsistent with Dr. Muffett's statement. Among barbarous races,

[18] *N. H.*, Lib. XVIII, Cap. XXVII.

CHURNING BUTTER

butter was largely employed as an unguent, to anoint the body, as Latins and Greeks used olive oil. At Rome, according to Horace, it was the practice to eat bread with salt or water-cresses,[19] while butter was used to rub on the bodies of infants or, when melted, was poured upon the sacrificial fires and upon the offering on the altar.[20] Butter spoils very easily, especially unsalted butter, and this, Sala says,[21] may have been the reason that the ancients thought so little of it that Athenaeus, among a large variety of foods and seasonings, never once spoke of it. In the commercial markets of the world butter is comparatively new.[22]

During many centuries cheese was the only dairy product which would keep long enough to reach distant markets. "The Irishmen," Dr. Muffett said rather sharply, in 1600,[23] "like to Plinies Barbarians, have not yet so much wit as to make Cheese of Milk; and our Welshmen want cunning to make it well," but in England and on the continent of Europe, cheese was a staple article of commerce. Throughout long ages, therefore, the commercial dairy industry was little more than the production and sale of cheese. As late as 1787, Mr. Joseph Twamley published in England a book entitled *Dairying Exemplified, or the Business of Cheese Making*, the very title of the book showing that a hundred and fifty years ago the sale of fluid milk was not then an important branch of the industry.

Cheese, therefore, was everywhere to be had, a nourishing food, a cheap and delightful obsonium of which Galen says that, when fresh, it is very good and wholesome. Stuckius says that cheese was

[19] *Satires*, Lib. II, No. II.
[20] *Les Indo-Européens* by Professor Albert Carnoy of the University of Louvain (Vroment & Cie., 37 rue de Lille, Paris, 1921).
[21] *De Alimentis*, Cap. XIII, p. 75.
[22] See chapter on Butter in *History of Inventions, Discoveries and Origins* by John Beckmann (Bohn, London, 1846), Vol. I, p. 499.
[23] *Health's Improvement* (London, 1655), Chap. XV.

a regular part of the ration in Roman armies[24] and was much liked
by the oarsmen in ancient vessels and by sailors.[25] In the old days,
however, when there was so little variety in diet, when bread held
so great a place while green vegetables and fruits were so little
used, it was important, if any cheese be eaten by persons who were
not accustomed to much physical exercise, that it be eaten spar-
ingly. Many persons, however, can not take cheese at all,—a subject on which Martin Schook, a Dutchman, wrote in 1664 an en-
tertaining little book entitled *The Dislike of Cheese*.

In this book, Schook quoted from Joseph du Chesne, a French
physician who wrote under the name Quercetanus, the statement:

Cheese is used generally and in many places, as Savoy and Switzerland,
where it is eaten very frequently so that men of all ranks take almost
no other obsonium but cheese. Thus it has come about that men of the
highest dignity from too constant indulgence in cheese have brought about
their own death.[26]

If this be true, Schook said, cheese may be the cause not of one
disease only but of an army of troubles. Galen thought that it
often produced indigestion, impaired the normal functions of the
body and tended to produce stone in the kidney, an opinion in
which other physicians agreed and which under the conditions of
the time may well have been true in many cases.[27] To add emphasis
to this caution, Schook quotes from Julius Capitolinus his account
of the death of Antoninus Pius, the great Roman Emperor. It is
reported, Capitolinus says, that it happened in this way:

When the emperor had eaten Swiss cheese at dinner very freely, he was

[24] *Antiquitates Conviviales* by J. G. Stuckius, Lib. I, Cap. XXI, p. 59
(Tiguri, 1597).
[25] *Antiquitates Conviviales*, Lib. II, Cap. VIII, p. 171.
[26] *De Butyro. De Aversatione Casei*, p. 220, citing, *Diaetetichon Polyhistori-
con*, Cap. 6, p. 463.
[27] *De Aversatione Casei*, pp. 219-223.

troubled in the night by nausea, and the next day had a fever. On the third day when he perceived that he was sinking, he commended the care of the State to Marcus, his adopted son, and of his daughter to the prefects then present, and directed that the golden figure of Fortune which was always placed in the royal bed be given to him. This done, he calmly made a sign to the tribune and, turning as though he would go to sleep, gave up his spirit.[28]

A physician of the present day would have some difficulty in determining from the facts stated the cause of death, but men of old knew that for them cheese could be the source of dangers. Symeon of Antioch thought all cheese bad.[29] Many other writers might be quoted who advised caution in its use, and the Latin saying—cheese is good which is taken with a sparing hand—would generally be approved at the present time. Indeed, there is an old French proverb going much farther:

> Jamais homme sage
> Ne mangea fromage,

which might be rendered in English by the lines:

> No wise man would please
> To eat any cheese.

Nevertheless, the world would be poorer without cheese. Eaten in moderation by persons whose digestion is good, it is a valuable food and has been the source of much pleasure to many persons. It is wonderful, said Pliny, that barbarous nations which live on milk should for so many ages have been ignorant of cheese.[30] And so having quoted proverbs against cheese, it would also be possible to quote them in its favor.[31]

[28] *Vita Antonini Pii, Imp.* by Julius Capitolinus (Zweibrucke, 1787), Vol. I, Cap. XII, p. 47.
[29] *De Facultate Cibariorum*, Tit. Caseus.
[30] *N. H.*, Lib. XI, Cap. XCVI.
[31] *Adagia*, Erasmus, Tit. Frugalitas.

In Pliny's time cheeses weighing a thousand pounds each, and undoubtedly originating in the Po valley, were shipped to Rome from the port of Luna on the borders of Liguria and Etruria and hence were stamped with a sign of the moon and were known as Luna cheeses.[32] Martialis has an epigram on the subject. Fifteen hundred years later Bruyerinus tells of the Placenta cheeses, known in France as Milanese, the best cheeses of his time, some of which were as large as a wagon wheel and, like Pliny's cheeses which came from the same country, weighed a thousand pounds apiece —all produced in the Po valley and carried thence to France.[33] Olivier de Serres said in 1600 that Lombardy cheeses were as big as millstones. The size had been reduced, however, for by this time they weighed no more than a couple of hundred pounds apiece, but this industry still continues, many cheeses of the present day being as large and heavy as those which de Serres described nearly three hundred and fifty years ago.

At Rome, Pliny says, where the good things of all the world were brought together in competition, the favorite cheese was that brought from the neighborhood of Nîmes, which Joannes Harduinus, who in 1773 edited a famous edition of Pliny's works, thought was the cheese known in his time as the fromage de Baux. The other cheese which Pliny liked and which came from Lesura and the district of Gabalicus, Harduinus says was the rich cheese made near Mende and which, like the fromage de Baux, had continued during all the intervening centuries and was still popular when Harduinus wrote.

Many cheeses were made in Holland, Flanders, Switzerland, Germany and England, of which a long history could be written, as also now in America, Canada, New Zealand and other countries.

[32] Pliny, *N. H.*, Lib. XI, Cap. XCVII.
[33] *De Re Cibaria*, Lib. XIII, Cap. VIII, p. 750. *La vie privée des Français* by Le Grand d'Aussy, Vol. II, p. 49.

It is possible in the international competition which has existed to trace no little national pride, as when Bruyerinus quotes Pliny as saying that the cheese to be preferred above all others was that which had both the taste of the Gallic cheeses and the effect of medicine![34] And if Sweden has been overlooked in this history, her champion is found in Olaus Magnus, Archbishop of Upsala, who gives his own account of the rise of the cheese industry:

If Parma or Placentium or other countries and cities of Lombardy may be commended for their many great, excellent cheeses, truly they must thank the original of it, which is the Peninsula Scandiana, and especially the country of the West Goths in the Northern Kingdoms; For those Vestrogoths above all Northern people, obtain this greatest commendation that no nation is like to them in making cheese. . . . Wherefore often they make such huge Cheeses that two strong men can scarce carry one of them a little way; yet men never have any hand in making them but only women; which from all the Villages near, bringing great quantity of milk, coming in Summer to the house of one that will make a Cheese, heat the milk in great Cauldrons and putting rennet to it they press it in a frame of Wood that is commonly square and they break all little cheeses dried in the Sun into small crumbles and put them into the same milk when it is almost scalding hot; as it is used in great Wells where by piling one stone upon another with mortar they are made the more compact. Nor is any man thought fit to be present at this work of the women, though he should beg of them never so much. For these most strong women have several offices in their houses that their husbands never meddle with; as Spinning, Weaving, baking of Bread, boyling Beer, to deck themselves, to make Beds and lay on blankets, to provide for Lambs, Calves and other small creatures, but men have greater labours to take care of . . . But the cheese of the Ostrogoths made of sheep's milk in large quantity is highly

[34] Pliny's text, as given by Joannes Harduinus, is: "Et caprarum gregibus sua laus est, Agrigenti maxime, eam augente gratiam fumo: qualis in ipsa Urbe conficitur, cunctis praeferendus. Nam Galliarum sapor medicamenti vim habet." *N. H.*, Lib. XI, Cap. XCVII. Bruyerinus' version is: "Cunctis (ut inquit Plinius) praeferendus, qui et Gallicorum saporem et medicamenti vim obtinet." *De Re Cibaria*, Lib. XIII, Cap. VIII, p. 750.

commended; so also is the cheese of the upper Sweden, especially among the Helfingi and Norwegians.[35]

The book, of course, is something of a curiosity and well deserves the treatment given to it by Count Grégoire.[36]

Our ancestors of three hundred years ago were more familiar with country life than are many residents of great cities at the present time. Undoubtedly not a few of them had enjoyed milk in the country, and this may be the origin of the small trade in fluid milk which we find arising in London in the seventeenth century. As milk was supplied the demand would, of course, increase, but under the conditions of the time a much increased supply was impossible. The history of the fluid milk trade, therefore, divides into two periods: First, the period before railways, when the trade was small and milk was delivered in the city by horse and wagon, direct from farms, or from cows kept in the city or its suburbs. Second, the period after railways, when the business of supplying fluid milk became one of the great agricultural industries.

Fluid Milk Trade before Railways. The beginning of the modern trade is suggested in a British statute of 1679[37] which dealt with the subject of Sunday observance, expressly permitting the crying and sale of milk on the streets on Sunday before nine o'clock in the morning and after four o'clock in the afternoon. Evidently there were those in London, even two hundred and fifty years ago, who were not afraid to use city milk and who wanted it on Sundays as on other days. One is curious to know when this street trade in milk began and to discover the purposes for which milk was used at that time. Of course, there were no large cities three hundred years

[35] *Historia Gentium Septentrionarum* (Bas. 1554). English translation entitled *Compendious History of the Goths, Swedes and Vandals and other Northern Nations* by J. Streater (London, 1658), Bk. XIII, Chap. VIII, p. 159.

[36] *Le théâtre d'agriculture* by Olivier de Serres (Paris edition of 1804), *Essai historique*, p. cxii.

[37] 29 Car. II, Cap. VIII.

ago. At the beginning of the seventeenth century, London was not much larger than Springfield, Mass., and Albany, N. Y., now are, while at the end of the century it was about the size of Pittsburgh or San Francisco. The number of persons who wanted milk was small, farms were near, and delivery in the city by horse and wagon direct from the farm was still possible. Apparently, however, there were at that time few, if any, householders who required a regular delivery of milk, such as is now the rule in American cities, making the street cry of milk for sale unknown in New York or Chicago. In London, on the other hand, the demand for milk seems to have been in some degree occasional in character, and milk was sold on the streets to buyers who asked for it, as fruit is often cried and sold on the streets of large cities at the present time. There was also a small demand for milk by physicians.[38]

As for the time when the trade began, it appears that on March 22, 1642, the House of Commons made an order directing that Sunday observance laws be more strictly enforced. In accordance with this order, the Mayor of London issued a proclamation to the effect, among other things, that no person should sell food in the streets on Sunday "or any Milkwoman cry Milke on that day." Two years later, on April 8, 1644, the law was changed by a statute whose terms, so far as concerns the sale of milk, were almost repeated in the Act of 1679.

Milk was, therefore, one of the street cries of London in 1642. It was not, however, among the cries of which John Lydgate wrote in *London Lyckpeny* in the early 1400's, nor of which Ben Jonson wrote in *The Silent Woman,* published in 1609. Probably, therefore, although milk was undoubtedly obtainable in London long before the seventeenth century, the milk trade in London streets be-

[38] *De Facili Medicina, per Seri et Lactis usum* by Joannis Costaeus, 1604; *De Lacte* by Conradus Gesnerus (Zurich, 1541) ; *Disquisitio Medica de Lactis Natura,* Gulielmus Hird (Edinburgh, 1751) ; *A Dissertation on Milk* by Samuel Ferris (London, 1785).

gan sometime in the first half of that century, and it is likely that the date was not before 1609 nor after 1641. It was a small trade at this time, and milk was not one of the common cries. Nevertheless, the trade existed. Supply of milk to the householders of the city of London had begun and has continued from that time to the present, a daily supply for three hundred years or more.

What were the purposes for which milk was used in London at that time? At the present day, milk is chiefly used in American cities,

1. For coffee and cereal at breakfast;
2. As a food raw, and when so used generally for infants, children and invalids;
3. For cooking.

1. In the first half of the seventeenth century, milk was not much needed for coffee, since coffee at breakfast was new and unusual. Breakfast itself was somewhat of an innovation, for in the 1500's, two meals were the rule,—dinner at ten or eleven o'clock in the morning and supper at five or six o'clock in the afternoon. Those who wanted something before dinner generally took bread or pottage and ale or wine.

In the 1600's oatmeal might appear at breakfast and if it did, Gervase Markham says,

some eat it with hony, which is reputed the best sauce; some with Wine, either Sacke, Claret or White; some with strong Beere or strong Ale, some with Milke as your ability or the accommodations of the place will administer.[39]

Apparently, milk was the last resort and only for those whose "ability" did not permit the purchase of liquor.

2. The use of milk as a food presented great problems to a world wholly unacquainted with chemistry and bacteriology.

[39] *The English House-Wife* (London, 1649), p. 241.

Sir Hugh Platt said, in 1590, that "a man may live with milk only, and it will serve instead of meat and drink and medicine."[40] Gulielmus Hird gives a pleasant account of persons who, being ill, would go in the spring to the mountains where they spent the summer in good air and quiet living, making a chief article of their diet the milk of animals on fresh pasture, and who, in the fall, to the great joy of their friends, would return home well and strong.[41]

Of course, if the use of milk always brought an easy cure there would have been no hesitation in taking it. The trouble was that it often brought more serious diseases than those for which it had been given, and many cases can be found in old books of distressing complications which followed the use of milk. To men of old, therefore, milk seemed almost like an explosive, being capable of doing great good and equally capable of destroying life, so that Dr. Frederic Hoffmann, who lived a couple of hundred years ago, one of the most eminent physicians of his time, said of it:

Although there is no better nourishment for man or beast than milk, so that it well deserves to be called the prince of foods, nevertheless there is hardly any in the whole list of foods that is so unsafe, so deadly, and which presents an opening for so great and so serious diseases, as does milk.[42]

It is impossible, however, to read of the work of those old-time students without admiring the way in which some of the many persons studying such questions as these tried to solve their problem. It would be much better, George Wolfgang Wedel said 250 years ago, if, instead of reading old authors and following traditions handed down to us in long succession from the ancients, we should make our own investigations, distinguishing true and false by the

[40] *Sundry New and Artificial Remedies against Famine* (London, 1683).
[41] *Disquisitio de Lacte* by Gulielmus Hird (Edinburgh, 1751), p. 19.
[42] De Saluberrima Seri Lactis Virtute by Fredericus Hoffmannus, *Opera Omnia* (Geneva, 1748), Vol. VI, sec. 3, p. 9.

test of experience.[43] To the same effect is the statement of Frederic Hoffmann that experience is the best teacher, superior to the most acute speculations of reason.[44] It was sought, therefore, to learn under what circumstances milk had been harmful.

Milk, obviously, was sometimes very beneficial. If at other times it was the cause of trouble, the reason—so it seemed—must be because the wrong milk was given, or because milk was given to persons who should not have it, or because it was given in the wrong way. Hieronymus Acorombonus, for example, in 1536, advocated milk for persons suffering from typhus fever, and when he was strongly attacked for such teaching he replied that there is a great difference in the milk of different animals and that it is impossible to say of all milk what may in fact be true of some kinds of milk.

In order therefore that we may not fall into the same ditch into which they have gone headlong, let us first say of what animals the milk should come into human use.[45]

A knowledge of the chemistry of milk was impossible four hundred years ago, but it was known that some milk contained much of the material that goes to make butter or cheese, while other milk contained less of these substances, and nearly 250 years after Acorombonus' work came Samuel Ferris who, having made many pioneering experiments, approved Acorombonus' conclusions to the extent that he advocated the use of buttermilk for persons suffering from typhus fever.[46] It is immaterial at this time whether the treatment advocated by these men is such as would be approved to-day or not. The fact of interest is that the subject was approached in as good a manner as the knowledge of the time permitted.

[43] Petrus Jonas Bergius, *Materia Medica* (Stockholm, 1782). Text quoted on fly-leaf without reference.

[44] Fredericus Hoffmannus, *Opera Omnia* (Geneva, 1748), Vol. VI, p. 2.

[45] *Tractatus de Lacte* by Hieronymus Acorombonus (Venice, 1536), p. D, ii.

[46] *A Dissertation on Milk* by Samuel Ferris (Edinburgh, 1785), p. 156.

Many methods were suggested by which it was hoped that milk could safely be used. It should be taken, some said, in the morning when the patient is well rested. Possibly it was best, too, when taken in small quantities, with exercise and rest between doses. It might be also that milk should be taken alone, and not with other food. Hird, in 1751, quoted Frederic Hoffmann who suggested something very like what to-day is known as pasteurizing, since milk, he said, should be drawn from the udder into a vessel placed in boiling water and thence should be poured into a bottle with a narrow neck, promptly corked to protect it from the air, and drunk before it became cold.[47] Long before Hoffmann's time, Galen had advised, in order to keep milk from acquiring undesirable qualities that, where ass's milk was used, the milch ass should be brought into the sick-room and this advice Hoffmann repeats.[48] Hoffmann advises too, as had others before him, that the milk be drawn, with very little exposure to the air, into the vessel from which it is drunk or, in other cases, that milk should be taken directly from the breast or udder.[49] Where a mother could not nurse her child, Sala says,[50] nearly everyone turned to goats, since their milk is like mother's milk.

As a food for infants, cow's milk was not common, partly because, as we can well understand, raw milk was not safe; partly because boiled milk brought its own difficulties, but largely also because the use of cow's milk was contrary to established customs

[47] Fredericus Hoffmannus, De Mirabili Lactis Asinini in Medendo Usu, *Opera Omnia*, Vol. VI, p. 1. "Lac ubere exprimendum in mulctrale aquae ferventi impositum, illico lagenae angustioris orificii indendum obturaculo muniendum et tepidum sic successive bibendum." Sec. 8, p. 8.

[48] *Ibid.*, "Animali adhuc aegro lectove ejus adstante." See also *Disquisitio de Lactis Natura et Usu* by Gulielmus Hird, p. 31.

[49] *De Lacte* by Conradus Gesnerus (Zurich, 1541), p. 26; *De Facili Medicina* by Joannis Costaeus, Lib. I, Cap. III; *Le gouvernement nécessaire à chacun pour vivre longuement* by La Framboisière (Paris, 1601), p. 65.

[50] *De Alimentis*, Cap. XXII, p. 133.

and, being unknown, was feared. Moreover, the nature of the milk provided for young animals was thought by some persons to have great influence on the development of the young to whom it was given, and few parents were willing to give milk from the lower animals to their offspring, with the danger that from it the infant would acquire the characteristics of the lower animals. Plutarch relates that Cato's wife nursed her servants' children "in order to beget in them an affection towards her son as having been brought up on the same milk,"[51] and this idea as to the effect of milk prevailed until a comparatively recent date, as can be learned from *The Boke of Chyldren*, written by Thomas Phayre and published in 1543, where, in the account given by Aulus Gellius (Lib. XII, Cap. I) of the opinions of the philosopher Favorinus, the statement is made:

If lambs be nouryshed wyth the milke of goates, they shall have coarse wolle, lyke the heare of gootes, and if kyddes in lyke maner suck upon shepe the heare of them shal be soft like wolle. Where by it doth appeare, that the milke and nouryshyng hath a marveylous effect in chaungying the complexion as we se lykewyse in herbes. . . . Wherefore as it is agreeing to nature, so it is also necessary and comly for the owne mother to nource the owne chylde. Whyche yf it may be done, it shall be most commendable and holesome, yf not, ye must be well advised in takyng of a nource, not of yll complexion and of worse maners; but such as shall be sobre, honest and chaste, well fourmed, amyable and chearful, so that she maye accustome the infant unto myrthe, no drunkard vycyous, nor sluttish for such corrupteth the nature of the chylde.

Thomas Becon, about the year 1542, emphasizes the dangers which attend employment of wrong nurses for, he says—

It many times comes to pass that children, being brought forth of godly and gentle parents, prove churlish and wicked, and utterly estranged from the nature and good disposition of the parents. For children by drinking in strange milk, drink in also strange manners and another nature.[52]

[51] *Life of Cato.*
[52] *The Catechism of Thomas Becon*, edited for the Parker Society by Rev. John Ayre, Cambridge. (Printed at University Press, 1844), pp. 347-348. See

Gerald de Berri, who during the thirteenth century wrote in Latin under the name of Geraldus Cambrensis, reports in his *Welsh Journey* a remarkable instance of this drinking in of strange manners and another nature, for he tells of a sow that when young had sucked a hunting dog and when grown proved to be strong in the pursuit of game even to a wonderful degree, so that in her keenness of smell she was found to be far better than hounds bred and trained for this purpose.[53] Stuckius says that it has been shown that if a young dog be fed on the milk of a cat he will, when grown, catch mice like a cat,[54] and both of these stories are applied as a warning to human beings of the influence which the nature of a nurse may have upon the character of the young whom she nourishes.

Similar views were expressed with no small emphasis by Dr. Thomas Muffett in his book, *Health's Improvement*, written about the year 1600 and published, "Corrected and Enlarged," by Dr. Christopher Bennet in 1655. Dr. Muffet said:

No man can justly doubt that a child's mind is answerable to his nurse's milk and manners; for what made Jupiter and Aegystus so lecherous, but that they were chiefly fed with goot's milk? What made Romulus and Polyphemus so cruel but that they were nursed by she-wolves? What made Pelias (Tynus and Neptune's son) so brutish but that he was nursed by an unhappy mare? Is it any marvel also that Giles the Abbot (as the Saints Register writeth) continued so long the love of a solitary life in woods and deserts, when three years together he suckt a Doe? [p. 123.]

Aulus Gellius lived in the second century of the Christian era, and it seems that his notions as to the feeding of infants still pre-

also Epistola VII in *Epistolae Medicinales* by Richard Carr (London, 1691). A copy of this book is in the library of the New York Academy of Medicine. See too *A Dissertation on Milk* by Samuel Ferris (Edinburgh, 1785), pp. 13 et seq.

[53] Geraldus Cambrensis, *Opera* (Rolls Series, London, 1868), Vol. VI, pp. 27-28.

[54] *Antiquitates Conviviales* by J. G. Stuckius, Cap. XVII, Lib. I, p. 37b.

vailed in parts of Europe at the time when the Pilgrim Fathers
landed in America. When artificial feeding was attempted, the one
resource was a mixture of bread and water, known as pap—the
mixture of which Margaret so ingenuously spoke to Faust in the
garden scene of Goethe's poem, dating no farther back than the
year 1774. Her mother, she said, was so weak after her infant's
birth,

> . . . 'twas vain for her to try
> Herself to suckle the poor babe, so I
> Reared it on bread and water all alone.[55]

The pap-boat, Miss Godfrey said in 1903, was a venerable institution superseded by the nursing bottle only in the latter part of
the nineteenth century.[56] There were, however, new notions stir-
ring in the seventeenth century, and an excellent discussion of the
feeding of infants by J. Dominicus Sala was published at Padua
in 1628. The best food for an infant, Sala says, is its mother's
milk, but if this be not available goat's milk is a good substitute,
and he suggests that young animals be secured which will permit
the child to nurse directly from the udder.[57] In times when nothing was known about sterilization of utensils, this latter suggestion
was important and had already been emphasized by Conrad Gesner
in 1541.[58] If goats be not used, Sala advises wet nurses, discussing
the subject at length, free from the influence of tradition and with
no reference whatever to Aulus Gellius or to the character of

[55] Trans. Anna Swanwick (London, 1851), p. 101.
[56] *Home Life under the Stuarts*, p. 6.
[57] *De Alimentis* by Jo. Dominicus Sala (Padua, 1628), p. 133.
[58] *De Lacte* by Conradus Gesnerus (Zurich, 1541), p. 26.
"Cujus materia . . . in verum transire alimentum potest . . . quum e mam-
milla naturali suo tepore, spiritu ac quasi anima adhuc turgidum exsugitur,"
(p. 5) ". . . praestat ut e mammis ipsi exsugant . . . quod facilius coquitur
ac minus corruptioni patet," (p. 19). *De Facili Medicina per Seri et Lactis
Usum*, Joannis Costaeus (1604). *Le gouvernement nécessaire à chacun*, etc.
by Nicolas de la Framboisière (Paris, 1601), p. 65.

Aegystus. A further indication of coming changes in ideas about food can be found in Thomas Tryon's *The Way to Health*, published in London in 1683, where it is said:

The best food for young children, next to their mother's milk, is good cow's milk, raw, with crums of bread in it, always observing that it first stand till it be cold, after 'tis milkt, before you give it them; for 'tis a great error in physicians and others to advise consumptive people to drink milk hot from the cow, for that heat is of a windy quality that swells the body and sends fumes into the head, and is harder of concoction [digestion] than the same milk is when 'tis cold. . . . I know mistress nurse will be offended that I talk of giving children raw milk; but I must tell her that properly the same ought not to be called raw, because it hath passed through several digestions and fermentations, even to the highest degree . . . and yet our good dames would think it a sad business if they should give their children unboiled milk.

These, however, were not the ideas which prevailed in the seventeenth century and, in view of the dangers which at that time attended the use of unboiled milk, perhaps it is as well that the natural method of feeding infants was the method approved. The proper care of children is an art which the human race has only very slowly learned. Queen Anne's children were eighteen in number and not one of them lived beyond childhood.[59]

3. There remains, then, the possibility that milk could be used in cooking—was that the whole story? Fortunately, Gervase Markham, in 1649, comes very near to giving us a complete answer to this question. He says:

Now for the profits arising from milk, there are three of especiall account, as Butter, Cheese and Milk to be eaten simple or compounded; as for Curds, sowr Milk, or Wigge, they come from secondary means and therefore may not be numbered with these.[60]

[59] *Families of the Past* by Miss Helen Grierson. Fortnightly Review, Vol. 127, N. S., p. 521, April, 1930.
[60] *The English House-Wife* (London, 1649), p. 195.

Rules for making butter follow, then rules for making cheese, and then, when we seem to be on the point of hearing the full story of raw milk in the seventeenth century, the discussion ends. The explanation of this sudden silence is in the fact that the subject of raw milk had been elaborately treated in previous chapters on "Skill in Cookery," "Skill in Distillations," and on compounding medicines in which milk was often used.

In the early part of the century, therefore, the milk sold on the streets of London was used almost entirely for cooking, for some old household beverages and for medicine.

The London *Punch* of June 10, 1936, in a short verse entitled "My Hero," raises the question who first used cream on strawberries.

> Some talk of Alexander
>   While others now acclaim
> Those who more swiftly wander
>   To record-breaking fame.
> Yet all who have created
>   Heroic standards seem
> To me to be deflated
>   By him—or her—(not stated)
> Whose fancy first soul-mated
>   The strawberry and cream.

The question which *Punch* thus presents is of no small interest, and as in the case of other great discoveries is not easily answered, for there are several claimants to the honor of making the first announcement.

The first is the learned Josephus Jacobus Plenck who, in his book *Bromatologia*, published at Vienne in 1783, says of strawberries that the odor is delightful, the taste agreeing with the odor, and he adds that they can be eaten by themselves or with wine or milk:

Hae baccae eduntur crudae vel vino aut lacte commixtae. [p. 115.]

172

This is like the statement of Petrus Jonas Bergius that strawberries "eduntur cum quales sunt, tum vino lacteve commixtae."[61] No mention is made of cream though it is an article with which both Dr. Plenck and Dr. Bergius were familiar, for Plenck advises (p. 312) that cream be eaten in summer with sugar, or used with coffee, and Bergius mentions it. Perhaps they sympathized on this subject with the view which Dr. Samuel Johnson expressed in a letter to Mrs. Thrale, July 3, 1771:

> I have never wanted strawberries and cream.

Dr. Johnson's preferences were disregarded, for one week later, July 10, 1771, he complained again to Mrs. Thrale,

> Toujours strawberries and cream!

Neither Dr. Johnson, Dr. Plenck nor Dr. Bergius deserves to receive from *Punch* the Hero's reward.

The next claimant is Thomas Venner, "Doctor of Physic in Bathe," England, who in his book, *Via Recta ad Vitam Longam*, published at London in 1650, amidst much interesting matter makes the statement on page 117: "Verily with strawberries and sugar, Creame is, for them for whom it is convenient, a very delicate and wholesome dish. And whosoever he be that delighteth to eat a dish of Creame, let him not be parsimonious of sugar"—a characteristically mediaeval recommendation in which many modern culinary artists would not agree. Right or wrong in this detail, however, the information is there, to which he added later, on page 172, the further statement that raspberries "are with us usually eaten with the very fattest and best part of the milk and sugar."

This announcement was made the year of Descartes' death and of Cromwell's victory of Dunbar. Dr. Venner belongs among the great men of history but unfortunately for his claim as a discoverer, the announcement of strawberries and cream had been made

[61] *Materia Medica* (Stockholm, 1782).

twenty-three years earlier by Dr. Ludovicus Nonnius, a Belgian
physician of note from the University of Salerno, who, in the
edition of his book *Diaeteticon* published at Antwerp in 1627,
presents the situation very clearly. He says:

Old writers have said little of strawberries and our own physicians appear to have guarded high silence. Pliny no more than mentioned them,
but Virgil in the third Eclogue (line 92), describes the fresh berries lying
close on the earth. Servius says that we see them occasionally growing in
the woods but now they have been introduced into our gardens and receive
great attention, though notwithstanding this and though the cultivated
berries are larger than the wild ones, they are not at all sweeter. Strawberries have great fragrance, somewhat like wine. Everybody likes them.
Many persons eat them with cream, some with wine, putting on a little
powdered sugar which in my opinion is well done.[62]

As between Dr. Venner and Dr. Nonnius, priority clearly belongs to the latter, but here we are met by a new claimant, none
other than Bruyerinus Campegius, La Bruyère-Champier, a Frenchman of Lyons and physician to Henry II, who presents his claim
in his book, *De Re Cibaria*, published at Lyons in 1560, a year
marked by the death of Melanchthon and the Queen Regent of
France, Mary of Guise, and the treaty of Edinburgh between
Mary, Queen of Scots and Queen Elizabeth of England. To the
world of such events, Bruyerinus Campegius made his announcement:

In summer especially, cream is wonderfully pleasant at the afternoon
meal, and in the evening for the dessert our ladies like it poured on strawberries. And they add sugar so that nothing in our part of the world shall
ever come to the table without some foreign importation.[63]

Then, as though the simple statement were not enough, Bruyerinus increases the debt which the world owes him by his comment

[62] *Diaeteticon*, Ludovicus Nonnius (Antwerp, 1627), Lib. I, Cap. XXIV, pp.
101-102.
[63] *De Re Cibaria*, pp. 741, 597.

which suggests that sugar was taken largely because it had become a fashion and that the world would be better off if less were used.[64] By whom the discovery of strawberries and cream was first made we do not know. It may have been enjoyed in silence by many generations of men.

Of the history of sugar, a very interesting account was given by Dr. W. Falconer in 1796 and published in the *Memoirs of the Literary and Philosophical Society of Manchester*,[65] with many references to ancient writers. Honey was the principal sweet of ancient times, but sugar, it appears, has long been known and used. Sugar cane is an Asiatic plant and reached the West from India. It is twice mentioned in the Bible.[66] Seneca speaks of an oily, sweet juice in Indian canes[67] as something of which he had heard, but with which he was not himself familiar. Lucan also speaks of a sweet juice of reeds which the people of India drank:

Quique bibunt tenera dulces ab arundine succos.[68]

Pliny says that sugar came both from Arabia and from India, but the best from India.[69] The practice of reducing this juice by evaporation so as to make a solid product was known in India at an early day and probably had reached the West by the first century of our era, for Dioscorides speaks of it as solid and easily broken by the teeth, like salt.

Of the practice of evaporation, Dr. Falconer quotes a statement written about the year 1100 that the sweet honeyed reeds which grow near Tripoli, in Syria, are

cultivated with great labor of the husbandmen every year. At the time of

[64] *De Re Cibaria*, pp. 562-563. "Millia gentium sine saccharo eleganter ac feliciter vivunt."
[65] Vol. IV, Part II.
[66] *Isaiah*, XLIII, 24; *Jeremiah*, VI, 20.
[67] Epistle LXXXIV.
[68] *Pharsalia*, Lib. III, line 237.
[69] *N. H.*, Lib. XII, Cap. VIII.

harvest, they bruise the cane when ripe in mortars; and set by the strained juice in vessels till it is concreted in form of snow or white salt. This when scraped they mix with bread, or rub it with water and take it as pottage; and it is to them more wholesome and pleasing than honey of bees.[70]

The same author, Dr. Falconer says, in his account of the reign of Baldwin, King of Jerusalem, speaks of eleven camels laden with sugar which were captured by the Crusaders, so we may assume that sugar was made at that time in considerable quantities. Arab physicians used sugar as a medicine and it is quite possible that the art of refining sugar came from them, about the time of the Arab conquest in the seventh century. The growth of sugar cane and the manufacture of sugar thereafter spread widely, reaching India in the East and Morocco, Spain and Sicily in the West.

In the age of discovery, the Spaniards carried the cultivation of sugar cane to Madeira and the West Indies.

During the middle ages, Venice was the great center of the sugar trade in Europe, and "toward the end of the fifteenth century, a Venetian citizen received a reward of 100,000 crowns for inventing the art of making loaf sugar."[71]

Possibly the use of sugar on fresh fruit was in 1560 a foreign innovation which came with the Venetian trade passing up the Rhone valley. It is noticeable that, when used with strawberries, the favor given to sugar constantly increased. Bruyerinus took his berries without this addition. He did not object to the sugar as a novelty, but rather because its use had become excessive, and also because, as he said: "praestantissimas etenim escas putamus quae suapte natura placent"—that is, the choicest foods are those whose natural flavor is most pleasing,—and he added: "Thousands of people have lived elegantly and happily without sugar."[72]

[70] Gesta Dei per Francos, p. 270.
[71] Ency. Brit., 9th ed., Tit. Sugar. Vol. 22, p. 625.
[72] De Re Cibaria, Lib. X, Cap. VIII, p. 563.

In the oldest times [John Beckmann said] mankind were so fond of sweet things, that the goodness and agreeable taste of every kind of food was determined according to the degree of its sweetness; and such is the manner of judging even at present throughout all the East, in Africa, and in America. This is the case among us with the greater part of the lower classes . . . and one might almost suspect that a taste for sweet things were in the inverse ratio of civilization.[73]

We may hope that the consumption of sugar in America a hundred and fifty years ago was less than Mr. Beckmann thought, and we may not be prepared fully to approve all the implications of his statement, but in substance his argument on taste is a strong one to epicures who consider the pleasures of the table one of the fine arts. It seems, however, that sugar eaters were not open to persuasion, for Ludovicus Nonnius, in 1627, advised a little powdered sugar when wine was used on strawberries and Dr. Venner, in 1650, would take sugar "with no parsimony."

We can, therefore, carry the use of sugar and cream with strawberries as far back as the year 1560. Possibly the practice may be traced to an earlier date in France, but it is noticeable that in England Hugh Latimer, when he preached his *Sermon on the Ploughers*[74] about the year 1547, though he spoke of strawberries, said nothing of cream. Moreover, an inventory of royal property taken in the second year of Edward III includes "1 furcam de argento pro strawberiis," from which we may infer that King Edward, if he had cream on his berries at all, was able to enjoy no more than his fork could carry.

If any writer before Bruyerinus made and published this discovery, his name should be known, the reference to his book should be given, and the world will not be long in awarding honor where honor is due. In the meantime, until it is known that the credit be-

[73] *History of Inventions, Discoveries and Origins* by John Beckmann, Vol. II, p. 337.
[74] *Arber's English Reprints*, No. 7 (Southgate, London, 1868).

longs to some other person, we must believe that Bruyerinus was the first to report the discovery.

Dr. Bergius apparently thought that the general use of strawberries made its way northward slowly because, he says, although the plants grow well in southern countries, they did not invite the attention of northern gardeners, since they bear comparatively few berries in the south and their fruit lacks sweetness.[75] This probably is not true of our present plants, but it is noticeable that, although wild strawberries were known in Italy during classical times, Bruyerinus writes in 1560 as though strawberries were a recent luxury to the French of his time.

There seems also to have been a fear that strawberries might contain poison, for Estienne and Liébault say that we should notice the innocence of strawberries as being almost miraculous for, although they creep close along the ground where they are continually pressed by serpents, lizards, adders and other poisonous animals, nevertheless they receive no infection nor acquire any poisonous savour—a sign that they have no affinity with poison.[76] It hardly seems, however, that it should have taken fifteen centuries for knowledge of such a fruit to travel from Rome to Lyons, and perhaps Dr. Bergius' suggestion may offer an explanation for part of this delay, though it should never be forgotten that conditions of life in Europe during many ages made any form of progress nearly impossible.[77]

By the middle of the seventeenth century the English public was becoming accustomed to the use of milk and cream as a food and in *The Accomplish't Cook*, published by Robert May in 1660, many receipts are given, not only for the use of milk in cooking,

[75] *Materia Medica* by Petrus Jonas Bergius (Stockholm, 1782), pp. 462-463.
[76] *La maison rustique*, p. 109; *De Re Cibaria*, Bruyerinus, p. 597.
[77] Count Grégoire, in his *Essai historique*, which forms an Introduction to the 1804 edition of Olivier de Serres' *Théâtre d'agriculture*, p. xcviii, mentions several other instances of slow movement of knowledge in regard to foods.

but for preparation of raw "whipt" cream, for cheese and cream, a dish in which both raw milk and raw cream were used, and for many other "creams"—snow, gooseberry, almond, clouted, etc.

The latter part of the 1600's was a time of change in England. Enclosures of public commons gave opportunity for private initiative. There was a great extension of market gardens at this time, and the use of roots as a field crop which, with the planting of grass seed, began at the end of the century, had a most important effect on the nation's food supply, for thereafter cattle, instead of being killed off every winter as in former times, were kept alive with turnips and hay so that fresh meat, butter and milk now became available the year round.[78]

Apparently the public were learning that milk could be a safe beverage, for Mr. George Walter Thornbury, in his book *Old and New London*, speaks of the Milk Fair at the end of the Mall in 1700 where "the noisy milk-fools in the park cried 'A can of milk, ladies! A can of red cows' milk, Sir.'" Pepys' *Diary*[79] shows that on June 17, 1666, he "went down to the Milke-house and drank three glasses of whey." Samuel Johnson in *The Idler*, No. 15, says of an acquaintance that in the evening she generally "takes the child out to give it milk in the park."

Apparently neither visitors to the Mall early in the eighteenth century, nor the child's mother much later, expected to find a supply of milk in their own homes.

The first of May was sacred to chimney-sweeps and milkmaids, and a footnote to Pepys' *Diary* explains that on this day

milkmaids used to borrow silver cups, tankards, etc. to hang them round their milk pails with the addition of flowers and ribbons, which they carried upon their heads, accompanied by a bagpipe and a fiddle, and went

[78] *Towards National Health* by Mr. James Anthony Delmage, p. 132.

[79] Transcribed from original MS. by Rev. Myners Bright and edited with additions by Henry B. Wheatley (G. Bell & Sons, London, 1893-99, 9 vols.).

from door to door, dancing before the houses of their customers in order to obtain a small gratuity from each of them.[80]

There was a good sale also for asses' milk even at the price of 3s. 6d. a quart, and milch asses therefore made daily rounds, which are described in a verse which Mr. Ashton quotes:

> Before proud Gates attending Asses bray,
> Or arrogate with solemn pace the Way;
> These grave Physicians with their milky Chear,
> The Love-sick Maid and dwindling Beau repair.[81]

In *The Spectator*, No. 251, Tuesday, December 18, 1711, a humorous description of the London street cries of this period can be found with the complaint that "Milk is generally sold in a note above E, la, and in sounds so exceeding shrill that it often sets our teeth on edge."

All this perhaps has its place in "the late refinements in knowledge running parallel to those of dyet in our nation," mentioned by Dean Swift in Section VII of the *Tale of a Tub*, published in 1696.

In the following years the conditions which surrounded the milk trade underwent great changes. Between 1750 and 1800 the population of England and Wales increased fifty-two per cent., and the city of London grew to be a great modern city, of which Mr. Trevelyan gives a vivid description:

The roads converging on London were an epitome of the activities of the nation. The great city of some seven hundred thousand inhabitants, more than a dozen times as large as Bristol, the next largest in the island, had daily to be fed from the fat of the land. Night and day hundreds of horses in relays were coming up at trot and gallop, from the South Coast and even from the Berwick and Solway salmon fisheries, bringing fresh to Billingsgate the best fish of every port. A hundred thousand head of cattle

[80] Vol. 6, p. 279. Pepys' *Diary*, May 1, 1667, mentions Nell Gwynn looking on at the dancing of milkmaids.

[81] *Social Life in the Reign of Queen Anne* by John Ashton (Charles Scribner's Sons, New York, 1925), p. 148. See John Gay, *London*, Trivia, Bk. II.

and three quarters of a million sheep yearly walked up to Smithfield for the slaughter, many of them from Scotland or from the borders of Wales. But strangest of all to the modern eye would be the droves of geese and turkeys, two or three thousand at a time, waddling slowly and loquaciously along all the roads to London for a hundred miles, between August and October, feeding on the stubble of the fields through which they passed. On one road, from Ipswich to London, 150,000 turkeys walked over the Stour Bridge each year.[82]

The demand for milk was constantly increasing, but by the beginning of the nineteenth century London was so large, and the quantity of milk needed was so considerable, that direct delivery from the farms was no longer possible. The problem how to supply the milk was difficult for, if it could not be carried to the city, the only other way to meet the needs of the situation was to keep the cows themselves in or near the city and carry their feed to them. It was not a very satisfactory solution, for the city is not a fit place in which to keep cows. The expense of such a milk supply, of course, would be great, and the number of cows which could be kept in this way would necessarily be small. Under the conditions of the time, however, there was nothing else to do. City dairies were established, and many references can be found to the hovels where cows were sheltered and to the revolting conditions under which they were kept. Perhaps the milk trade would be no better to-day if we had no rapid transportation from farm to city and if modern cows had to be kept in the crowded space of great cities. Whether this excuse be valid or not, these were the facts.[83] Milk was de-

[82] *British History in the Nineteenth Century* by Mr. George Macaulay Trevelyan, p. 11.

[83] *Cattle, Their Breeds, Management & Diseases* by William Youatt (London, 1834), pp. 260-265. As to conditions in Paris dairies, see note by editor of *Le théâtre d'agriculture* by Olivier de Serres, Vol. I, pp. 612-615, edition of 1804. As to conditions in New York, see *Essay on Milk as an Article of Sustenance* by Robert M. Hartley, New York, 1842, reprinted in 1850 under the title *The Cow and the Dairy*. See also *Milk Trade in New York and Vicinity* by John Mullaly (New York, 1853).

manded and milk was provided. Mr. Timbs said, however, in 1855, that there was no such thing in London as new milk at that time,—"It is all boiled skim-milk."[84] It was also dirty and adulterated, but bad as it was, the world wanted it. John Ashton, in his book on *The Dawn of the Nineteenth Century in England,* gives an interesting account of this trade. He says:

> Curiously enough, the carriage and delivery of milk—by no means a light task whether looked at from the distance walked or the load carried—was entirely in the hands of women, strapping country wenches, principally recruited from Wales. The cows were kept in hovels in and near London and a "milkmaid's" daily life began at from 4 to 6 A. M. when the cows had to be milked; they then delivered the milk at the various houses until near 10. Then there were the dairy vessels to wash, and at noon the cows again to be milked. The delivery of milk again occupied them until nearly 6 P. M. when they had to wash up all cans for the evening. In 1808 it was reckoned that about 8500 cows were kept in London and its vicinity; one cow-keeper at Islington owning between 800 and 900 cows. It is sad to read, however, in 1804, that milk is sold at four pence per quart to five pence for a better sort; yet the advance of prices does not insure its purity, for it is generally mixed in a great proportion with water by the retailers before they leave the milk house! The adulteration of the milk, added to the wholesale cost, leaves an average profit of cent. per cent. to the vendors of this useful article.[85]

After this explanation, one is not surprised to hear that the city milk of those days went by the name of "London blue," nor is it surprising—in view of the high price which it brought—that the trade continued to be small. Mr. John Lawrence,[86] who signed the name Bonington Moubray to his book on *Poultry, Swine, Milch Cows and Bees,* published in 1824, said that milk had never been

[84] *Curiosities of London* by John Timbs (David Bogue, London, 1855), p. 249.

[85] *The Dawn of the Nineteenth Century in England* (New York, 1886) p. 219. See also *Social Life in the Reign of Queen Anne* by John Ashton (Charles Scribner's Sons, New York, 1925), p. 148.

[86] See *Dictionary of National Biography*, Vol. 32, p. 265.

WATER CARRIERS, WOMEN AT THE WELL, INDIA

within the reach of the laboring population in England, even in the dairy counties.

The water supply of London as it now exists, with water pipes running into every house, is of comparatively recent history.[87] Three hundred years ago, or less, water was sold on the streets of London as milk was sold,[88] and as it was still sold in Paris and Madrid in the middle of the nineteenth century. Not until 1818 were water pipes laid to any house in Edinburgh,[89] and as late as 1936, milk was, and may still be, produced and sold in Liverpool and Edinburgh from cows kept in those cities. There was a description of London edited by Charles Knight and published in 1851, in which, after describing the water carriers in the Spanish city of Madrid, Mr. Knight says:

But the number of persons thus employed compared with the London milk carriers, is no doubt small. The cry of "Milk" or the rattle of the milk pail, will never cease to be heard in our streets. There can be no reservoir of milk, no pipes through which it flows into the houses. The more extensive the great capital becomes, the more active must be the individual exertion to carry about this article of food. The old cry was "Any milk here?" and it was sometimes mingled with the sound of "Fresh cheese and cream!" It then passed into "Milk, maids below," then was shortened into "Milk below" and was finally corrupted into "Mio," which some wag interpreted into "Mi-eau"—demi-eau—half water. But it must still be cried, whatever be the cry. The supply of milk to the metropolis is one of the most beautiful combinations of industry we have.[90]

It is said that a milk dealer in Baltimore, Jacob Fussell, "really

[87] For a description of London water supply, see *Social Life in the Reign of Queen Anne* by John Ashton, pp. 52-54.

[88] Oliver Cob, one of the characters in Ben Jonson's play, *Every Man in his Humour*, is a London water-bearer who "serves water" at the house of Master Kitely, another character in the play.

[89] *Scotland* by Mr. Robert Laird Mackie (Harrap & Co., London, 1916).

[90] *London*, edited by Mr. Charles Knight (Bohn, 1851), Vol. I, p. 129. Readers of Du Maurier's novel *Trilby* will remember the call of "Milk below!" with which the heroine of the book introduces herself.

started the ice-cream industry in the United States in 1851,"[91] but the history of frozen milk and cream goes far back of 1851, to very early times.

Something like ice-cream has probably been known for ages. Conrad Gesner in 1541[92] gives a good account of what he calls aphrogala, which he thinks was the preparation which Galen, in the second century after Christ, said was known at Rome as melca, but he adds:

Since neither the names are the same, nor are any descriptions of the thing for which they stood extant, so far as I know, among Greek or Latin authors, it is left for us to guess what it was, even though we cannot be sure. Therefore I shall say at once that by this name aphrogala I understand nothing else than what the same word now means among the Germans, i. e., creamy milk, which is so shaken in long jars that nothing but foamy cream appears. It is made in upper Switzerland at the beginning of winter since by the cold the cream is hardened and lasts longer, can be transported as desired, and its coldness is pleasant to the stomach. Some persons call this snow, because in appearance and coldness it is like snow. In different places it is prepared in different ways. If any person understand by aphrogala merely the light floating cream of milk, I do not object since in either case, shaken or not shaken, you supply cold cream to the warm stomach. To me, however, it is pleasanter shaken because that form of the preparation contains less of the fat.

Probably it was a rich milk which in the beginning was put into the long jars, for milk must contain much fat or it will not foam when shaken. If left to stand, however, as Galen advises, the cream will rise and when frozen would surely be ice-cream. This was not what Gesner liked, but there were others who did like it four hundred years ago. Gesner preferred his aphrogala when the cream and milk were shaken together first and then frozen— and in a rich milk that is not very different from ice-cream.

[91] *The Fundamentals of Dairy Science* by Associates of Lore A. Rogers (New York, 1935), p. 16.
[92] *De Lacte et Operibus Lactariis*, p. 37b.

Perhaps the principal difference between aphrogala or melca and modern ice-cream is that ice-cream of the present day is sweetened and flavored, a practice of which Bruyerinus gave a suggestion in 1560:

There is also another food from milk which is made of milk sweetened with honey and frozen, for the cream of the milk floats on top. Some persons call it the flower of milk, some call it cream. . . .[93]

In reading these descriptions of frozen cream, we recognize that with the story of individual experiences we are receiving also the story of long traditions which extend back into the past for unknown centuries of prehistoric time. Living in fixed dwellings or in the movable shelters of the nomad, protection against the cold of winter was but slight, and men, who with their flocks and herds inhabited cold countries, could not fail to make early acquaintance with frozen milk and cream.

The process of sweetening and flavoring the ancient aphrogala, nevertheless, made a steady, even if not a very rapid, progress of which at times we are given casual, unexpected glimpses. Louis Lémery, who in 1702 covered nearly the entire range of European food resources, might well have given an account of ice-cream, but his book contains no mention of the subject. On the

---

[93] *De Re Cibaria*, Lib. XIV, Cap. III, p. 741. The word *"refrigeratus,"* here translated frozen, was commonly used in Roman times to mean chilled. Galen, however, in the passage which Gesner quotes, speaks of the cream as hardened by the winter cold, so that it can easily be carried and would last longer. Apparently, therefore, both melca and aphrogala were sometimes frozen and it is to these foods that Bruyerinus refers.

The word used by Galen and by Bruyerinus which is here translated cream is *"spuma,"* as it had also been used by Pliny in the phrase, "spuma id est lactis" and of this use Harduinus says in his edition of Pliny's works, *N. H.* (Paris, 1723), Vol. I, p. 637, note 20: "Hoc est, pingue lactis, quod, ut in oleo, superne fluitat, instar spumae." Willichius Resellianus, a contemporary of Gesner and of Bruyerinus, twice speaks of cream as spuma. "Crema lactis, Graece ἀφρόγαλα, id est, spuma lactis." *Ars Magirica*, p. 46. Also, "butyrum ex spuma lactis cocta fit." *Ibid.*, p. 47.

other hand, an unpublished manuscript of about Lémery's time, which recently appeared on the London market, goes fully into the subject which Lémery omitted.

In the catalogue, *Food and Drink through the Ages*, issued in 1937 by Maggs Brothers, London dealers in rare books and manuscripts, one of the articles offered for sale was an anonymous manuscript of 84 pages, of which the date, fixed by a water-mark in the paper on which it was written, is given as "circa 1700." This manuscript is entitled *L'art de faire des glaces*, and it is described as:

A manuscript on ice-cream making. The first paragraphs describe the refining and pearling of sugar, then follow the freezing process and recipes for all sorts of ices: cherry, orange and apricot ices, violet, rose, chocolate, coffee, caramel ices, etc., and finally recipes for soufflé dishes.

This manuscript gives a full account of the way in which French cooks made ice-cream in 1700. The art apparently was not new at that time but had travelled northward from Italy[94] where the making and use of ice was well known. Possibly it was from Italy that the knowledge came which in 1413 supplied a dish for the banquet at the coronation of King Henry V of England, for there, according to the Holkham manuscript, *A Noble Boke of Cookry*, edited by Mrs. Alexander Napier and published in 1882, a part of the third course was "creme frez."[95] If this name stood for ice-cream, its appearance on this occasion is the earliest mention yet found of the dish at any public banquet.

So far as is known, the first public advertisement of ice-cream ever made was published by Philip Lenzi, a confectioner, in the *New York Gazette* on Monday, May 12, 1777, of which a facsimile is shown on the opposite page. That was not a good time for the

[94] Chapter on Artificial Ice and Cooling Liquors in *History of Inventions, Discoveries and Origins* by John Beckmann.

[95] *A Noble Boke of Cookry* (Elliot Stock, London, 1882), p. 5.

PHILIP LENZI,

Confectioner from London,

Having removed from Dock-ſtreet to Hanover-Square,
No. 517.

TAKES this method to return his ſincere thanks to all his friends and cuſtomers for their paſt favours, and hopes for a continuance ; and will have in this pre-ſent ſeaſon, a very great variety of the beſt ſweetmears ; preſerves marm-lades, jellies &c. in brandy, at very reaſonable rate as the times will permit, for ready money only ; and every thing of the ſaid branch will be execu-ted to all perfection as in the firſt ſhops in London.

Said Lenzi will, in the enſuing ſeaſon. give a very good price for the very beſt ſort of fruit, ſuch as ſtraw-berries, gooſeberries, cherries, raſberries, peaches, pine apples, green gages, apricots, &c. &c.

May be had almoſt every day, ice cream ; likewiſe ice for refreſhing wine, &c.

N. B. Wanted to the ſaid buſineſs, an apprentice.--- Premium is expected.

The New York Gazette and *Weekly Mercury*
Monday, May 12, 1777

introduction of luxuries into America and the ice-cream trade was long in finding a place.

Fluid Milk Trade since the Building of Railways. Delivery of milk by milkmaids on London streets, from cows kept in city hovels, was not the modern milk trade and was incapable of development beyond the stage which has been described. The great fact, therefore, which is of controlling importance if dairymen are to understand the present situation of their business, is that so far as concerns the commercial sale of fluid milk in markets not near their farms, dairying, instead of being an old industry, is one of the most recent developments of modern times. Its infancy goes back no farther than the latter part of the nineteenth century. Men may still be living who might have seen the first can of milk carried into New York City by railroad for sale in the city trade. As a means of furnishing an adequate supply of food to great populations, the dairy industry is hardly a hundred years old. During all the centuries previous to 1840, when starving populations needed food, there was no dairy industry such as the modern world knows.

What the transportation of milk was at that time is well told by Mr. Robert M. Hartley in his *Essay on Milk as an Article of Sustenance*, written in 1841 and published in New York in 1842. Of the trade as it then existed, Mr. Hartley said:

The idea of bringing milk from a distance is not an untried experiment. Many pioneers in the work have tested its practicability and prepared the way for future success. For more than three years past it has been brought by Messrs. Husted and Mead from Connecticut in excellent condition, alternately by wagon and steam-boat, without a failure. The milk is placed in large canisters fitted to a square box. In hot weather the interstices are packed with ice and a similar precaution would be sufficient to protect it from the greatest heat. The city of Boston is also largely supplied from Worcester, forty miles distant. The system having been in operation several years has been subjected to a fair trial and though but five cents a quart is paid for the milk [by the consumer] the result is highly satisfactory to all engaged in the business. Many, we learn, are making arrangements for very extensive operations. [p. 337]

Since 1840 the growth of the dairy industry has been one of the most conspicuous developments in modern times. Of the entire agricultural income of America from animals and from crops combined, approximately one quarter is produced by the dairy industry, which in 1937 had a gross return exceeding a billion and a half dollars.

In the States north of the latitude of Virginia and east of the Mississippi River, the earnings of the dairy industry are much more than a quarter of the total agricultural income, for Wisconsin alone produces nearly 30 million pounds of milk a day every day in the year, winter and summer. New York produces 20 million pounds and the little State of Vermont produces 3½ million pounds a day. In 1937 there were 25 million cows and heifers kept for milk in America, with 10 million heifers and heifer calves maturing as replacements. In Europe since the War, agricultural expansion is most marked in the increase of cereals and potatoes, but it also appears in dairy products.[96]

The dairy industry on its present scale arose, therefore, as a result of the introduction of machinery during the nineteenth century at a time when there was much new land available for cultivation and when population was small. Under these circumstances, cattle could have ample space and abundant food without reducing food supplies for the human race. These conditions, however, cannot last forever. Population is increasing and, as numbers grow, food animals tend to disappear. "They are secondary products of agriculture using up food not much more effi-

[96] League of Nations, Economic Intelligence Service, World Economic Survey, Fifth Year, 1935-36, p. 53.

ciently than human beings and forming thereby the most expensive part of our dietary system."[97] This is conspicuously true of beef cattle, but it is also true, in smaller degree, of our present dairy cattle which are not as efficient producers of food for mankind as they might well be.

A quart of 4% milk containing 13.4% solids has a total solid content of 4.6 ounces of food in 29.79 ounces of water, and of course the transportation and handling of this water adds greatly to the price which the consumer must pay for the food contents of the milk.

Of the 4.6 ounces of solid contents, there are nearly 2 ounces of lactose and minerals, substances easily and cheaply obtained without the use of fluid milk. The valuable food elements in the quart of milk are $1.37\frac{1}{2}$ ounces of butter-fat and $1\frac{1}{4}$ ounces of protein, of which the protein is the more important, and these elements, at the present price of milk, make an expensive food.

Unless, therefore, the protein content of milk can be increased and the cost of producing and delivering fluid milk can be lowered, the use of fluid milk in cities and towns is likely, as time passes, to have a constantly smaller place among food industries.

[97] *Mankind at the Crossroads* by Professor Edward M. East, pp. 161-162.

CHAPTER X

FIVE CENTURIES OF POULTRY HISTORY

WHAT would life be without modern agricultural machinery? There would be great suffering, of course, and a return to simpler conditions in a much smaller population, but the world lived in that way until very recently, having no more food than could be raised for the most part by hand labor, with the population pressing upon the food supply, so that for many centuries Hunger and Want were man's daily companions, not unknown even in America.[1] As recently as 1781, in the time of great-grandparents of men still living, and five years after the establishment of American Independence, M. Parmentier wrote his well-known *Observations on Such Nutritive Vegetables as May Be Substituted for Ordinary Food in Times of Scarcity*, a book that dealt with a subject of great importance in days when the supply of food in civilized countries was never adequate to the needs of the population.

When food, then, was lacking for man and beast, we can be sure that very little was left for chickens. Poultry, Columella says, are especially subject to disease in cold weather when food is short[2] and, indeed, like other creatures, probably could not live long at any season when they could find nothing to eat. The poultry industry, as a regular source of food in winter as well as in summer, is a recent luxury industry. It could not exist until agricul-

[1] See, for example, *Narrative of a Tour through Vermont in 1789* by Rev. Nathan Perkins (Elm Tree Press, Woodstock, Vt., 1920), pp. 21-22.
[2] Lib. VIII, Cap. V.

190

tural machinery and modern knowledge brought to mankind the degree of abundance which the western world first began to know during the nineteenth century. Of course, in all places where poultry was kept, during former ages, food for poultry came with vegetation in the spring. Eggs were, therefore, an appropriate celebration for Easter, and Le Grand d'Aussy describes a practice of egg-rolling in Auxerre[3] which modern visitors in Washington can see every year at Easter on the White House lawn. It is a striking phenomenon of history that though the egg is one of the oldest human foods, the business of producing eggs on a large scale is hardly older than the manufacture of motor cars and radios. In 1859 the process of candling eggs as carried on in Washington and Fulton Markets, New York, was apparently regarded in England as a novelty of some interest,[4] notwithstanding that this method of determining the condition of eggs had long been known.[5]

Virgil draws a pleasant picture of the farmer's life when the very fruitful earth, almost of its own accord, produced from the ground an easy living for the farmer, but sober history gives no such pleasant representation of ancient conditions. The experience of the race is that advanced civilization and primitive agriculture are incompatible. When food and other necessaries must be supplied by hand labor, the cost of living is high and the standard of living is low.

There has been a doctrine—very popular in recent years—that high prices make a high standard of living, and something could be said for this belief if we could receive high prices for what we sell without paying high prices for what we buy. Unfortunately, however, the standard of living and the cost of living are very

[3] *La vie privée des Français*, Vol. II, p. 40.
[4] *Curiosities of Food* by P. L. Simmonds (Richard Bentley, London, 1859), pp. 139-140.
[5] See Impatience des femmes, *La maison rustique*, Estienne and Liébault, p. 42b.

closely related. We cannot have many comforts unless comforts are cheap. The great ideal of a happy people can be realized only when the necessaries of life are so low in price that industry and thrift will make them available to persons of the smallest means. Machinery does not reduce employment, for machinery multiplies occupations and makes available to everybody things which but recently were luxuries rarely enjoyed even by princes.

We need not go back far into the past to discover the sort of life which hand work supported, and to learn the history of comfort such as we see about us, and the first thing we discover is that hand work makes a high-priced product, a small market and low wages. Of Scotland less than two hundred years ago, it was said that there was not work for more than half the population of the highlands at wages of three shillings a week.

Everything was done in the slowest and most wasteful manner. When a plow was used, from six to a dozen oxen were harnessed with ropes of straw and four men watched its progress; but more often the ponderous spade was used. . . . Neither barley nor oats was threshed properly. The barley was beaten on "the knocking stone" while the oats were "graddened," that is, the straw and husks were burned away, leaving the blackened grain.[6]

It is obviously the old story of mind and body weakened by want, but Scotland was only coming slowly out of the condition in which all Europe had been for ages. The mediaeval farmer was able by hand labor to raise but a small quantity of grain. Very little of this could be spared for poultry, and men working long hours at heavy labor had no time whatever in which they could take care of birds. The work, therefore, which had once been the pleasure of an Emperor,[7] went as a chore to the women of mediaeval households, already burdened with family and household cares,

[6] *Scotland* by Mr. Robert Laird Mackie, p. 501.
[7] Gibbon, *Decline and Fall*, Chap. XXIX, Vol. III (Harper, N. Y., 1905), p. 303.

spinning and weaving, brewing, milking the cows and doing the work of the dairy.[8] The method by which poultry are to be fed de Serres passes over very lightly, the subject being so fully understood, he says, that "les plus simples femmelettes" knew all about it.

The net result was that, except perhaps in Egypt or other favored spots where grain was easily raised and seasons were long, the poultry had very little attention and not much food beyond that which they could find for themselves. As M. Parmentier says in his note to Olivier de Serres' *Le théâtre d'agriculture*, the good thing about poultry was that they were strong and willing to eat anything, so that when the farmyard, storehouse, stables and manure heaps gave out they could pick up their own living of insects and seeds which they found along roads and hedgerows.[9]

To supplement this rather uncertain source of food, de Serres describes a method by which an artificial supply of worms can be produced.[10] Professor Bradley, in his English version of Noël Chomell's *Dictionnaire oeconomique*, published in Dublin in 1727, describes this method as follows:

There is an Invention of gathering together a great many Worms; what will be advantageous in this Case arises from the Pleasure the Poultry take in eating those Insects, which contribute at a small charge to maintain a great many of them, and by this means to make them fat, with the Help of a little Corn.

To gather these Worms, dig a Ditch . . . throw into it a bed of Rye straw chopped very small, to which join a Bed of Horse dung . . . upon which pour the blood of an Ox or Goat, the gross Substance of Grapes, Apples, Oats and Wheat-bran . . . adding other Ingredients . . . Offals

[8] *La maison rustique*, Estienne and Liébault, Liv. I, Chap. XV, p. 39b. *Le théâtre d'agriculture* by Olivier de Serres, 1600, Cinquième Lieu, edition of 1804, Vol. II, p. 3, and notes, pp. 152 et seq. *The English House-Wife* by Gervase Markham, 1649.

[9] *Le théâtre d'agriculture* by Olivier de Serres, Vol. II, p. 156.

[10] *Ibid.*, Chap. II, pp. 9-10 and note, pp. 157-158.

or Garbage of Sheep and other Beasts . . . cover with thick bushes . . . and the rain will . . . breed Worms, the End and Benefit aimed at by this Composition.

The plan comes so near to an easy production of something out of almost nothing of value that its popularity was assured from the start, and it can be found with full directions in many of the old books.[11] It is the true secret of cheap poultry food, Liger says,[12] and so it is a good plan to have two or three verminières always ready so that one can be used after the other.

So much, then, for the problem of feeding. It is true that de Serres cautions his readers that poultry need good care and food, but times change. What might have been considered good care and food in the days of which he wrote would not be adequate for man, beast or bird to-day. Four hundred years ago there were few farmers, or farmers' wives, who had either time or food to give to their birds, and the result was that in most cases the birds got along as well as they could, so far, at least, as their owner was concerned, uncared for and unfed.

A hen house, Olivier de Serres says, that is eight or nine feet square and about the same height, is of reasonable capacity, the chief requirements being that it can be closed at night to protect the birds from thieves and prowling animals and that it shall be well equipped with roosts and nests.[13] Some books say that the hen house should be placed near the oven, chimney or kitchen,[14] but de Serres would have it far from the dwelling on account of the noise and odors of the birds. Apparently, however, poultry houses were not at all necessary for the keeping of poultry, since there are

[11] *La maison rustique*, Estienne and Liébault, p. 40b.
[12] *Le nouveau théâtre d'agriculture* (Paris, 1713), p. 108.
[13] *Le théâtre d'agriculture*, Cinquième Lieu, Chap. I.
[14] *Four Bookes of Husbandry* by Conrad Heresbach, translated by Barnaby Googe (London, 1578), Bk. 4, p. 162. *A Way to Get Wealth* by Gervase Markham (London, 1648), Bk. 2, Chap. 15, p. 153.

many warnings of trouble which may come from poultry droppings in horse and cow stables and pig pens, while the practice of keeping birds in human dwellings is shown in many books and in many ways, among others by the curious ancient superstition that a cross on the chimney keeps the birds from leaving the house.[15] In ordinary cases, therefore, it appears that poultry were kept in small flocks to consume what would otherwise be wasted. Neither food nor care nor space could be given to them,[16] but scraps from the kitchen and litter from the farm were enough to keep a small number of birds alive.

From these birds the chief source of income was in their eggs,[17] and Heresbach quotes a statement which, he says, "our experience approveth," that some hens "laie . . . every daie, some twice a daie; some are so fruitfull, as thei kill them selves with laiying,"[18] a statement which suggests Dr. Johnson's remark, "to count is a modern practice, the ancient method was to guess; and when numbers are guessed they are always magnified."[19]

On the other hand, Warburton, in his *Treatise on the History, Laws and Customs of the Island of Guernsey*, published in 1682, refers to "an ancient paper, pretending to be an account taken by John Fresingfeld and John de Ditton, judges itinerant, sent into Guernsey 2 Edw. II, 1309," which tells of the monks who were considerable landlords on the island in the tenth century and who let out their lands on shares, reserving among other things

[15] *English and Other Proverbs* by Vincent Stuckey Lean (London, 1903), Vol. II, Part I, p. 60.

[16] *Loudon's Encyclopaedia* (1857), Sec. 7433.

[17] *Le théâtre d'agriculture*, Olivier de Serres (Paris edition, 1804), Vol. II, p. 4, and note by M. Parmentier, pp. 154-155.

[18] *Four Bookes of Husbandry* by Conrad Heresbach (London, 1578), Bk. 4, p. 162. See Aristotle, *History of Animals*, Bk. VI, Chap. I, Sec. I.

[19] *A Journey to the Western Islands. Works of Samuel Johnson* (London, 1810), Vol. 8, p. 327.

"a duty . . . called ponnage, which was as many eggs as a couple of hens might ordinarily lay in the space of a year, which has since been ascertained to be 40 eggs,"[20] an average of 20 eggs per hen per year! It does not seem likely that the Guernsey farmers were more astute than the monks, but the estimate is probably too low.

The unknown author of the book on *Hosebonderie*[21] expects 115 eggs from every hen every year,—a figure which is probably much too high. Between the various estimates an experienced poultry-man will not go far wrong in judging the productive ability of mediaeval hens. It is probable that twenty or twenty-five years ago the native egg-producing ability of hens, like the milk-producing ability of dairy cattle, was no greater than it had been in days of ancient Greece. In recent years the progress of egg-laying poultry in the best yards has greatly increased but with dairy cattle, contrary to the common impression, progress is so slight that it can be said that the work of improving the commercial qualities which make dairy cows valuable has hardly begun.

Of course, as in everything which comes to us from the middle ages, we have to deal with superstitions and the mysterious effects of appearances. Type was very important five hundred years ago, so that the color, shape, size and carriage of cocks were minutely described. Type also extends to the egg and Horatius considers that long eggs have a better flavor than round eggs.[22]

There has also been a long debate whether males come from long eggs and females from the eggs that were round or whether it was just the other way,—males coming from round eggs while females came from the long ones. In this debate Aristotle,[23] Pliny,[24]

[20] Reprint by Dumaresq and Mauger, Guernsey, 1822, pp. 23, 24.
[21] Edition published with Walter of Henley's book (Longmans, Green & Co., London, 1890), p. 75.
[22] *Satirarum*, Lib. II, No. IV, lines 12-13.
[23] *History of Animals*, Bk. VI, Chap. II.
[24] *N. H.*, Lib. X, Cap. LXXIV.

Columella,[25] Olivier de Serres,[26] Coelius Rhodiginus,[27] Ludovicus Des Prez,[28] Estienne and Liébault,[29] and many other eminent scholars, including Albertus Magnus, Avicenna, J. C. Scaliger, Duns Scotus, Vincentius and Antigonus Caryotius have taken part.[30] For over two thousand years the question was debated with some of the greatest names in human history on one side or the other, while no effort appears to have been made to learn the truth by experiment until Louis Liger in 1713,[31] and Parmentier in 1804,[32] described their experiments and showed that the shape of the egg had nothing to do with the sex of the chick hatched from it.

It is sometimes said that nothing is ever settled until it is settled rightly, and we may hope that this is true though, apparently, some things can never be settled at all, for M. Parmentier's and M. Liger's experiments are rarely mentioned and many poultrymen can be found who still believe the old story. It was repeated, for example, not long ago by a correspondent of a modern agricultural paper[33] and can doubtless be found in many other publications that are not yet very old. Nevertheless, the question is decided and it has all been done so easily and quietly that even the names of the poultrymen who settled the mighty argument are, for the most part, unknown. The question itself, indeed, is unimportant. The

[25] Lib. VIII, Cap. V.

[26] Le théâtre d'agriculture, Cinquième Lieu, Chap. II, Vol. II, p. 14.

[27] Antiquae Lectiones, Lib. XXVII, Cap. XVII. Coelius was a learned Italian—Coelio Ludovico Iricchieri, who lived about 1450-1525.

[28] Q. Horatii Flacci, Opera, Satirarum (Delphine edition, Paris, 1691), Lib. II, No. IV, note 2, p. 672.

[29] La maison rustique, p. 42b.

[30] See Aristotelis de Animalibus Historiae Libri X, 4 Vols., edited by J. G. Schneider, Leipsic, 1811. Vol. IV, p. 251, contains Scaliger's version of Aristotle's text. Vol. III, p. 403, contains Schnider's notes.

[31] Le nouveau théâtre d'agriculture, Liv. I, p. 111. See Lémery, Traité des aliments (Paris, 1702), Chap. XXV, pp. 357-358.

[32] See Le théâtre d'agriculture by Olivier de Serres (Paris, 1804), Vol. II, p. 161, note.

[33] Dairy Farmer, Ipswich, England, August, 1936, p. 19.

nature of long eggs and of round eggs, whether one produces males and the other females, is of no consequence. Application of the experimental method to the processes of nature was the great thing. When this was done, the doors of progress opened.

Advances, such as the later nineteenth century began, could not be achieved by syllogisms or tradition, and the poultry of a hundred and fifty years ago were probably as little changed from the poultry which Aristotle knew, as the question which Aristotle raised had been changed by the contributions of later times.

Such the poultry industry was four hundred years ago, and such it remained until very recent years. As late as 1878, Chambers' *Encyclopaedia* described poultry keeping much as it might have been described by Gervase Markham. The *Encyclopaedia* said:

In general the rearing of poultry is regarded as a very subordinate branch of rural economy, and it is pursued chiefly where agriculture is in a somewhat primitive state, the skillful and enterprising farmer deeming it beneath his attention, or finding that he has not time to attend to it, and often looking on the feathered inmates of his farm-yard almost as a nuisance because of their invasion of his fields. It may pretty safely be asserted that there is no good reason for this, and that poultry, properly cared for, would always be found a source of profit. The farm-yard affords great advantages for the keeping of poultry, and the increasing demand of the market promises a sure return. In some parts of Britain and in Ireland, where the farms are small, poultry are very extensively kept by farmers and cottagers; but the north of France and Pomerania exceed all other parts of Europe in poultry keeping, which there is not unfrequently the leading object of husbandry . . .

There is very commonly no building erected for the special accommodation of poultry; but perches and places for nests are provided for them in a cow-house, or some other farm building; or, in very many cases, when kept by cottagers, they roost on the joists of the roof within the door of the cottage itself.[34]

The birds were still housed in human dwellings in 1878 as

[34] Chambers' *Encyclopaedia*, 1878, Title, Poultry.

European travelers, indeed, find them even at the present day, and "type," although it receives scant attention nowadays, is not entirely forgotten, as appears from the recent statement of a poultryman:

If I were thirty-three and interested in poultry I would surely be a fancier. If egg production and market poultry were all there is to it I know that I would soon tire of the whole business and take up something else . . . the spirit of the fancy will go on forever.[35]

Even the verminière is not wholly out of date, for one of the most recent writers, in speaking of the food value of eggs, says:

Eggs, like butter, are food supplies that one does well to get as directly as possible and from an observed source of supply in the country. It is particularly important that eggs should not be from chickens that are fed artificially and kept confined as in the large poultry farms, but are allowed to run in the fields and eat their necessary ration of grasshoppers, worms and other country life and fresh seeds and grass. The mechanized poultry farms produce eggs which are just as undesirable in their way as is the milk from the mechanically managed dairy where the cows are kept indoors, and fed as mechanically and as routinely as a boiler is stoked with coal or oil.[36]

Robert Burton, in *The Anatomy of Melancholy*, reports the belief in which, however, he did not share, that:

. . . fat standing waters make the best beer, and that seething doth defecate it as Cardan holds . . . innoxium reddit et bene olentem.[37]

Possibly modern writers can be found who would agree with the opinion which Burton disapproves, for it is seriously said of butter prepared by modern careful methods that, as compared

[35] New England Poultryman, April 15, 1934, p. 42.

[36] *Eat, Drink and Be Wary* by F. J. Schlink (Covici, Friede, New York, 1935), p. 296.

[37] Part I, Sec. II, Mem. II, Subsec. I, Vol. I, p. 256. "The clearer the water, the less it fatneth," *Health's Improvement* by Dr. Thomas Muffett, Chap. II, p. 10.

with old-time butter, it

. . . will be far more uniform in flavor and perhaps in some cases bacteriologically safer, but it will be nutritionally less wholesome.[38]

It is evident, then, that progress is not a matter merely of our date. The past is always with us. We carry it on our shoulders but, as Samuel Johnson said, "life is surely given us for higher purposes than to gather what our ancestors have wisely thrown away,"[39] and among the things wisely discarded we may safely class the verminière, foul water, dirty butter, and fanciful distinctions of type which make it harder for men to earn their living.

It must not be thought, however, that during this long period of five hundred years no progress has been made in poultry keeping, for though the distinguishing characteristics of our modern industry are very recent, these advances would have been impossible without the new agriculture, farm machinery, improved seed, chemical fertilizers, and above all without the personal freedom from which all progress springs. Every one of these things has come to us from the past, and the future brings happiness only to those who hold fast the good which the past has brought.[40]

Where poultry are kept in small numbers to consume what would otherwise be wasted about a house or farm, the natural method of hatching eggs is simplest and best. Artificial incubation is essentially a method which looks forward to the existence of a great poultry industry, when chicks must be hatched in large numbers. This was the industry contemplated by René Antoine Ferchault de Réaumur, one of the great names of agricultural

[38] *Eat, Drink and Be Wary* by F. J. Schlink, pp. 296, 297.
[39] *The Rambler*, No. 121, May 14, 1751.
[40] For the history of domestic fowl, see W. C. L. Martin, *The Ox, Sheep, Hog and Poultry* (London, 1847-48). The same treatise is in Vol. II of *The Farmer's Library* (Charles Knight, London, 1848). For history of the Dorking breed, see Samuel Copland, *Agriculture, Ancient and Modern* (London, 1866); Morton's *Cyclopedia of Agriculture* (Blackie and Son, Glasgow, 1855), Vol. 2, p. 707.

history ranking with "Coke of Norfolk," Jethro Tull, the Duke of Bedford, George Washington and, in modern times, with many men in America and elsewhere, of whom Professor Gras says:

For the most part the heroes of the agricultural revolution were distinguished amateurs. They were gentlemen first and farmers second.[41]

It is natural that men who have leisure should be conspicuous among those who apply to the arts the fruits of their study. Natural philosophy, Francis Bacon said, has attracted but few wholly devoted followers, unless it be some monk working in his cell, or some gentleman in his country house.[42] There has been no "hampering tradition of the country gentleman,"[43] such as is sometimes assumed by uncritical democrats, and of Réaumur it was said in "the year XII" of the French Republic (1804), a time when radical opinions might be expected to depreciate his services:

We may well wish that another man like Réaumur would appear in France, a property owner learned, rich and zealous for the welfare of his country.[44]

Other countries also have known the value of the country gentleman.

I heard it remarked by a professor at Copenhagen, [Malthus said] that the reason why the agriculture of Norway had advanced so slowly was that there were no gentleman farmers to set examples of improved cultivation, and break the routine of ignorance and prejudice in the conduct of farms. . . . From what I saw of Norway I should say that this want is now in some degree supplied.[45]

Development of a great poultry industry was impossible until poultry food was available in sufficient quantity to keep the birds

[41] *A History of Agriculture* by Professor N. S. B. Gras, pp. 217, 224.

[42] *Novum Organum*, Pars II, Cap. LXXX.

[43] See Article by Secretary Henry A. Wallace in Saturday Review of Literature, New York, March 23, 1935.

[44] *Le théâtre d'agriculture* by Olivier de Serres. Note by M. Parmentier to edition of 1804, Vol. II, pp. 170-171.

[45] *An Essay on the Population*, Bk. II, Chap. I, p. 162.

alive and in good condition, and mechanical methods of incubation and brooding on a large scale were developed. All this being done, progress comes with the establishment of strains of poultry capable of laying many eggs of good size. This made it necessary:

1. To identify the best producing birds, and
2. To use for breeding purposes only those birds which have high-producing offspring.

Trap-nests. The history of these very simple contrivances, by which producing birds can be identified, shows a strange vagary of the human mind.

In 1854 a patent was issued in the United States for a nest which closed upon the entrance of the hen. Thereafter many such patents were issued—all for the purpose, however, of protecting the hen on the nest from annoyance and all alike permitting her to escape at any time. It had not yet occurred to the world that identification of high-producing birds was desirable. As the Journal of Heredity remarks:

> The poultry-minded inventors of America of that time seem to have been very much wrought up over the psychological and other hazards to which the hen was exposed.

The ideas of sympathetic poultrymen are well shown by the illustration on the opposite page, reproduced with a little freedom from the specifications accompanying the application for the Hayward patent of 1868.

It is possible that as early as 1869 new ideas in regard to poultry breeding were making their way, for in that year a patent was granted to Mr. D. P. Leich for a trap-nest, no suggestion being made in the papers that the laying hen could escape from the nest. What Mr. Leich actually intended to accomplish by the nest which he patented is not clear. *The Origin of Species* had been published ten years before the Leich patent was issued, but the history of the poultry industry does not indicate that the work of keeping records

FOILED AGAIN!

of egg-production by individual hens had begun at the time of the Leich patent. It was not, indeed, until thirty years later, when the patent of 1899 was issued to Mr. George I. Lytle, that any statement was made of the function of the trap-nest in breeding poultry for egg-production. The Journal of Heredity in speaking of this trap-nest said:

This patent was filed on October 17, 1898, so that this statement dates from the same year in which Gowell's experiment began. Gowell lived in Maine and Lytle in Wisconsin, so the basic idea of using trap-nests for poultry selection seems to have been quite wide spread at that time.[46]

Selection of Breeding Stock. If development of the trap-nest for the purpose of identifying high-producing birds was slow, development of the idea that only those birds should be used as breeders which had high-producing offspring was still slower. If the Romans were slow in learning how horses should be harnessed, and the middle ages slow in using oats for porridge, surely our own age was slow in discovering that the best breeding stock consists of those animals which have the best offspring. No principle, it seems, could be more obvious. To quote again the statement of Johannis Herengius, already used in another connection:

Res tam utilis et tam obvia, ad quam natura ipsa ducit, non potuit, non debuit diu quaeri.[47]

It surely should have taken neither long time nor great genius to discover anything so useful and so simple, to which nature herself shows the way. The human mind, however, took a different turn.

In 1586, three hundred and fifty years ago, John Baptista Porta, an ingenious Neapolitan gentleman, published a book entitled *A Method of Knowing Inward Virtues of Things by Inspection.*

[46] Journal of Heredity (Baltimore, Md. and Washington, D. C.), Vol. 28, pp. 424, 425, December, 1937. See also Vol. 28, pp. 344-345, October, 1937.
[47] *De Molendinis* (Frankfort, 1625), p. 44.

It is not likely that many teachers of poultry husbandry or many poultrymen are familiar with this book and, nevertheless, *The Standard of Perfection*, a book prescribing the type and plumage which birds should have, has long been and still is an accepted guide in poultry breeding,—a book which could only have been written or followed by believers who enjoyed a simple, unquestioning faith in Porta's method.

During the last twenty-five years, however, great advance has been made in poultry keeping, especially by:

1. New methods of artificial incubation and brooding.
2. The science of genetics.
3. Recent knowledge of nutrition.
4. Discoveries which are just beginning to enable poultrymen to reduce their losses from poultry diseases.

The poultry industry of the present day is a serious business engaged in supplying a food which is essential to the comfortable maintenance of the American people and which is in competition with many other industries supplying foods in the markets of the world. In comparatively few years, poultry keeping has risen from a very minor position to become one of the great interests of the country. In 1840, Mr. Miller Purvis says,[48] the value of all the poultry in the United States and Territories was given in the census of that year as $12,176,170—almost exactly the value of the poultry and eggs sold in Kansas in the year 1934.

In 1933 there were approximately 400,000,000 hens on American farms and poultry yards and they produced eggs at the rate of 1,000 per second every second of every minute throughout the year, both day and night.[49] Of these eggs, the total value at the price of 13.6 cents a dozen amounted to nearly three hundred

[48] *Ramblings Through Red History*, Rhode Island Red Journal, July, 1936, Vol. XXV, p. 3.

[49] The Egg & Poultry Magazine for January, 1937, quoting article in Poultry Craftsman and Pacific Poultryman.

sixty million dollars; to which, if the value of dressed poultry sold that year be added, it will be seen that even at the low prices prevailing in hard times, the poultry industry in America has a gross annual income exceeding half a billion dollars.

Methods of preserving eggs have been sought for many years, and the old books tell of putting eggs down in water, in oil, in sand, bran, ashes, salt or saw-dust. Froissart says that when Charles VI of France provisioned his fleet in 1386 for an attack upon England, he included "the yolks of eggs in powder and rammed in barrels."[50] Réaumur advised coating eggs with melted suet and the Abbé Nollet dipped eggs in a varnish made of Spanish wax dissolved in alcohol.[51] No method, however, was satisfactory until in very recent years eggs have been preserved by many housewives in water-glass and by commercial dealers on a large scale throughout the country in cold-storage warehouses.

Very recently, dried eggs and frozen eggs have been imported into America from China, about eight million pounds being imported during the year 1936.[52] This is not a large figure, being no more than the equivalent of a quantity which American hens produce every $3\frac{1}{2}$ days, but since eggs can often be bought in China for three or four cents a dozen, the possibilities of Asiatic competition have raised some alarm in the poultry trade. Now, however, eggs are dried in America and an excellent high-grade product is on the market which is easy to ship, cheap to buy, convenient to keep and to use. Poultrymen, therefore, like dairymen, face an ever increasing, widening competition in which only those plants that are best located and best managed can survive.

[50] *Chronicles*, trans. by Thomas Johnes (London, 1808), Vol. VIII, Chap. VII, p. 32.

[51] *La vie privée des Français*, Vol. II, p. 41.

[52] Egg & Poultry Magazine, Vol. 43, p. 334.

CHAPTER XI

ABUNDANCE

THE seventeenth century was the great century when, as Mr. Trevelyan says, the appearance of England "was being gradually changed from open landscape to enclosed fields, by the substitution of modern for mediaeval tillage,"[1] and when, with this new tillage, there came such political progress that "never perhaps in any other century have such advances been made towards freedom."[2] We have here, then, the association of an efficient agriculture with political progress, that is, of food and freedom, an association which well deserves attention.

In England, the great change from land used in common to fields held and used in severalty, from community planning to individual control and private initiative, began in the seventeenth century. There had, it is true, been some enclosures before the year 1600, but they had been too few to make much change in the conditions of life. After that year they were numerous, and the result was a degree of individual enterprise such as British agriculture had never before known. The early part of the century saw the introduction from Flanders of the art of cultivating market gardens. Later in the century came what was known as Dutch agriculture, including the use of clover in the rotation. At the end of the century Dean Swift, impressed, apparently, as much by the improved conditions of living as by the intellectual progress of the times, spoke of the "late refinements in knowledge running parallel to those of dyet in our nation."[3]

[1] *England under the Stuarts* by G. M. Trevelyan, p. 36.
[2] *Ibid.*, p. 516.   [3] *Tale of a Tub*, Sec. VII.

In the eighteenth century, enclosures increased rapidly both in number and in the extent of ground enclosed. At the beginning of the century, little had been done to improve British sheep and cattle, and their weight at Smithfield market in 1710 was less than half that of ordinary sheep and cattle in 1785.[4]

About the middle of the eighteenth century Robert Bakewell began farming. Private property and freedom provided the opportunity, and, when it came, the man was not lacking. Lord Ernle said that Bakewell, by the improvement of British live stock, added to national wealth as much as Arkwright added by his invention of the spinning frame, or Watt by his work with steam engines,[5] while Mr. James Sinclair says of the Shorthorn breed that it has not only raised the standard of living, but "if the monetary value of the improvements it has effected could be ascertained, it would rank as one of the greatest sources of financial profit that has ever been discovered."[6]

So much, then, for the advance which came in political freedom and in increased comforts of life when men were given the opportunity to work out their own salvation.

It will be noticed that the market gardens, the new agriculture and the productive cattle, all of which had contributed so much to British progress, came from the Netherlands, where, as Richelieu said, there was "only a handful of people confined to a corner of the land where is nothing but water and meadow and who, nevertheless, supply almost all the nations of Europe with a great part of their necessaries." We would like to know how they did it, but as Count Grégoire remarks, "there never was a people with such a flourishing agriculture, who wrote less about it."[7] Surely

[4] *England under Queen Anne* by G. M. Trevelyan, pp. 14-15.
[5] *English Farming Past and Present*, 4th ed., p. 181.
[6] *History of the Shorthorn Breed*, Chap. I, p. 2.
[7] *Essai historique, Le théâtre d'agriculture* (Paris edition of 1804), Vol. I, p. xcv.

theirs was an astonishing achievement for a handful of people, but they did more than this, for they built up a commerce extending to the remotest corners of the earth and some of them, the Dutch, established a free republic which, for many years, held its own against the greatest empires of the world.

The arts, however, which had such a flowering in the Low Countries in the fifteenth and sixteenth centuries, did not originate in Flanders or Holland but can be traced directly to the broad plains of the Po valley and earlier still to the agriculture of the Moors in southern Spain.

In the turmoil of nations which followed the fall of the Roman empire and the invasion of northern tribes, the Iberian peninsula in southwestern Europe was occupied by the Visigoths, under whose rule, very fortunately for Spanish peasants, the feudal system did not exist. Even before the Moorish conquest, therefore, the agricultural population of Spain enjoyed a degree of freedom hardly known to the cultivators of the soil elsewhere in Europe at that time.

After the overthrow of the Visigoths in the year 711 and the establishment of the Moors in Spain during following years, cultivation of the fields was left to the natives, working their properties for their own benefit. "The air of the country," Mr. S. P. Scott says, "like the air of the Desert, seemed congenial to independence."[8] There was no religious persecution, acts of violence were punished, the countrymen were left to rebuild their cottages and resume their labors.

The Moors, however, brought more than order to the conquered country and independence to the cultivators of Spanish land, for, as Mr. William Gifford Palgrave says, it is to the Moors that we owe, directly or indirectly, the revival of learning in western

[8] *History of the Moorish Empire in Europe* by S. P. Scott. (Lippincott, Philadelphia, 1904), Vol. III, p. 600.

Europe and "to them also, at least indirectly and by deduction, are due most of the useful arts and practical inventions laboriously perfected by later nations."[9] Under these favoring conditions, there developed in Spain an agricultural system of remarkable excellence.

A considerable portion of the country which had never been subjected to tillage because of its aridity became suddenly metamorphosed as if by the wand of an enchanter. Barren valleys were transformed into flourishing orchards of olives, oranges, figs and pomegranates. Rocky slopes were covered with verdant terraces. In districts where, according to ancient tradition, no water had ever been seen, now flowed noisy rivulets and broad canals. Where marshes existed, the rich lands they concealed were drained, reclaimed and placed under thorough cultivation.[10]

There is hardly a civilized country in the world, Mr. Scott says, which has not benefited by the agricultural achievements of Moorish Spain eleven hundred or more years ago.

From Spain the movement extended to northern Italy which, like the Low Countries, is a well-watered, fertile land of rich herbage, where fields are irrigated and cattle are pastured throughout the winter months. In the second century of the Christian era, Plutarch said of the region later known as Lombardy:

All the country is planted with trees, has pleasant and rich pastures and is well watered with rivers. It contains eighteen large cities well situated for trade and for obtaining all the accommodations and pleasures of life,[11]

a land where food was abundant and where later the beginnings of freedom showed themselves in the many free cities which maintained their independence and protected their citizens.[12]

In the ninth century these cities began to establish republican governments protecting their own liberty and the liberty of the

[9] *Ency. Brit.*, 9th ed., Tit. Arabia, Vol. 2, p. 265.
[10] *History of the Moorish Empire in Europe*, Vol. III, p. 600.
[11] *Life of Camillus*, Vol. I, p. 379.
[12] Hallam, *Middle Ages* (London, 1853), Vol. I, Chap. III, p. 393.

occupants of neighboring territory over whom they extended their rule. Long before Runnymede, there was freedom in Italy such as other countries did not know until much later. Subjects of the Moors in Spain had enjoyed a degree of independence by the polity of their rulers, but liberty for modern Europe, one may almost say, was born in Italy.

Of the Italians to whom we owe this great achievement, Jacobus Vitriacus, early in the twelfth century, said that they were

in consiliis circumspecti, in re suâ publicâ procurandâ diligentes et studiosi; sibi in posterum providentes; aliis subjici renuentes; ante omnia libertatem sibi defendentes; sub uno quem eligunt capitaneo, communitati suae jura et instituta dictantes. . . .[13]

or, in other words, that they were prudent in counsel, diligent and careful in their affairs, foresighted, unwilling to submit to the rule of others and concerned above all things to defend their liberty, serving under a captain whom they choose, and establishing for themselves the laws and institutions of their own State.

As early as the tenth century, Sismondi says, these cities developed a degree of wealth, intelligence, energy and independence unknown in feudal countries.

So skilful was the agriculture of Lombardy and Tuscany that, after the lapse of five centuries, it is affirmed that the lands formerly comprised in the territories of these republics can be distinguished from those which continued under the sway of the feudal lords.[14]

We would like to know the history of this agriculture, but as in the later case of Flanders, so in Lombardy during the tenth and the following centuries, no record was left. "Some grave chroniclers," Sismondi said, "preserved the memory of an im-

[13] *Gesta Dei per Francos . . . Historia Hierosolymitana*, Vol. II, p. 1085, quoted by Dr. William Robertson in *History of Charles V*, Vol. I, note xiv.

[14] *Democracy in Europe* by Sir Thomas Erskine May (Armstrong & Son, New York, 1895), Vol. I, p. 292.

portant crisis, but in general the cities passed whole centuries
without leaving any written memorial."[15] Of the free cities in
Lombardy and northern Italy, in the thirteenth century, the century
for which Mr. Walford's description of famines and want in other
parts of Europe has already been quoted, Sismondi gives an at-
tractive picture:

The aspect was of a prodigious prosperity which contrasted so much
more with the rest of Europe that nothing but poverty and barbarism was
to be found elsewhere. The open country appertaining to each city was
cultivated by an active and industrious race of peasants, enriched by their
labor, and not fearing to display their wealth in their dress, their cattle
and their instruments of husbandry. The proprietors, inhabitants of towns,
advanced them capital, shared the harvests, and alone paid the land tax;
they undertook the immense labor which has given so much fertility to
Italian soil—that of making dikes to preserve the plains from the inunda-
tion of the rivers, and of deriving from those rivers innumerable canals
of irrigation. The naviglio grande of Milan, which spreads the clear
waters of the Ticino over the finest parts of Lombardy, was begun in
1179, resumed in 1257 and terminated a few years afterwards. Men who
meditated and applied to the arts the fruits of their study, practiced already
that scientific agriculture of Lombardy and Tuscany which became a model
to other nations; and at this day, after five centuries, the districts formerly
free, and always cultivated with intelligence, are easily distinguished from
those half-wild districts which had remained subject to the feudal lords.[16]

"Such is the fertility of this country," Thomas Coryat wrote
in 1608, "that I thinke no Region or Province under the Sunne may
compare with it. For it is passing plentifully furnished with all
things, tending both to pleasure and profit, being the very Paradise
and Canaan of Christendome. For as Italy is the garden of the
world, so is Lombardy the garden of Italy, and Venice the
garden of Lombardy. It is wholly plaine, and beautified with such
abundance of goodly rivers, pleasant meadowes, fruitful vineyards,

[15] *History of Italian Republics* (London, 1832—1 Vol.), Chap. III, pp. 78-79.
[16] *History of Italian Republics*, Sismondi, pp. 107-108.

fat pastures, delectable gardens, orchards, woodes, and what not, that the first view thereof did even refocillate my spirits and tickle my senses with inward joy."[17]

A little later, looking out from a tower in Milan, Coryat returned to the subject. The country, he says, "was so pleasant an object to mine eyes, being replenished with such unspeakable variety of all things, both for profite and pleasure, that it seemeth to me to be the very Elysian fields, so much decantated and celebrated by the verses of Poets, or the Tempe or Paradise of the world. For it is the fairest plaine, extended about some two hundred miles in length, that ever I saw, or ever shall if I should travell over the whole habitable world: insomuch that I said to myselfe that this country was fitter to be an habitation for the immortall Gods then for mortall men."[18]

During the twelfth and thirteenth centuries, Dr. William Robertson, in his *History of Charles V*, says that the commerce of Europe was almost entirely in the hands of the Italians, commonly known in those ages by the name of Lombards,[19] and he gives a good account of the trade which they carried on at this time in the Low Countries with Flemish and Dutch merchants and with the merchants also of the Hanseatic League. In this way, Italian culture was carried along the channels of trade to the Netherlands, where the influences which had produced abundance and freedom in Lombardy produced abundance and freedom also in the Netherlands. It is important thus in tracing the rise and progress of freedom to notice how widely, when once established, it spreads its influence into every human activity. The Director of the South Kensington Museum in London, Mr. A. S. Cole, writing on Lace in the *Encyclopaedia Britannica*, remarks that pictorial art first flour-

[17] *Coryat's Crudities* (London, 1611), pp. 92-93.
[18] *Ibid.*, p. 99.
[19] Vol. I, Sec. I, *A View of the State of Europe* (Boston, 1857), p. 92.

ished and attained high perfection in two widely distant regions of Europe—North Italy and Flanders—and that these were precisely the places where lace-making first became an industry of artistic and commercial importance.[20] The fine arts, then, first appeared in the modern European world in regions which already were conspicuous in the early history of European food and freedom, but this is only part of the story for, as Mr. Hallam says, "Italy supplied the fire from which other nations in the revival of letters lighted their own torches."[21] "All that is great," Sir Thomas Erskine May says, "in the intellect and arts of Italy, is associated with the history of her freedom."[22] Lombardy teaches, however, not only how comfort comes, but also, unfortunately, its later history teaches how comfort disappears even from a land which seems made to be a permanent abode of happy peoples.

Nature, Walter Harte says, seems to have contrasted want and plenty in the same picture and so, he adds, quoting Burnet's *Travels*, written in 1685-1686, that Lombardy, although it "seems the most desirable place in the world to live in; yet after all, the government is so excessively severe, that there is nothing but poverty and beggary over all this rich country."[23]

The history of Lombardy, then, gives us both aspects of the subject. In her early prosperity we see freedom and plenty closely related as cause and effect, while in her later adversity we see the loss of freedom related with poverty and beggary.

[20] *Ency. Brit.*, 9th ed., Vol. 14, pp. 183, 184.

[21] *Literature of Europe* (London, 1843), Part I, Chap. I, Sec. 81. Lanfranc, Anselm, Peter Lombard and Gratianus are all in one way or another associated with the history of the Po valley. Johannes de Janua wrote the first Latin dictionary since Roman times, finished in 1260 and published in Mayence in 1460, and Venice, 1487, and Leonardo da Pisa wrote the first European treatise on algebra in 1175.

[22] *Democracy in Europe* (Armstrong & Son, New York, 1895), Vol. I, p. 291.

[23] *Essays on Husbandry* (London, 1770), p. 75. See *Letters Containing an Account of Switzerland, Italy*, etc., by Bishop Gilbert Burnet (London, 1724), pp. 45, 111.

Of the Netherlands in 1550, Mr. William H. Prescott gives a description strikingly like the description which Sismondi had given of conditions in Lombardy three centuries earlier:

The country, fertilized by its countless canals and sluices, exhibited everywhere that minute and patient cultivation which distinguishes it at the present day, but which in the middle of the sixteenth century had no parallel but in the lands tilled by the Moorish inhabitants of the south of Spain. The ingenious spirit of the people was shown in their dexterity in the mechanical arts, and in the talent for invention which seems to be characteristic of a people accustomed from infancy to the unfettered exercise of their faculties. . . . The humbler classes, in so abject a condition in other parts of Europe at that day, felt the good effects of this general progress in comfort and civilization. It was rare to find one, we are told, so illiterate as not to be acquainted with the rudiments of grammar; and there was scarcely a peasant who could not both read and write;—this at a time when to read and write were accomplishments not always possessed, in other countries, by those even in the higher walks of life.[24]

It is a very remarkable history which is thus traced from Lombardy in the tenth, eleventh, twelfth and thirteenth centuries, to Holland and Flanders in the fourteenth, fifteenth and sixteenth centuries, and to England in the seventeenth, eighteenth and nineteenth centuries, but it is no less remarkable that the trade which carried the seeds of all this progress passed through France, where neither freedom nor abundance was known until long afterward. What is the reason that the Netherlands could take so much while France could take so little? This is the question which troubled Count Grégoire and which he debated in his very scholarly *Essai historique*.[25] If, he says, the Flemings were distinguished in agriculture even before the sixteenth century, to what circumstance of climate or soil or laws or customs do they owe their success? How much is due to their canals, how much to the spirit of liberty which

[24] *History of Philip II* (Boston, 1859), Vol. I, pp. 367, 373.
[25] See *Le théâtre d'agriculture* by Olivier de Serres (Paris edition, 1804), Vol. I, p. cxv.

214

they manifested and how much to the government which neglected to stifle these precious germs? And why did Flemish agriculture keep its success within such strait limits that it did not spread to their next-door neighbors? If these questions are not their own answer, Count Grégoire has no further suggestion to offer, but an answer can be found in the Fifth Book of Taine's *History of the Ancient Régime* with such wealth of detail, giving the effects of heavy taxation and governmental control of human activities, that the reader is not surprised by the statement of Arthur Young that, in the year 1789, French agriculture had not passed beyond the agriculture of the tenth century. In the eighteenth century France suffered eight famines, culminating in the short crops of 1788, which were one of the causes of the Revolution.

Count Grégoire says that an Italian writer of 1605 had devoted a chapter to prove that abundance was good and that famine was an evil, a proposition, Count Grégoire remarks, which in his time it would have been unnecessary to argue. The same comment can be made on taxation and regulation—that in the twentieth century it should be unnecessary to argue that freedom is good and that taxation and regulation are bad. Taxation in France before the Revolution, and regulation in England before the days of enclosures, were the cause of endless misery.

Of course, there have been governments which of set purpose caused suffering among their subjects. Rulers have been insane, intoxicated with power or revengeful, but it was not the purpose of the Bourbons in France or the Stuarts in England to make their peoples unhappy. They wanted to hold their thrones, and they wanted their peoples to be contented, because it is only contentment among subjects that promises permanence to the ruler. They would have said of their system of taxation and regulation that its purpose was nothing less than the purpose of a recent American statute which a high authority in the American government de-

215

scribed as a "supreme effort to stabilize for all time the many factors which make for the prosperity of the nation."

The Bourbons and the Stuarts, nevertheless, failed, as the American statute failed, because it is not given to any man to understand at once all humanity, its past and future. The manager of even a small store cannot stabilize its policy for all time. Something must be left to wiser heads, to experience and to to-morrow. This, however, is but a description of freedom, and it was freedom which saved the world.

Freedom in Italy, Holland, and in England after enclosures had been made, brought abundance and leisure, giving to men the opportunity, in Sismondi's phrase, to apply to the arts the fruits of their study, an opportunity which has brought to the service of mankind all the scientific advance of the last two hundred years.

It is a very serious reflection for modern times that the human race in our own part of the world has so recently raised itself from such an abyss of want and suffering as history describes, but it is a more serious reflection that the available surplus, which gives the western world security from want, is still small and that a brief interruption in the process of supply would once more bring back the old trouble of which we read but never yet have seen. A little interruption by the American government in the raising of corn, united with a drought, resulted during 1935 in an increased importation of corn amounting to 7,265.3 per cent. over the average of the preceding five years. America fed its domestic animals upon Argentine corn, and if Argentine production had been short, or Argentine prices high, there would have been need in America. The decrease in the number of swine which the American government effected resulted in making what is ordinarily the cheapest meat an expensive dish and further increase of governmental regulation might have brought a serious shortage of food. America has known local food shortage on a small scale and could easily know it on a large scale.

The history of agricultural methods and of the food supply seems to indicate that hard conditions make strong governments, and that the liberalism of the eighteenth century, which increased from small beginnings until it dominated the politics of the nineteenth century, was after all in some of its aspects merely a consequence of easier conditions of living. Men have talked of abundance in many by-gone ages, but they never had it to enjoy until within the span of life of men now living. We have had Abundance and Freedom and Democracy, and it may be that these are not three sisters as we had thought them, but three names for one heavenly visitor whose stay on earth may be short. In America we have long had such great abundance that there has been very little to suggest what the world has known in the past as want and famine, and America has always been a democratic country. It is quite possible, however, with increasing population, that as to the supply of necessaries for each individual there is a perceptibly smaller margin of safety than there was a few years ago. Certainly, unless the food supply increase as population grows, there will once more arise the condition, which existed so long in Europe, of an insufficient margin and of occasional periods of inadequate supply. If that time come, the days of democracy will be drawing to an end. "In the labors of husbandry," Mr. Hoskyns says, "we recognize the humble but persevering antagonist of various elements of international and social disorder."[26]

All persons, therefore, who are interested in having an adequate food supply for the nation, and in maintaining democratic institutions, are vitally concerned in the reduction of taxes and in protecting industry and agriculture from political control. "It is the

[26] *An Inquiry into the History of Agriculture* by Chandos Wren Hoskyns (London, 1849), p. 10.

217

cardinal principle of our national life," Mr. Wendell Phillips said, "that God has given every man sense enough to manage his own affairs."

The potentialities of food supply in America are abundant for our present population, but permanent abundance of all needed articles is impossible in a constantly growing population. What are the prospects that numbers will increase so as to make American life less comfortable than it has been?

Beyond Ortygia, Eumaeus told Ulysses, there is an island rich in flocks and herds, abounding in grain and wine. It is not very thickly settled, however, and into this land dearth never comes nor does hateful sickness fall upon unhappy men.[27] In that short statement, made nearly three thousand years ago, is the gist of the problems of our great modern populations. A small population in a fertile land can thrive while a large population under similar conditions will suffer want and all the diseases which want brings. This is the lesson the modern world must learn.

About a hundred and forty years ago, Thomas Robert Malthus wrote his famous *Essay on the Population* which was published in 1798. His principal thesis was that there is a constant tendency of all animated life to increase beyond the nourishment and other necessaries available to it. The ultimate check to population appears then to be a want of food, but this is never the immediate check except in cases of actual famine. Independent of scarcity there are causes, moral or physical, constantly operating to keep numbers down. The physical checks are diseases, epidemics, wars, plagues and famines, with other causes which weaken the human frame or shorten the duration of life. Beyond these, however, there is in man that distinctive superiority in his reasoning faculties which enables him to calculate distant consequences. He cannot look around him and see the distress which frequently presses upon

[27] *Odyssey*, Bk. XV, lines 403 et seq.

218

those who have large families without considering what the consequences would be if he should marry and have children. The substance of Malthus' doctrine as he stated it is this:

It is observed by Dr. Franklin that there is no bound to the prolific nature of plants or animals but what is made by their crowding and interfering with each other's means of subsistence. Were the face of the earth, he says, vacant of other plants, it might be gradually sowed and overspread with one kind only, as for instance with fennel; and were it empty of other inhabitants, it might in a few ages be replenished from one nation only, as for instance with Englishmen.

This is incontrovertibly true. Through the animal and vegetable kingdoms Nature has scattered the seeds of life abroad with the most profuse and liberal hand; but has been comparatively sparing in the room and the nourishment necessary to rear them. The germs of existence contained in this earth, if they could freely develop themselves, would fill millions of worlds in the course of a few thousand years. Necessity, that imperious, all-pervading law of nature, restrains them within the prescribed bounds. The race of plants and the race of animals shrink under this great restrictive law; and man cannot by any efforts of reason escape from it.

In plants and irrational animals, the view of the subject is simple. They are all impelled by a powerful instinct to the increase of their species; and this instinct is interrupted by no doubts about providing for their offspring. Wherever, therefore, there is liberty, the power of increase is exerted; and the superabundant effects are repressed afterwards by want of room and nourishment.

The effects of this check on man are more complicated. Impelled to the increase of his species by an equally powerful instinct, reason interrupts his career, and asks him whether he may not bring beings into the world for whom he cannot provide the means of support.[28]

Of course, the means of producing food and other necessaries of life a hundred and forty years ago were very different from those with which present times are familiar. Malthus knew nothing of agricultural machinery, of modern sanitation and hygiene, of

[28] *An Essay on the Population*, T. R. Malthus (Everyman's Library, Dutton, New York), Bk. I, Chap. I, pp. 5-6.

the luxury of our standard of living or of the methods of easy birth-control with which so large a part of our population is familiar. All these things, nevertheless, affect the ratio between the growth of the population and the increase of food and all other supplies, which in varying conditions are regarded by different persons as neces-saries of their lives. The ratio of the present time is therefore dif-ferent from the ratio which Malthus knew, but he was not writing on machinery, hygiene or contraception. His subject was the ever-continuing tendency of life to increase beyond the possible supply of necessaries and his moral was self-control.

No one could expect such doctrines to be popular. "A modest country parson," Professor Ezra Bowen said, "Malthus called down upon his head a stream of vituperation sufficient to sink a navy. Nevertheless, it did not occur to those who contributed to this torrent of abuse that a fire which could not be put out with a smaller stream must be the very fire of truth itself. This quiet rural scholar and parson was accused of defending small-pox, slavery and child-murder; of denouncing soup-kitchens, early mar-riage, and parish allowances; of having the impudence to marry after preaching against the evil of families; of thinking the world so badly governed that the best actions do the most harm—in fine, of taking from life all its joys and virtues."[29]

The book, nevertheless, was not so misinterpreted by everybody. M. Joseph Garnier, who published in Paris in 1857 a book on *The Population*, put on its title-page the text:

It depends on man whether growth of population brings Progress or Misery.

Of Malthus, M. Garnier says that his name is one of the most unpopular in the world; that public opinion, ignoring the nature and importance of his work and his noble idea of service to human-

[29] *Malthus, A Revaluation* by Professor Ezra Bowen. Scientific Monthly, May, 1930, pp. 465-471.

ity, considered him the leader of an aristocratic doctrine opposed
to the interests of the masses, the joys of the family hearth, the
growth of the people—and yet, notwithstanding all this, Professor
Edward M. East, who calls attention to M. Garnier's book, is able
to add:

> The law of population enunciated by Malthus, shorn of its unnecessary
> subsidiary propositions, is considered incontestable by nearly all the emi-
> nent economists who have expressed themselves and by all the biologists
> who have looked into it carefully.[30]

"Darwinism," Mr. Robert H. Murray said, "is Malthusianism
on the largest scale: it is the application of the principle of population, animal and vegetable." The phrase "struggle for existence"
was used by Malthus and it was the study of his *Essay on Population* which led Darwin and Wallace to frame the theory of evolution. "Indeed, Sir Charles Lyell is so much impressed by these
conclusions that he even denied the originality of Darwin and Wallace."[31] Malthus' position in history may be regarded, therefore,
as secure, and his teaching as sound.

The world which has witnessed the operation of Malthus' doctrines has, however, during the last 139 years, become very different from the world Malthus knew. "It is well to realize," Mr.
Henry Pratt Fairchild says, "that the whole great spurt which the
world population took in the nineteenth century was absolutely
unique in human experience. . . . In one century, humanity added
much more to its total volume than it had been able to add during
the previous million years."[32] In 150 years, the population of
Europe rose from 200 millions to 600 millions.

What continued growth of numbers can do to a country, to prog-

[30] *Mankind at the Crossroads* (Scribner, New York, 1923), pp. 59, 50-51.

[31] *Malthus and the Principle of Population* by Mr. Robert H. Murray. The
Contemporary Review, Vol. 146, p. 691, December, 1934.

[32] *When the Population Levels Off* by Henry Pratt Fairchild. Harper's
Monthly Magazine, Vol. 176, p. 596, May, 1938.

ress and, in the end, to mankind, is well stated by Professor Humphrey Michell:

The Ultimate Stage of Agriculture

A curious social phenomenon is to be found in the almost completely static condition of such Eastern races as the Chinese. There we find a people, industrious, intelligent and with an age-long tradition of culture, who seem to have halted, to have even turned back in the path of progress. When the Western nations were mere barbarous tribes, the Chinese were a civilised and cultured race. There are few modern inventions which had not been anticipated many centuries ago by the Chinese, for instance, printing. Not only have they not progressed, they have even retrograded. It is well known that centuries ago Chinese doctors understood the principles of anaesthesia for the performance of difficult surgical operations, to mention but one instance. To-day the Chinese doctors are the crudest of their kind, they have forgotten their ancient arts. Of course, it is easy to point to Confucianism, to the worship of ancestors, as providing the necessary stabilising force, but a little reflection will show that such can only be a symptom and not a cause. We must look deeper.

China, India and large parts of Japan have enormous populations which are able only by the most assiduous application to agriculture to support life at all. These countries have reached the ultimate stage of agriculture, where all the efforts of the population are required to win from the soil a livelihood just sufficient to support so many and no more. Having reached that stage, society with them has become static; even the struggle to retain, to remember their ancient arts and learning becomes almost too much for them, their energies are absorbed in the one preoccupation of winning from the earth their daily food. But, it may be argued, the agriculture of China, the transportation system, the means of distribution, are all primitive. Production there is on a small scale, with modern methods it would be possible to support a far greater population than at present. In answer to this two replies may be made: in the first place, the population is already so dense that if new methods were to make possible a still further increase in numbers the newcomers would have to seek a livelihood by emigration. Secondly, if the new methods did permit a greater population, then the Chinese would, in a very short space of time, breed up to the new possibilities of subsistence and the last case would be as bad as the first.

From whatever way we look at it, we must see that China, and a large part of India and Japan, have reached the ultimate stage beyond which it is practically impossible to go.

A contemplation of this may well arouse within us long and serious thoughts of the ultimate stage of the world's population, when it shall definitely have reached the point when no more people can be supported and the energies of vast numbers are devoted to the support of life, not to the production of a surplus. Economically speaking that will mean the extinction of most if not all free capital, that is to say, surplus wealth destined for the production of further new wealth. Progress in invention will be halted, the creative mind of man, his ingenuity and his daring, his restless ambition and his spirit of adventure will be baulked, it will turn back upon itself. It is no accident that the Chinese are a pre-eminently unwarlike people; they have no time for war, they must work to keep body and soul together.

And so, if our forecast is correct, such will be the state of the world two centuries hence, when men will beat their swords into ploughshares and their spears into pruning hooks for the compelling reason that only thus may they support life. A period of vast disorder, an age of strife, political and industrial, as nations and classes, men and women, feel the oncoming and relentless grip of growing scarcity and rising prices; and then, slowly and inevitably, the coming of the ultimate state of society, the static.[33]

Possibly we may see in the international relations of European and Asiatic nations, and in the domestic politics both of Europe and America, a suggestion of such disorder as that which Professor Michell thinks is coming. It is to be hoped, however, that no part of our western world will ever reach the depths of degradation of the Asiatic peoples which have been described, but it must always be borne in mind that the natural tendency of life is to reproduce regardless of consequences, and that if America and Europe are to escape the fate of Asia it can be only by an appeal to the distinctive superiority, of which Malthus spoke, in man's reasoning faculties which enables him to calculate remote consequences. If

[33] *A Restatement of the Malthusian Doctrine* by Professor Humphrey Michell. The Contemporary Review, November, 1924, pp. 628-637.

the peril be avoided in this way, it will be, as Mr. Robert Morrison MacIver says, for the first time in recorded history.[34]

It is impossible to foretell the future of our population in any western country. We know, however, that the birth rate is falling, and that if it continue to do so, and death rates remain constant, the total numbers before long will cease to increase.[35] Unfortunately, however, the decline in the birth rate is not equally spread through all classes of the people but is greatest among those who have the best education and the widest cultural resources. Apparently, low incomes and unemployment produce a high birth rate, while higher incomes and steady employment produce a lower birth rate. "The force of this influence," Messrs. Lorimer and Osborn say, "though imperceptible, is by no means negligible. Such a tendency, if continued for many generations, would result in a serious lowering of capacity for cultural-intellectual progress by the American people."[36]

[34] *Society, A Text Book of Sociology* (Farrar and Rinehart, New York, 1937), p. 98.

[35] *Dynamics of Population* by Mr. Frank Lorimer and Mr. Frederick Osborn (Macmillan, New York, 1934), p. 340.

[36] *Ibid.*, p. 344.

CHAPTER XII

THE EFFECT OF ABUNDANCE ON THE HUMAN MIND

WE HAVE followed the effect of want upon the mental life of mankind during the long ages when supplies were insufficient for the needs of the population. What, then, has been the influence of the abundance which began in the latter half of the eighteenth century, but which has been most conspicuous since the year 1800 and especially since the use of machinery?

At first, abundance showed itself chiefly in the supply of food, but, as time passed, conveniences and luxuries became available at prices which put them within the reach of a large part of the population, and in recent years hours of work have become shorter, holidays have increased in number, while amusements have become a principal interest, with graphophones, automobiles, radios, moving pictures and travel always inviting attention. The air is filled with music, speeches, stories and plays, and the theatres are many and well attended. What effect has all this upon the mental life and character of mankind? The Athenians, Montesquieu says, dreaded Philip as the enemy, not of their liberty, but of their pleasure, so that they made it by law a capital offence for any person to propose applying the money designed for the theatres to military service.[1] Is there any danger that pleasure can have a similar debasing effect upon democracies of the modern world?

The idea of progress with which we are so familiar was not one

[1] *Spirit of Laws*, tr. by Thomas Nugent (Bell, London & New York, 1892), Bk. III, Chap. 3, Vol. I, p. 23 and footnote.

which mankind readily accepted a hundred and fifty years ago. Odus de Odis was not the only person who had noticed that an advance in the useful arts was exceedingly rare, for Dr. Samuel Johnson in 1751 quoted La Bruyère that "we are come into the world too late to produce anything new," and Saint Cyprian long before had said that the world is old, that it hath not those forces which formerly it had, neither is imbued with that vigour and strength wherewith it formerly was and itself proclaims its declination by the experience of all things declining in it.[2] "The opinion of the World's decay," Bishop Hakewill said, "is so generally received, not onely among the Vulgar, but of the Learned, . . . that the very commonness of it, makes it current with many without any further examination: That which is held, not onely by the multitude, but by the Learned, passing smoothly for the most part without any checks or controle."[3]

Into a world, therefore, of hard conditions, in which there were many who had little hope of better things, there came the developments which followed the slow rise of human freedom.

The great change began, as has been said, with an increase in the supply of food. There was a hope that famine could be abolished, but the first thought of every observer, naturally, was of scepticism. So large a part of human misery comes from human improvidence that, without a change in man's nature, it was impossible to believe that great reduction in the amount of human want could be made. "It seems," Professor Bouthoul says, "that French economists and philosophers lived during the eighteenth century under the haunting memory of the famines with which that century began, especially the famine of the winter of 1709 when, according to the figures of the time, more than a million per-

[2] *The Fall of Man* by Godfrey Goodman (London, 1616). *An Apologie of the Power and Providence of God* by George Hakewill (Oxford, 1627).
[3] *An Apologie of the Power and Providence of God*, Bk. I, Chap. I, Sec. I.

sons died out of a population of twenty millions, five per cent. of the inhabitants of France."[4]

No such haunting memory troubled persons not economists and philosophers, nor did it affect those whose judgment was uninfluenced by history. To many persons the world is always new, and to such the conditions at the end of the eighteenth century were intoxicating.

So, a hundred and fifty years ago, changes in living had some of the effects which extreme changes sometimes have elsewhere. Many men were content that life was improving. The intoxication of change was for the few only, but it came in ways which recall the common experience that although growth is slow decay is rapid.

We wonder sometimes, when we read the books of one or two centuries ago, that the thoughts of our forefathers could so insistently have dwelt on sin and its punishment, on death and the wrath of God. We wonder that men of those days could not have enjoyed the beauty of a landscape as we do and that the world could not have seemed to them, as to so many since their time, a beautiful world made for man's comfort and pleasure.

Perhaps, could we have expressed these views to some English contemporary of Elder Brewster or Thomas Hooker, he might have answered:

You speak as though you had never known want. Landscapes feed no man. I lost a son last spring who would never have been ill could I have given him last winter the food he needed. My wife is troubled with the stone and we can not cure her nor relieve her pain. I have sat with her night and day when I have thought her sufferings would slay us both— but this is the common lot of man. Death and pain are in every house, and I like to think that they too are God's creatures for He is plenteous in mercy if we rightly seek Him, knowing that tribulation worketh patience, patience experience and experience hope.

[4] *La population dans le monde* by Gaston Bouthoul, pp. 142-143.

227

It is almost impossible for us to realize how our own recent ancestors lived, or the overturning effect of the new knowledge which, beginning in the eighteenth century and increasing throughout subsequent years, brought not only necessaries of life but comforts and luxuries as well.

Of course abundance came as a release, freeing mankind from much want that had pressed so heavily, from starvation because the right food was not known, from unnecessary pain and disease, from weakness and anxiety. So abundance has been and is a means to strengthen human bodies and human minds to carry burdens and to increase usefulness both to present and future ages. There were men, however, upon whom the dawning hope of freedom and plenty had no such sober effect as has been described. With nations as with individuals, indulgence is easy, denial and perseverance are hard— and so it comes that a civilization built up by centuries of effort, industry and courage may be destroyed in a short period of prosperity.

The prophet of the new order was Jean Jacques Rousseau, of whom David Hume said in 1766:

He has read very little during the course of his life and has now totally renounced all reading: he has seen very little and has no manner of curiosity to see or remark: he has reflected, properly speaking, and studied very little: and has not, indeed, much knowledge: he has only felt during the whole course of his life: and in this respect his sensibility rises to a pitch beyond what I have seen any example of, but it still gives him a more acute sense of pain than of pleasure.[5]

Rousseau, then, was a man of little education who was subject to great emotion, and he influenced the emotional part of mankind to a degree that others can understand only with difficulty. He was able, nevertheless, to move the feelings of the world in a way that

[5] Letter to Dr. Hugh Blair, *Letters of David Hume*, edited by J. Y. T. Grieg (Clarendon Press, Oxford, 1932), No. 314, Vol. II, pp. 28, 30.

fortunately does not happen often. Napoleon said that without Rousseau, France would have had no Revolution.[6] Sir Henry Maine said of him:

We have never seen in our own generation—indeed the world has not seen more than once or twice in all the course of history—a literature which has exercised such prodigious influence over the minds of men, over every cast and shade of intellect, as that which emanated from Rousseau between 1749 and 1762.[7]

David Hume, writing from Paris in 1765, said:

It is impossible to express or imagine the enthusiasm of the nation in his favor; . . . no person ever so much engaged their attention as Rousseau.[8]

Mr. Herbert Paul, in his Introduction to the *Letters of Lord Acton to Mary Gladstone*,[9] quotes the statement of Lord Acton:

Rousseau produced more effect with his pen than Aristotle, or Cicero, or Saint Augustine, or Saint Thomas Aquinas or any other man who ever lived.

We read of ladies dressing to go to a ball, who would pick up a volume of Rousseau and, becoming absorbed in it, would forget their dress, forget the ball, forget the carriage waiting at the door and read until the ball was over and the carriage had to be dismissed.

One turns, then, to Rousseau's writings with vivid anticipations. We expect to be absorbed in such literature as the world has never seen more than once or twice in history, but when we take up his books we find them almost unreadable. *The Social Contract* begins with a striking sentence:

Man was born free, but everywhere is in chains,

[6] *Foreign Reminiscences* by Lord Holland (London, 1850), p. 261.
[7] *Ancient Law* (Henry Holt & Co., New York, 1887), p. 84.
[8] *History of Civilization in England* by Thomas Henry Buckle, Vol. II, Chap. XIV, notes 12, 13, citing Burton's *Life of David Hume*, Vol. II, p. 299.
[9] *Letters of Lord Acton to Mary Gladstone* (Macmillan, 1904), p. 10.

yet nothing that follows justifies the hope which this sentence awakes. Rousseau is not without readers, even at the present time, and nevertheless for most persons he is dull. The sparkle is gone. No lady will ever again forget either her dress or her ball to read anything which he ever wrote. Rousseau once said of his own productions:

I dread that my writings are good for nothing at bottom, and that all my theories are full of extravagance,[10]

and to a modern reader Rousseau's dread seems well-founded. What, then, was the secret of his power? Just this—that he spoke of freedom to a world enslaved, and the delight of the thought was enough to make readers in those days forget everything else.

Of what has been referred to as slavery, no description is required. It is not a pleasant subject. It was well said of ancient Europe—and something from these conditions survived into the eighteenth century:

Far the greater part of society were everywhere bereaved of their personal liberty and lived entirely at the will of their masters. Everyone that was not noble was a slave; the peasants were not in better condition; even the gentry themselves were subject to a long train of subordination under the greater barons, or chief vassals of the crown, who, though seemingly placed in a high state of splendor, yet, having but slight protection from the law, were exposed to every tempest of the state, and by the precarious condition in which they lived, paid dearly for the power of oppressing and tyrannizing over their inferiors.[11]

The world has had every opportunity through long ages to learn the truth of Shelley's statement in *Queen Mab*:

> Power like a desolating pestilence
> Pollutes whate'er it touches; and obedience,
> Bane of all genius, virtue, freedom, truth,
> Makes slaves of men. . . .

[10] Letter of David Hume to Dr. Hugh Blair, March 25, 1766. *Letters of David Hume* (Clarendon Press, Oxford, 1932), Vol. II, No. 314, pp. 28, 31.

[11] *History of England*, David Hume, Chap. XXIII (Harper & Brothers, New York, 1879), Vol. II, p. 510.

To a world which we would think well described in this way, Rousseau brought dazzling possibilities and something like intoxication. Many persons of our times, who have had freedom all their lives, do not know that such liberty as we enjoy is a new thing in human history, but to a world that had never known freedom, Rousseau seemed to promise the immediate coming of a millennium of happiness. Mankind is perfectible and men will perfect themselves. William Godwin, whom a recent writer in The Contemporary Review well called "the father of anarchy,"[12] described in 1793 the future for which he looked:

There will be no war, no crimes, no administration of justice as it is called, and no government. Besides this, there will be no disease, no anguish, no melancholy and no resentment. Every man will seek with ineffable ardor the good of all. Mind will be active and eager, yet never disappointed.[13]

Condorcet, in his *Tableau historique des progrès de l'esprit humain*, gave a similar account of coming conditions and it is quite evident that the woods were ablaze. That the fire still burns can be seen by those who read Mr. J. B. S. Haldane's *Possible Worlds*.

Very clearly, therefore, if want can hinder intellectual advance, so also can that degree of freedom from want which in different minds is sufficient to deprive judgment of the sobriety which gives it value.

It would be a mistake to think that such writings are too fanciful to be important. One of the most influential papers in America

[12] *André Gide on Soviet Russia* by Miss Barbara Ward, The Contemporary Review, No. 869, pp. 578, 580, May, 1938.

[13] *Political Justice and its Influences on Morals and Happiness* by William Godwin (London, 1796), Vol. II, Chap. IX, p. 521. This work, edited and abridged by Mr. Raymond A. Preston, was recently published as part of the Political Science Classics under the general editorship of Professor Lindsay Rogers of the Faculty of Political Science, Columbia University. In this edition, however, the part of Godwin's book from which the foregoing quotation is made was not included.

recently published on the first page of its Sunday Book Section a review which asserted, among other things:

> Of all the curious ways of living which humanity has tried, that governed by the ferocious doctrines of self-help and business enterprise may some day seem the strangest.

If this be true, progress is but a delusion and stagnation is the law of man! Here, indeed, is justification for the statement:

> Plenty and peace breeds cowards; hardness ever
> Of hardiness is mother.[14]

What would Odus de Odis have thought of the notion that the world must hereafter supply mankind not merely with a bare living, but with all comforts which the industry of the nineteenth and twentieth centuries has taught us to enjoy?

Surely, these ideas have had little relation to human history, and are

> . . . to be chid
> As we rate boys, who being immature in knowledge,
> Pawn their experience to their present pleasure.[15]

Mr. W. E. H. Lecky, in the Preface to his book, *Democracy and Liberty*, repeats the comment of a friend who "could not understand the state of mind of a man who, when so many questions of burning and absorbing interest were rising about him, could devote the best years of his life to the study of a vanished past." The study of science which is so important to-day leads men's minds easily toward the opinion expressed by Mr. Lecky's friend, and so we hear sometimes the suggestion that retrospect is not helpful, and that in any difficulty we should consider not how we got there

---

[14] *Cymbeline*, Act III, Sc. vi.

[15] *Antony and Cleopatra*, Act I, Sc. iv, following the reading which Richard Grant White considers most plausible. *Works of William Shakespeare* (Little, Brown, & Co., 1893), Vol. 12, p. 134.

but how we can get out, as if, said Edmund Burke, we should "consult our invention and reject our experience." Here, indeed, is to be found one of the causes of the increasing excitability of American politics. Invention is the parent of Utopias, socialism, radicalism of all kinds. Experience is the parent of improvement, progress, conservatism. Possibly the human race has found some profit in all the misery it has had to endure, for if trouble can be crushing, prosperity, too, brings its dangers.

Bulwer Lytton in his novel, *Kenelm Chillingly*, published in 1873, describes a country parson who speaks of

. . . a citizen of a great republic, trying his best to accomplish an experiment in government in which he will find the very prosperity he tends to create, will sooner or later destroy his experiment.

Forty-seven years earlier William Hazlitt, in his *Notes of a Journey through France and Italy*, had made a similar statement, that,—

The Americans will perhaps lose their freedom, when they begin fully to reap all the fruits of it; for the energy necessary to acquire freedom, and the ease that follows the enjoyment of it, are almost incompatible.[16]

The world has not passed beyond its age of need. Machinery has come to man's aid so recently that persons now living enjoy great supplies while population is still comparatively small. It has been our extraordinary fortune to live in a transition stage during which mankind enjoyed new and unheard-of abundance. If, however, we judge the future by the past, this happy condition is but transitory.

To a world that has known little of abundance, a world that throughout history has lived in want and fear, the idea of permanent abundance may seem impossible to realize. Perhaps it is im-

---

[16] *Works*, Vol. 9, p. 257.

Our civilization, Mommsen says, is destined perhaps some day to experience "the decay of productive power in the satiety of contentment with the goal attained." *History of Rome* (Scribner, 1870), Introduction, Vol. I, p. 24.

possible, but we have great new forces at our command. The conception of happiness as something which should be within reach of all having reasonable prudence, industry and thrift is surely a conception which we will not willingly surrender. It can be attained, however, only by conscious effort.

Specifically, food, clothing, shelter and relaxation can be brought within the reach of all only by making the cost of living low. Human progress, as has been seen, is measured by the ease with which the necessities of life are provided.

Ben Jonson has given us a picture of the farmer who plans his welfare on hopes of scarcity,—

> . . . a precious, dirty damnèd rogue
> That fats himself with expectation
> Of rotten weather . . .

who says to himself:

> O, I shall make my prices as I list;
> What though a world of wretches starve the while?
> He that will thrive, must think no courses vile,[17]

whose thirst for gain would make others "hunger and thirst with poverty."[18] Shakespeare touches the same subject when he describes in *Macbeth* the drunken porter who imagines himself opening the gates of hell for the "farmer who hanged himself in expectation of plenty,"[19] but these characters, which have been the sport and scorn of the theatre, faithfully represent the agricultural policy which many persons in America have seriously approved.

Readers of *John Halifax, Gentleman* are shocked by the story of the miller who threw his grain into the water rather than to have it seized by a hungry mob. Similar acts, however, by government or by combinations of men in present days, seeking to maintain or

[17] *Every Man out of his Humour*, Act I, Sc. i.
[18] *Ibid.*, Act III, Sc. ii.
[19] *Macbeth*, Act II, Sc. iii.

raise prices or wages, are approved by persons who condemn the conduct of the miller. Evidently, the happy effect of abundance in softening men's manners and preventing cruelty gives way before personal interest as surely to-day as in former ages. We still say, with Piso, that cruelty does not please us, and with Bacon that pity is the tenderest of human affections, but human conduct seems to have changed little in two thousand years.

Liberal government, as America has known it, is one of the greatest blessings ever enjoyed, but it has been liberal government under the Constitution. Without the Constitution, it would be government by popularity,—by appetite rather than by principle.

Comfort is not wholly new to humanity. History tells of two previous periods when man had what seemed to him like plenty, and both of these periods proved to be the result of temporary conditions.

When savage man learned to keep flocks and herds, he had greater supplies than ever before, until population rose and the days of comfort and abundance passed.

When agricultural civilization developed, man had abundance again a second time, a Golden Age when the earth willingly poured forth her treasure, but its reign was short for population rose once more and brought want, with ever recurring famine and pestilence.

Now, for the third time, after a long interval the world again has what, in comparison with the past, must surely be called abundance. We of the present are favored beyond all men who ever lived, in that our lives are cast in a period which future generations are likely to call a truly Golden Age, and the problem before us is to do what we can to prolong the happy conditions of our time, to make its comforts available, so far as possible, to persons of small means, and to ensure the permanence of these conditions. If this be in fact the purpose we intend, there is but one course to follow,—to reduce the cost of production and make neces-

235

saries, comforts, and even luxuries, cheap and plentiful. There
is no such over-production as is often described. The world never
had too many good things and what is called over-production is
commonly but a misleading name for high prices with the small
market which high prices bring.

The western world has been conspicuously successful during the
last century and a half in producing scientists, inventors, and men
of genius able to organize the great business enterprises which are
needed in order to put into practical service on a large scale the intellectual advances which scientists and inventors have made. Commercial developments have thus kept pace with scientific progress,
and mankind has been rescued from a world of want so quickly
that the sons do not know how their fathers lived. Here, indeed, is
an explanation of the dissatisfaction with conditions of life so often
expressed, since men who never knew want such as that in which
the world lived during many by-gone centuries, are unable to value
at its true worth such abundance as now exists, and are unhappy
because it is not greater.

As Mr. H. G. Wells recently said, "The primary source of our
present troubles is the complete incompatibility between our his-
torical traditions and the new, more exacting conditions of life
created for us by invention and discovery,"[20] and although Mr.
Wells had not in mind the effect of an almost sudden abundance
upon a hungry world, his statement still is true in this application.
Progress, indeed, has been so great, and mankind so readily becomes accustomed to ease that past sufferings are almost forgotten,
and what to our fathers were great luxuries, uncovenanted mercies,
are now thought of as daily necessaries which we would exact as
of right. It is very pleasant to be told, and to believe, that general
material conditions of the world have improved, and will always

[20] *The Poison Called History.* The Nineteenth Century and After, Vol.
CXXIII, p. 521, May, 1938.

improve, so that we can safely accept as our example the conduct of Mr. Micawber "whose irreducible gift for expecting something good to turn up was justified in the end,"[21] but lasting welfare can not be built on groundless hopes. Every person in our western world should know that there is no assurance that present conditions of comfort can continue, and that the question whether there is to be progress and happiness in the future depends upon our ability to maintain industry, prudence and thrift among our people, and upon our capacity to continue to produce in the future such men as those to whom we owe our progress in the past. We want genius in all its forms, executive, scientific, literary and aesthetic. What price would be too great to pay if by paying we could bring into existence such men as those to whom we owe the Conquest of Hunger and the degree of abundance that we have to-day? Few, indeed, would wish to reduce the incentive to enterprise and, nevertheless, there are, in no inconsiderable numbers, those who would reduce the rewards of achievement.

One danger, therefore, which threatens the maintenance of comfort and abundance is that individual energy and initiative will be destroyed by the very conditions which abundance itself brings.

There is, however, another danger not less serious.

If one were asked to name the two most conspicuous features of western history during the last hundred and fifty years, the answer would probably be that these features were the invention of machinery and the spread of liberal ideas,—the two being so closely associated that liberalism has sometimes seemed to be a by-product of the steam-engine. As comforts increased, liberalism has increased, making its way not only in politics and theology, but also in literature, in painting, sculpture, architecture, in manners and dress—more even than this, we have liberalism as well in the realm

[21] See *The Shifting of Poverty*, Quarterly Review, Vol. 270, p. 327, April, 1938.

of morals. Classicism is a search for the laws of progress and an effort to achieve progress through these laws when discovered. It "is the product," Sir Herbert Grierson says, "of a nation and a generation which has consciously achieved a definite advance, moral, political, intellectual; and is filled with the belief that its view of life is more natural, human, universal and wise than that from which it has escaped."[22]

Liberalism,—in its beginning contemporary with the Romantic movement, and closely related to it,—demands relief from burdens, and sometimes relief from obligations.

Both classicism and liberalism, as thus described, are necessary for progress. Every right-minded man is at once a classicist and a liberal and no one would wish to go back to the conditions in which the western world lived when liberalism began its great campaign. There is danger, however, that the spirit of revolt may go too far and the danger of this excess is never greater than when liberalism questions old standards of moral conduct. When Pleasure is on trial, Plato said, we are not impartial judges. Nevertheless, as soon as we begin to put into practice the life of passion and imagination of which the poets and novelists during the Romantic movement wrote, if we find emotional interests occupying our leisure thoughts, it is well to reflect that virtue and industry with steady discipline and self-control make a tranquil, cool life but that they are the only foundations on which a happy future can be built, and that they are even the basis upon which our present safety rests.

[22] *The Background of English Literature* (Henry Holt & Co., New York, 1926), p. 266. See also *The Romantic Agony* by Mario Praz, translated by Angus Davidson (Oxford Press, 1933).

If food, and other necessaries of life, are adequate in quantity and variety and if men are free, there will be industry. If savings are secure from confiscation and debasement, there will be thrift, and an industrious, thrifty people make a prosperous and rich nation.

LIST

OF

SOME OLDER BOOKS QUOTED IN THIS VOLUME, AND NAMES OF LIBRARIES IN WHICH THEY CAN BE FOUND, TOGETHER WITH BRIEF BIOGRAPHICAL NOTES OF THEIR AUTHORS

To discover the degree of want and scarcity which existed in Europe before the days of machinery, we need contemporaneous records and, unfortunately, few old books deal directly with the subject of want. There were, however, books on food and on the treatment of disease, and some of these books occasionally give valuable information, as for example, in Plenck's statement of corvus corax,

"Caro a misserimis hominibus non sine fastidio degustatur,"

or of felis catus domesticus,

"Caro leporinae similis esse dicitur et a quibusdam hominibus in Hispania, Gallia, Hollandia comeditur."

Such books can not take the place of later critical histories, but so far as they treat of conditions amidst which the writer lived as did the men of many previous centuries, they are original sources of information. The full significance of the books listed below can, however, best be understood when studied in connection with old books on agriculture, such as those of Barnaby Googe and Mascall.

Acorombonus, Hieronymus. Girolamo Acoramboni was an Italian physician and writer who was born in Gubbio, Umbria, and died in 1535. He taught medicine in Padua and, besides Tractatus de Usu Lactis, wrote also De Catarrho (Venice, 1536) and De Putredine (Venice, 1534).

Tractatus de Usu et Natura Lactis, Venice, 1538, the edition to which notes in the present volume refer.

Surgeon General's Office, Washington, D. C.

Also published in Nürnberg in 1538 and in Basel in 1578.

British Museum, London

241

Aussy, Pierre Jean Baptiste le Grand d'
See
Le Grand d'Aussy, Pierre Jean Baptiste

Bagellardus, Paulus. Italian physician, born at Fiume, probably a professor at the University of Padua, author of the first text dealing specifically with children's diseases. Died in 1494.

Opusculum Recens Notum de Morbis Puerorum, cum appendicibus magistri Petri Toleti, Lugduni, 1538. The Index Catalogue of the U. S. Surgeon General's Office enters this work under Toletus, Petrus—with the note: "The first part is the work of Paulus Bagellardus: De egritudinibus infantium, Pataviae, 1472, with an appendix after each chapter by Toletus."

pp. 119-203 are the work of Odus de Odis,—De Coenae et Prandii Portione.

Oddo degli Oddi was born in 1478 in Perugia of a noble family, taught philosophy in the schools of his native city and later practised medicine in Venice. Thence he was called to teach in the University of Padua, where he died in 1559. He was the author of many books.

De Coenae et Prandii Portione, libri duo.

> Bibliothèque Nationale, Paris
> British Museum
> New York Academy of Medicine Library
> Richmond Academy of Medicine, Richmond, Virginia
> Surgeon General's Office

Baruffaldus, Hieronymus (1675-1755). Italian ecclesiastic, poet and playwright.

De Armis Convivalibus Schediasma; in: Sallengre, Albert Henri de. Novus Thesaurus Antiquitatum Romanorum. 3 vols. Hagae-Comitum, 1716-1719, the edition to which notes in this volume refer.

> Detroit Public Library, Detroit, Michigan
> Harvard College Library, Cambridge, Massachusetts
> Library of Congress, Washington, D. C.
> Newark Public Library, Newark, New Jersey
> New York Public Library, New York City
> Peabody Institute, Baltimore, Maryland

University of Chicago Library, Chicago, Illinois
University of Illinois Library, Champaign, Illinois
University of Michigan, Ann Arbor, Michigan

Other editions can be found in:

Bibliothèque Nationale
British Museum
Department of Agriculture Library, Washington, D. C.
Edinburgh University Library, Edinburgh
Surgeon General's Office

Beckmann, John. German technologist, called the father of technological science; professor of philosophy at Göttingen, later of agricultural economics at the same university. Born 1730, died 1811.

Beyträge zur Geschichte der Erfindungen. Leipzig, 1782, (1780)-1805. 5 vols.

British Museum

Other German editions can be found in:

Bibliothèque Nationale
John Crerar Library, Chicago, Illinois
Library of Congress
New York Public Library
U. S. Geological Survey Library, Washington, D. C.

A History of Inventions, Discoveries and Origins . . . translated from the German by William Johnston. Fourth edition carefully revised and enlarged by William Francis and J. W. Griffith. London, 1846, 2 vols., (Bohn's Standard Library), the edition to which notes in this volume refer.

Bibliothèque Nationale
British Museum
Brooklyn Public Library, Brooklyn, New York
Edinburgh University Library
Fall River Public Library, Fall River, Massachusetts
John Crerar Library
Library of Congress
Massachusetts State Library, Boston, Massachusetts
New York Public Library

243

Peabody Institute
Rutgers University, New Brunswick, New Jersey

Other editions can be found in:

Arnold Arboretum, Cambridge, Massachusetts
Boston Athenaeum, Boston, Massachusetts
Bowdoin College, Brunswick, Maine
Columbia University Library, New York City
Detroit Public Library, Detroit, Michigan
Engineering Societies' Library, New York City
Harvard College Library
Michigan College of Mining & Technology, Houghton, Michigan
Surgeon General's Office
U. S. Military Academy, West Point, New York

Bonamicus, Franciscus. An Italian physician, native of Florence, who lived in the second half of the sixteenth century.

De Alimento, libri V. Florentiae, 1603, the edition to which notes in this volume refer.

Bibliothèque Nationale
Bibliothèque Royale de Belgique, Brussels
British Museum
Surgeon General's Office

Bruyerinus Campegius, Johannis. Jean Baptiste La Bruyère-Champier was born at Lyons, France, and lived during the first half of the sixteenth century. He was attached to the court of Francis I, later becoming the physician of Henry II. His uncle, Symphorien-Champier, was a well known writer mentioned pleasantly by Thomas Coryat in his book, Crudities, and the nephew, like the uncle, wrote many books.

De Re Cibaria, libri XXII. Lugduni, 1560, the edition to which notes in this volume refer.

Bibliothèque Nationale
Bibliothèque Royale de Belgique
British Museum
Columbia University Library
Department of Agriculture Library
Library of Congress
Surgeon General's Office

244

BIBLIOGRAPHY

Other editions can be found in:

> Edinburgh University Library
> Princeton University Library, Princeton, New Jersey

Bulengerus, Julius Caesar. French historian, a member of the Jesuit order, born at Loudun in 1558 and died at Cohors in 1628. He was the author of many books.

De Conviviis, libri IV. Lugduni, 1627.

> Library of Congress

Ciacconius, Petrus (Chacon, Pedro). A learned Spaniard born at Toledo in 1525, died at Rome in 1581. He was appointed Canon of Seville by Gregory XIII and charged with the duty of editing the Bible and works of the Fathers. He was the author of many books. "His immense erudition was admired by Baronius, de Thou, Casaubon and other contemporary savants." Nouvelle Biographie Générale, Vol. 9, p. 547.

Liber Singularis de Triclinio Romano, seu de Modo Convivandi apud priscos Romanos et de conviviorum apparatu. Amstel, 1689, the edition to which notes in this volume refer.

pp. 112-382 are an Appendix by Fulvius Ursinus, an eminent classical scholar born at Rome, 1529, died 1600.

pp. 383-413 are Lib. I, Cap. XI, De Accubitus in Coena Antiquorum Origine from the book, De Arte Gymnastica by Hieronymus Mercurialis (1530-1606), an Italian physician, professor of medicine at Padua, whose book from which this chapter is taken was published in 1569.

pp. 414-445 are an Appendix by Mercurialis to the foregoing chapter, in which, among other things, Mercurialis states that much of the material in the books and writings of Ciacconius and Ursinus was taken from his earlier book, De Arte Gymnastica.

> "Petrus Ciacconius et Fulvius Ursinus rerum antiquarum peritissimi: quique multis annis post meam gymnasticam de triclinio scripserunt, procul dubio ad veritatem accubitus accesserunt, atque si aequus lector nostras cogitationes illorum scriptis comparare velit, certe statim animadverteret, fere quicquid hac de re boni dixerunt, e nostro libro accepisse." (p. 416) Robert Burton and Sir Hugh Platt would have approved this protest.

> Boston Public Library

Other editions can be found in:

> Harvard College Library
> Library of Congress
> Newark Public Library
> New York Public Library
> U. S. Surgeon General's Office

Combles, de. French agronomist, born of a noble family at Lyons towards the beginning of the eighteenth century and died about 1770. The name is sometimes erroneously given as de Combes.

L'école du jardin potager . . . par l'auteur du Traité de la culture des pêchers. Paris, 1749. 2 vols.

> Bibliothèque Nationale
> Department of Agriculture Library
> Library of Congress

........Paris, 1752, the edition to which notes in the present volume refer.

> Bibliothèque Nationale
> Department of Agriculture Library
> Library of Congress

Other editions can be found in:

> British Museum
> Massachusetts Horticultural Society, Boston, Massachusetts

Costaeus, Joannis. Giovanni Costeo was born in Lodi and occupied the first chair of medicine established in Torino. In 1581 he became professor of medicine in Bologna, where he died in 1603. He was the author of many books.

De Facili Medicina per seri et lactis usum. Papiae, 1604.

> Bibliothèque Nationale
> British Museum
> Surgeon General's Office

Forster, John. Nothing seems to be known about this John Forster. The British Museum describes him as "of Hanslop, Bucks." An exami-

BIBLIOGRAPHY

nation of Buckinghamshire histories reveals a sixteenth century John Forster at Hanslope, but he is evidently not our John.

England's Happiness Increased, or a sure and easie remedy against all succeeding dear years; by a plantation of the roots called potatoes, whereof (with the addition of wheat flower) excellent, good and wholesome bread may be made, every year, eight or nine months together, for half the charge as formerly. Also by the planting of these roots, ten thousand men in England and Wales, who know not how to live, or what to do to get a maintenance for their families, may of one acre ground, make thirty pounds per annum. Invented and published for the good of the poorer sort, by John Forster. London, 1664.

> British Museum
> Department of Agriculture Library
> New York Public Library

Gastius, Joannis (Petroselanus, Joannis Peregrinus). Theologian, born in Breisach, came to Basle shortly after the Reformation, and died there in 1572.

Convivalium Sermonum Liber . . . Basileae, 1541.

> Bibliothèque Nationale
> Harvard College Library

Other editions can be found in:

> British Museum
> Library of Congress
> Newberry Library, Chicago, Illinois
> University of Chicago

Gesnerus, Conradus. Of Conrad Gesner, Mr. Henry Hallam in his Introduction to the Literature of Europe (London, 1843), Vol. I, p. 492, said that he was "the most comprehensive scholar of the age," adding, Vol. II, pp. 234-235: "In the year 1551 was published the first part of an immense work, The History of Animals, by that prodigy of general erudition, Conrad Gesner . . . This work of the first great naturalist of modern times . . . says Cuvier, may be considered as the basis of all modern zoology." Gesner was born at Zurich in 1516 and died in December, 1565.

Libellus de Lacte et Operibus Lactariis. Tiguri, 1541.

> Bibliothèque Nationale
> British Museum
> Edinburgh University Library
> Ghent Université Bibliothèque
> Surgeon General's Office

Goodman, Godfrey, Bishop of Gloucester. Born 1583; Chaplain to the Queen-Consort, Anne of Denmark, 1616; Bishop of Gloucester, 1625-1643; imprisoned for refusing to sign new canons against popery, 1642-1643; died a Roman Catholic, 1656. A defender of King James in his Court of James I.

The Fall of Man, or The Corruption of Nature, proved by the light of our naturall reason . . . London, 1616, the edition to which notes in this volume refer.

> British Museum

Hakewill, George. English divine, born 1578, died 1619, Chaplain to Prince, later King, Charles, Rector of Exeter College, one of the writers whose style helped form that of Samuel Johnson.

An Apologie or Declaration of the Power and Providence of God in the Government of the World. Consisting in an examination of the common errour touching nature's perpetuall decay. Oxford, 1635, the edition to which notes in this volume refer.

> British Museum
> Chapin Collection, Williams College, Williamstown,
>   Massachusetts
> Edinburgh University
> Harvard College Library
> Henry Huntington Library, San Marino, California
> Newberry Library
> Union Theological Seminary, New York City
> University of California, Berkeley, California
> University of Chicago
> University of Michigan

Other editions can be found in:

> American Antiquarian Society, Worcester, Massachusetts
> Bibliothèque Nationale

BIBLIOGRAPHY

Boston Public Library
Engineering Societies' Library
Library of Congress
New York Public Library
Princeton University
University of Iowa Library, Iowa City, Iowa
University of Oregon Library, Eugene, Oregon
Vassar College, Poughkeepsie, New York

Herengius, Johannis. A native of Oldenburg, born in 1599, died in 1658. He was a lawyer and, besides his book on milling, of which John Beckmann, in his article on Corn Mills (History of Inventions, Discoveries and Origins, Vol. I, p. 150, note 2), says it is "a very confused book, which requires a very patient reader," Herengius wrote also Discursus de Appelatione etc. ad Judicium Dei in Valle Josaphat, 1632.

De Molendinis, Frankfort, 1625.

Bibliothèque Nationale
Harvard Law Library

........Edition of 1663.

Harvard College Library

La Framboisière, Nicolas Abraham de. A French physician, born at Guise in 1577, died probably in 1640. He was a professor at the Collège Royal in Paris and physician to the king.

Le gouvernement nécessaire à chacun pour vivre longuement en santé . . . Paris, 1601, the edition to which notes in this volume refer.

Other editions can be found in:

Bibliothèque Nationale
Bibliothèque Royale de Belgique
Ghent Université Bibliothèque
Surgeon General's Office
University of Wisconsin, Madison, Wisconsin

Le Grand d'Aussy, Pierre Jean Baptiste. A French writer and member of the Order of Jesuits. Born at Amiens in 1737. Died in Paris in 1800.

Histoire de la vie privée des Français. Paris, 1782. 3 vols., the edition
to which the notes in this volume refer.

> Bibliothèque Nationale
> Boston Public Library
> British Museum
> Edinburgh University
> Library of Congress
> Princeton University

Other editions can be found in:

> Ghent Université Bibliothèque
> Harvard College Library
> New York Public Library
> Peabody Institute

Lémery, Louis. A French physician, born at Paris in 1677, died in 1743.
A man of great reputation and author of many books.

Traité des aliments. Paris, 1702, the edition to which notes in this volume
refer.

> Bibliothèque Nationale
> British Museum
> Ghent Université Bibliothèque
> Library of Congress
> Surgeon General's Office

Other editions can be found in:

> Bibliothèque Royale de Belgique
> John Crerar Library

Trattato degli Alimenti, Transportato dal francese Venezia, 1704.

> New York Public Library

Another edition in:

> Harvard College Library

A Treatise of All Sorts of Foods. London, 1704, 1745.

> Bibliothèque Nationale
> Boston Public Library

BIBLIOGRAPHY

Brown University Library, Providence, Rhode Island
Edinburgh University
Harvard College Library
John Crerar Library
Library of Congress
New York Public Library
Surgeon General's Office

Mercurialis, Hieronymus—See note under Ciacconius, ante.

Muffett, Thomas. An English physician and author, born in 1553, died in 1604. Studied at Cambridge and Basle; practised in Ipswich, London and Wilton. He was a Fellow of the Royal College of Physicians and a member of Parliament. The second Earl of Pembroke was his patron.

Health's Improvement; or, Rules comprizing and discovering the nature, method, and manner of preparing all sorts of food used in this nation . . . Corrected and enlarged by Christopher Bennet. London, 1655, the edition to which notes in this volume refer.

Bibliothèque Nationale
British Museum
Henry Huntington Library
John Crerar Library
Library of Congress

. . . . .To which is now prefix'd a short view of the author's life . . . by Mr. Oldys, and an introduction by R. James. London, 1745.

British Museum

. . . . .London, 1746

Edinburgh University Library
New York Public Library
Surgeon General's Office
University of Pennsylvania, Philadelphia, Pennsylvania

"This" (Health's Improvement) "is a rare treasure, not because it adds anything to the sum total of human knowledge, but because of the fact that Muffett, who was a considerable traveller, collected in his travels and from the various authors of earlier times, a lot of quaint material dealing with the subject of dietetics and he is, as far as I know, the first English physician to write a book devoted solely to this subject."

John Ruhräh, M.D., in Medical Record, New York, 1921; Vol. 99, p. 636.

Nonnius, Ludovicus. A Flemish physician, Louis Nunez, son of a Portuguese surgeon who followed the Spanish armies into the Low Countries. Nonnius was born at Antwerp about 1555. He was a man of great learning of whom it was said that he excelled not less in poetry and history than in the exercise of his profession. He was a correspondent of learned men and wrote many books, but of the events of his life nothing is known, beyond the fact that he was living in 1645 and not far from ninety years old when he published the second edition of Diaeteticon.

Diaeteticon, sive De Re Cibaria, libri IV. Antverpiae, 1627, the edition to which notes in this volume refer.

> Bibliothèque Nationale
> British Museum
> Department of Agriculture Library
> Surgeon General's Office

Other editions can be found in:

> Bibliothèque Royale de Belgique
> Edinburgh University Library
> Ghent Université Bibliothèque
> Library of Congress

Odis, Odus de—See note under Bagellardus, ante.

Parmentier, Antoine Augustin. A French agronomist born at Montdidier in 1737, died in Paris in 1813. Parmentier wrote many books and his work with the potato is well known.

Recherches sur les végétaux nourissants qui, dans tous les temps de disette, peuvent remplacer les aliments ordinaires. Paris, 1781. This work developed from a memoir crowned in 1772 by the Academy of Besançon.

> Captain John Curtis Memorial Library, Brunswick, Maine
> Department of Agriculture Library

Observations on Such Nutritive Vegetables as May Be Substituted in the Place of Ordinary Food in Times of Scarcity. "Extracted from the French of M. Parmentier." London, 1783, the edition to which notes in this volume refer.

> Department of Agriculture Library
> Library of Congress
> New York Public Library
> Surgeon General's Office

Peutingerus, Conradus. A celebrated German humanist, born at Augsburg in 1465. Died at the same place, 1547.

Sermones Conviviales, in the collection of Schardius. Argentina, 1506, the edition to which notes in this volume refer.

> University of Michigan

Other editions can be found in:

> Boston Public Library
> Harvard College Library
> Library of Congress
> University of Chicago

Platt, Sir Hugh. Born in 1552, died about 1611, a man of wide attainments, author of many books on agriculture, gardening and other subjects. Of the account of his experimental work in gardening, it is said that he "is careful to state the name of his informant in all cases where he has not done the work himself." D. N. B., Vol. XLV, p. 406. Like Robert Burton, therefore, Platt could boast, "I have wronged no authors but given every man his own—sumpsi non surripui,"—an honorable distinction. See Burton's Letter to the Reader prefixed to The Anatomy of Melancholy.

Sundrie New and Artificial Remedies against Famine, written upon the occasion of this present dearth. London, 1596.

> Boston Public Library
> British Museum
> Harvard College Library
> Henry Huntington Library

Plenck, Josephus Jacobus, Ritter von. A German physician, born in Vienna, 1738, professor at the University of Vienna in chemistry, botany and therapy. Died in Vienna, 1807.

Bromatologia seu doctrina de esculentis et potulentis . . . Viennae, 1783, the edition to which notes in this volume refer.

> Bibliothèque Nationale

Other editions can be found in:

> British Museum
> Department of Agriculture Library
> Ghent Université Bibliothèque
> Library of Congress
> Surgeon General's Office

Bromatologie, oder Lehre von den Speisen und Getränken. Wien, 1784.

> British Museum

Other German editions are in the following libraries:

> John Crerar Library
> Surgeon General's Office

Sala, Johannis Dominicus. Giovan Domenico Sala was born in Padua in 1579. He was professor of medicine in his native city from 1607 to the time of his death on March 1, 1644. Besides his treatise, De Alimentis, he was the author of a book on the Ars Medica and of another entitled De Natura Medicinae.

De Alimentis. Patavii, 1628, the edition to which notes in this volume refer.

> British Museum
> Surgeon General's Office

Schoockius, Martinus. A Dutch critic and miscellaneous writer, 1614-1669. According to the Rothampstead Catalogue, Martin Schook was a physicist, philosopher, philologist and man of letters, professor at the University of Utrecht.

Tractatus de Butyro. Accessit ejusdem Diatriba de Aversatione Casei. Groningae, 1664, the edition to which notes in this volume refer.

> British Museum
> Princeton University
> Surgeon General's Office

BIBLIOGRAPHY

Segni, Giovanni Battista. Segni was an Italian prelate born in Bologna probably about 1550 and died in Ferrara in 1610. He was the author of many books. A good account of his life can be found in Notizie degli Scrittori Bolognesi, raccolte da Giovanni Fantuzzi, Bologna, 1784-1794, 9 vols. See Vol. VII, p. 377.

Trattato sopra la Carestia e Fame. Published by Giovanni Rossi, Bologna, 1602, the edition to which notes in this volume refer.

........Edition of 1591.

British Museum

Sethus, Symeon. A Byzantine writer and magistrate of Antioch, 1034-1074.

De Alimentorum Facultatibus. Basileae, 1538, the edition to which notes in this volume refer.

British Museum
Surgeon General's Office
University of Chicago

Other editions can be found in:

Edinburgh University Library
Grosvenor Library, Buffalo, New York
Harvard College Library
Illinois State Library, Springfield, Illinois
Library of Congress
Newberry Library
New York Public Library
Preussische Staatsbibliothek, Berlin
Princeton University
University of Iowa
University of Michigan

Stuckius, Johannis Guilielmus. The Allegemeine Deutsche Biographie gives a long account of this writer whose name was Johann Wilhelm Stucki. The date of his birth is very uncertain, the Allegemeine Biographie giving it as May, 1521, while the History of the German People by Johannis Janssen, translated by A. W. Christie (Kegan Paul, Trench, Trubner and Co., 1909), Vol. XIII, p. 181, says that he was born in 1563, and the Universal Dictionary of Biography, published by J. B. Lippincott

Company in 1901, says that he was "born in Zurich about 1550." He died in Zurich in 1607. Stucki was a well known theological scholar and an able writer, the author of several books.

Antiquitates Conviviales, libri III, in quibus Hebraeorum, Graecorum, Romanorum aliarumque nationum antiqua conviviorum genera, mores, etc. explicantur, etc. Tiguri, 1597, the edition to which notes in this volume refer.

> Harvard College Library
> Princeton University
> Peabody Institute

........Tiguri, 1582.

> Library of Congress

Sacrorum Sacrificiorum gentilium brevis et accurata descriptio. Tiguri, 1598, the edition to which notes in this volume refer.

> Harvard College Library (bound with Antiquitates
>   Conviviales, Tiguri, 1597)
> Union Theological Seminary

Operum Omnium, containing both Antiquitates Conviviales and Sacrorum Sacrificiorum. Lugduni Bat., 1695.

> Harvard College Library
> Library of Congress
> Newberry Library
> Princeton University
> University of Chicago

Ursinus, Fulvius—See note under Ciacconius, ante.

Venner, Thomas (Tobias). An English physician, born in 1527, died in 1560. He studied at Oxford, and practised in Petherton and during the season in Bath. Of his Via Recta, Raymond Pearl (in his paper, Tobias Venner and his Via Recta, Johns Hopkins University, Collected Papers, 1933; Vol. 7, p. 558 ff.) says that it is "one of the bibliographic landmarks in . . . gastronomy," and that "the latest treatise on personal hygiene of to-day contains little of any importance that is not in the Via Recta in one form or another, or little advice that differs in any essential way from old Dr. Venner's."

BIBLIOGRAPHY

Via Recta ad Vitam Longam . . . Much more enlarged than the former impressions. Whereunto is annexed . . . a . . . treatise of the baths of Bathe with a censure of the medicinall faculties of the water of St. Vincent's Rocks near Bristoll; as also . . . concerning tobacco. All which are likewise amplified since the former Impressions. London, 1650, the edition to which notes in this volume refer.

> British Museum
> Edinburgh University
> John Crerar Library
> Richmond Academy of Medicine
> Surgeon General's Office

Other editions can be found in:

> Harvard College Library
> Henry Huntington Library
> Library of Congress
> New York Public Library
> Union Theological Seminary

Willichius Resellianus, Jodocus. Jodocus Willich or Wilcke was born in Rössell, East Prussia, in 1501. He was the author of many books and an important man in Germany, for the German Dictionary of Biography contains a long account of his work.

Ars Magirica, hoc est Coquinaria, Tiguri, 1563, the edition to which notes in this volume refer.

> Surgeon General's Office
> New York Public Library

INDEX

Abandonment and exposure of infants, 18-19, 24

Abundance, xi, 10, 135, 206-224
  beginning of, 3, 60
  effect of, on human mind, 225-238
  in ancient Rome, 67, 209
  in England, 63, 206-207
  in middle ages, 61, 213
  relation of, to machinery, 34-35
  relation of, to poultry industry, 191
  three periods of, 235
  to-day, 217, 233, 237

Accomplish't Cook, The, 112, 116n., 178

Acorns
  storing, 89
  use of, 87-93, 96, 100

Acorombonus, Hieronymus, 166

Aelianus, 109n.

Agricultural machinery, 13, 22, 37, 65, 66, 190, 191
  restricted use of, 146

Agriculture
  beginnings of, 24-31
  Dutch, introduction into England of, 13, 143, 206, 207
  French, 215
  improvement of, 135
  in middle ages, 15-18, 20
  interest in, of Romans, 121
  management of, by village communities, 15
  ultimate stage of, 221-224

Albertus Magnus, 197

Alcibiades, 40

Ambition, 11, 14, 20, 26, 34, 37, 179, 206, 223

American Revolution, 2, 31

Anaesthesia, 222

Anatomy of Melancholy, 37n., 74n., 108n., 116, 136n., 155n., 199

Ancient Egyptian Paintings, 45

Ancient Régime, 68

Anderson, James, 17, 38

Anglo-Norman Social Life, 72

Animal food, 108, 111, 135

Animal husbandry, 28, 109-112, 207

Animal power
  in classical times, 43-49
    inefficiency of, 46-47
    maximum loads, 47
  in the middle ages, 49-50

Anselm, 213n.

Antoninus Pius, 158

Aphrogala, 184-185

Arbuthnot, John, 31

Archimedes, 2, 51

Aristotle, 49, 140, 195n., 196, 197n., 198, 229

Arkwright, Richard, 207

Ars Magirica, 102n., 108, 110n., 124n.

Artos (bread), 84n.

Ashton, John, 180n., 182, 183n.

Athenaeus, 57n., 64, 73n., 157

Aulularia, 76

Ausonius, 60, 86

Avicenna, 197

Babeau, Albert, 19, 61, 103, 105n.

Babes in the Wood, 20

Bacon, Francis, 52n., 140, 201, 235

Bakewell, Robert, 17, 38, 207

Baldwin IV, King of Jerusalem, 138, 176

Bark, making bread from, vii-viii, 66

Baruffaldus, Hieronymus, 81

Beckman, John, x, 19n., 40n., 74n., 81n., 119, 127n., 157n., 177, 186

Becon, Thomas, 168

Bede, 138

Bedford, Duke of, 200-201

Benet, Christopher, 169

Bergius, Petrus Jonas, 166n., 173, 178

Berri, Gerald de, 110, 169

Birth control, 220

Birth rate
  falling, xii, 224
  rising, xi, xii, 55
    relation of, to food supply, 69, 218

259

INDEX

263

INDEX

Po valley
  agriculture in, 27
  arts in, 208
  cheeses in, 160
  history of, 213n.
Praz, Mario, 238n.
Prescott, William H., 214
Pressure on food supply, 137, 145, 190, 217
Priestley, 2
Primitive man, 22-24, 235
  food of, 89
Printing press, 69
Private ownership, as stimulation to ambition, 37, 147, 179, 206, 207
Production
  cost of, 1, 235-236
  relation of, to consumption, 53
Progress
  and food, 140-144, 147
  conditions of, 145-146
  dependence of, on machinery, 35
  in France, slow, 214
  intellectual, dependent on moral fibre, 51
  slight until eighteenth century, 2, 33
  stages of, 33, 37, 145
  with agriculture, 25-26
Protecting hoofs of animals, 46, 49
Pseudolus, 76n., 124
Public opinion, 220
Puls, 41, 86, 126, 141
Punch, 172, 173
Purvis, Miller, 204

Quality of people, xii
Queen Mab, 230

Raleigh, Walter, 128, 129
Reaping, 30-31
Reason, awakening of, 12
Réaumur, René Antoine Ferchault de, 200, 201, 205
Recognition of individual rights, 35
Reeve's Tale, The, 102
Rham, W. L., 65n.
Richelieu, 81, 207
Robertson, Edmund, 13, 14
Robertson, William, 210n., 212
Rogers, Lore A., Associates of, 184n.

Roman law, 32
Roman life in ancient days, 39-43, 59-60
  deficiency of grain, 60-61
  few pleasures of, 71
Roots
  as field crop, 179
  eating of, 136n.
Rose, A. C., 45n.
Ross, Edward Aylesworth, 25
Rosset, 151n.
Rotation of crops, 16, 120, 135, 143, 206
Rousseau, 22, 228, 230, 231
  and the Revolution, 229
Row, Henry, 29
Roze, Ernest, 131
Ruaeus, Carolus, 75n., 117n.
Rules for the Preservation of Health, 151
Russel, F. York, 137

St. Anthony's fire, 62, 105
Sala, Johannis Dominicus, vii-viii, 24n., 86n., 87, 106n., 114, 115, 118, 125, 131, 132n., 134, 135, 148, 157, 167, 170
Salaman, Redcliffe N., 128, 130, 131n.
Sargent, Charles Sprague, 90
Savagery, 1, 24
  to-day, x
Savoy, Emile, 28, 43n., 44, 100, 101n.
Scaliger, J. C., 197
Schlink, F. J., 199n., 200n.
Schoockius, Martinus, 105, 120, 158
Scipio Africanus, 33
Scotland, conditions in at beginning of nineteenth century, 29-30, 192
Scott, John A., 57, 58
Scott, S. P., 208, 209
Segni, Giovanni Battista, 10n., 26n., 92, 103n., 141
Self-control, 220, 238
Seneca, 67, 175
Serfage, 50
Sermon on the Ploughers, 177
Serres, Olivier de, 5n., 42, 64, 85n., 113n., 127n., 131, 160, 162n., 178n., 181n., 193, 194, 195n., 197, 201n.
Sethus, Symeon, 113, 114n.
Shakespeare, 21, 106, 232n., 234
Shelley, 230
Short, Thomas, 6, 7

267

INDEX